Chris Maclennan   1B1

SECOND EDITION

MARION R. BROER, Ph.D.

Professor of Physical Education,
University of Washington

Photographs by E. F. MARTEN

EFFICIENCY OF HUMAN MOVEMENT

W. B. SAUNDERS COMPANY

Philadelphia and London

W. B. Saunders Company: West Washington Square,
Philadelphia, Pa. 19105

12 Dyott Street
London, W.C.1

Reprinted November, 1966, November, 1967 and April, 1969

Efficiency of Human Movement

To

RUTH B. GLASSOW

whose early vision and constant enthusiasm
for gaining and promoting an understanding
of human movement has been a very
great inspiration

Preface to the Second Edition

In revising this book I have attempted to clarify those ideas about which there may have been some question and to expand material where necessary to make it more meaningful. Students' and colleagues' questions about, and suggestions for clarification of, material in the first edition have led to many changes. The additional experience gained in the six years since the first edition has resulted in change of some previous concepts and formation of some new ideas and, therefore, corrections and additions were required.

As in the first edition, the intent of Part Four, Application of the Basic Mechanical Principles to Sports and Dance, is not to present a complete mechanical analysis of all sports. Rather the purpose is to give a few examples of the application of principles to a sample group of different types of activities, in the hope that the material presented will spark an interest and stimulate each student and teacher to think through the activities of interest to him, so that he will discover *for himself* the principles basic to the effective execution of the movements involved.

Although the format of the book is the same, many changes have been made in each chapter.

MARION R. BROER

Seattle, Washington

Preface to the First Edition

Movement problems have had to be met by each of us practically since we were born. Some of us have experienced greater success in the solution of these problems than have others. This book is written, not only as an aid to the teacher of movement, but also for any individual who desires to improve his efficiency. Since movement is involved in some way in every task, improvement in the efficiency of movement has far-reaching implications in the lives of all.

This book considers the questions: "What is efficient movement?" "Upon what is it based?" "What are the most basic laws which govern movement?" "What problems are involved in everyday, work, and recreational activities and what are the factors that must be considered in their solution?"

The basic laws governing movement are discussed in simple language and explained so fully that a background in the science of physics is not needed in order to understand this discussion. The final section of the book is written to aid the teacher of students of all levels of ability in understanding the reason(s) for a student's inefficient performance, so that teaching can be geared to the correction of the *basic* cause(s) rather than to a description of a set series of movements established authoritatively. Since the value of a foundation course in the physical education activity program is being debated so widely, the final chapter is devoted to a discussion of the possibilities of this type of movement education.

It is my sincere belief that the generality of movement calls for a generality of understanding that cannot be gained through the limited experience of learning a specific method for performing a few specific activities, but rather through experiences which, even though they may be limited, lead to an understanding of the factors involved in movement and in the various methods for approaching the solving of motor problems.

This book does not give answers to those who seek definite descriptions of *the correct form* for various movement situations. It discusses problems involved in the execution of a variety of activities and the principles which must be considered in their solution. For example, the discussion of the golf drive does not in any way establish the "correct" length of backswing. It seeks to assist the reader in gaining an understanding of the *relationship* of the length of the backswing to the control of the clubhead and to the force which can be produced, so that the reader can choose intelligently that length of backswing which will be most efficient according to *his* strength and the *particular* purpose involved at any specific time.

The book is the result of over ten years of study and of experimentation with basic principles of movement. I am greatly indebted to many students as well as colleagues whose clear thinking has led to questions and discussions which have aided in the clarification of many of the ideas expressed. Since every discussion, whether with an individual or a class, brings greater understanding, the ideas that can be brought to bear on this subject will never be assembled completely and, in this sense, a book dealing with this subject will never be "finished."

It is my hope that the ideas which *are* expressed will stimulate the reader to question some of the traditional materials and methods and to search for *basic* causes so that through each movement experience, whether his own or that of one of his students, he will continue to increase his own understanding and thus will experience the thrill that comes with a new idea and the satisfaction that results from seeing the greater progress of his students, not only in the efficiency of their movement but also in their ability to think through problems and to make intelligent decisions.

It would not have been possible to write this book without the understanding, patience, encouragement, and concrete assistance of many individuals. For their constructive suggestions concerning various portions of the manuscript I am greatly indebted to Ruth Wilson, Katharine Fox, Elizabeth Culver, Ruth Abernathy and Laura Huelster; for the many hours willingly spent in the performance of the activities photographed, to Elizabeth Culver; for his excellent photography, to Mr. E. F. Marten; for assistance in lettering the photographs, to Helen Hamilton and Joan Armstrong; for encouragement to put these ideas into print, to many of my students of the past years as well as my colleagues; and finally, and most important, for stimulating me to question and to search I shall always be grateful to Ruth Glassow.

MARION R. BROER

Seattle, Washington

Contents

Part One

Concepts of Efficient Movement

1   Efficient Movement 3

2   Prerequisites to Efficient Movement 25

Part Two

Basic Mechanical Principles Underlying Efficient Movement

3   Gravity and Buoyancy 35

4   Equilibrium 41

5   Motion 48

6   Leverage 60

7   Force 69

8   Angle of Rebound and Spin 82

9   Projectiles 94

Part Three

*Application of the Basic Mechanical Principles
to Fundamental Physical Skills*

10   Standing 107

11   Walking 124

12   Running 143

13   Hopping, Jumping, Leaping, and Landing 151

14   Falling 159

15   Sitting 163

16   Pushing and Pulling 181

17   Holding, Carrying, Stooping, and Lifting 192

18   Throwing and Catching 209

19   Striking 224

Part Four

Application of the Basic Mechanical Principles to Sports and Dance

Introduction to Part Four 251

20   Golf 252

21   Badminton and Tennis 273

22   Bowling 283

23   Basketball 299

24   Swimming 308

25   Tumbling 324

26   Other Activities 337

Part Five

Movement Education

27   Teaching Efficient Movement 363

28   The Foundation Course and Its Application to
      Physical Education Activities 374

Index 383

Part One

*Concepts of
Efficient Movement*

1

Efficient Movement

Movement is used in some way, to some degree, in every task accomplished by human beings. Every individual needs to understand human movement so that any task – light or heavy, fine or gross, fast or slow, of long or short duration, whether it involves everyday living skills, work skills or recreation skills – can be approached effectively.

Although the variety of movement tasks that confront man is endless, those involving the large muscles of the body might be organized under four main headings. A task may be *supportive*, and the purpose may be only to support the body itself, or it may involve supporting some object or objects. It may demand *suspension* of the body. While an object may be suspended from the body, some part of the object is always supported and therefore, objects can be considered under supportive tasks. While a suitcase is suspended from the hand, the fingers are under the handle and thus it is actually supported. The task may involve *motion* of the body as a whole or of one or more body segments, or of an object. And finally, the task may concern the problem of *receiving force*, either for the purpose of absorbing it, or resisting it so that the force will be returned to act on the object. For clarity various types of human movement tasks are outlined in Chart 1.

3

CHART 1. ORGANIZATION OF LARGE MUSCLE MOVEMENT TASKS

I. Supportive Tasks
    A. Supporting the body
        1. On more or less solid surface—standing, sitting, lying, kneeling
        2. On water—floating
    B. Supporting an object—holding

II. Suspension Tasks—Hanging
    A. From a solid object (e.g., bar)
    B. From an object free to move (e.g., rope, rings, etc.)

III. Tasks Involving Motion
    A. Moving the body
        1. Entire body
            a. On solid surface—walking, running, skipping, sliding, galloping, taking off for jump, dive, vault, hurdle, etc.
            b. On an object free to move—climbing rope, performing on rings, paddling canoe, rowing boat, etc.
            c. Through the air
                1). With no support—diving, jumping, falling, etc.
                2). While suspended—pole vault, on rope, trapeze, etc.
            d. Through the water—swimming
        2. Body parts
            a. Neck and trunk—rotating, bending, stretching, etc.
            b. Extremities—bending, stretching, swinging, rotating, etc.
            c. Pelvis—tilting
    B. Moving Objects
        1. Force supplied to object directly by body
            a. Giving initial velocity by keeping object in contact with body, or with object held by body, and then breaking contact and allowing object to move under the influence of gravity and other forces such as air resistance and friction, i.e., throwing, rolling
            b. Giving sudden impetus to object by momentary contact with a body part or an object held by body, i.e., striking
            c. Moving object by more or less constant application of force over distance and time, i.e., lifting, pushing, pulling, carrying
        2. Force applied to object indirectly by the body. Force of the body acts on elastic or some other type structure which in turn supplies the force to move the object. Body action essentially a push or pull, e.g., shooting bow, sling shot, gun, etc.

IV. Tasks Involving Receiving Force
    A. Of moving body
        1. Landing   a. On solid surface
        2. Falling (weight out of control)   b. On non-resistive surface,
                                          e.g., mats, pits, water, etc.
    B. Of moving object
        1. Body gains possession of object—dissipates force, "gives" to reduce jar of impact, i.e., catching
        2. Object rebounds from body or object held by body—body resists force of impact so force is returned to object, i.e., striking

---

With this variety of human movement tasks, the problem is to determine how, in a relatively short period of time, each individual can gain skill—not only in a few isolated motor activities (most of which are recreational), but also efficiency in movement in general.

Movement can be, and has been analyzed from many points of view. Many questions have been asked and each has led to a somewhat different approach to the study of human movement. The first question which comes to mind is, "What does the movement look like?" This has been studied by observation and by analysis of still and motion pictures. Observation is the oldest, and for years has been the most widely used (and probably the most misused), method of analyzing movement.

To answer the question, "What muscles function to produce the movement?" students have gone to anatomy and kinesiology texts. These have traditionally analyzed motion according to the positioning of the origins and insertions of the muscles crossing the joint or joints involved in the particular movement. More recently, this question is being answered by use of *electromyography* and the newer texts are reporting these findings.

While rhythm is as important in swinging a golf club, shooting a basket or swimming the crawl stroke as it is in dancing the rhumba, the dancer has, in the past, given more attention to the question, "What is the rhythmic pattern of the movement?" and thus to the time-force-space relationship of various movements, than have others interested in movement analysis.

The area of movement analysis represented by the questions, "How does the movement feel?" "What kinesthetic sensations are involved?" has many interesting possibilities and, as Steinhaus[1] indicated, it has very powerful implications since it is so vitally involved in the formation of many basic concepts such as those of the third dimension, roundness, etc.

Psychologists and physical educators are trying to answer the question, "What emotions are elicited by the movement?" The emerging importance of self-image concepts as they relate to response to movement is one interesting result.

Regardless of the approach to analysis, the first question which must be considered is, "What is the purpose of the movement that is to be executed?" This can be answered in very specific terms such as "to get the ball into the basket with a lay-up shot," or it can be answered in more general terms such as, "to produce force to lift the body as high as possible and to move the ball upward with just enough force and spin to carry it over the rim of the basket." The method of movement analysis will vary according to the approach to purpose.

In approaching analysis from the standpoint of observation, too frequently every detail in the performance of the expert has been described, regardless of whether a particular position or movement was really basic to success or was simply some inconsequential matter of the expert's style. Many physical education texts analyze skill only by describing, in minute detail, how the performance of the expert looks. Thus they imply that all who are attempting to learn the skill should attempt to reproduce all of this detail. This, despite the fact that no two individuals have the same tool for movement. Body builds differ; psychological and emotional make-ups differ; no two persons can ever perform a skill in *exactly* the same way.

To be effective, observation must be concentrated on the methods employed for applying the basic principles of movement in order to accomplish the purpose of the particular movement. Observation must be accompanied by the question "Why?" in the mind of the analyst. In other words, the analyst must ask, "What does each particular position or movement contribute to the performer's success?"

The basic tool for the performance of any movement task is the human body. Since the body cannot be "turned in on a new model" as can a car when its efficiency decreases, either it is used well or the individual fails to accomplish his purpose and/or suffers from fatigue or pain due to wasted energy or strain. It is not possible to anticipate every activity which each individual will sometime in his life be called upon to perform, and if this were possible there would not be time to learn them all specifically. Happily, this is not necessary.

Since the human body is made up of weights (mass of body segments), levers (bones), and devices for producing force (muscles and nerves), it responds to the laws of mechanics much as any other system of weights and levers. The problem is to determine how the body weights can be handled so as to maintain stability at rest or in motion (or to use instability to advantage), and produce and control force, in the performance of various types of tasks so that a desired result can be obtained with the least strain and a minimal expenditure of energy.

As various skills are analyzed from the standpoint of mechanics involved, it becomes obvious that there are some basic patterns of movement which require only slight adjustments according to the various purposes. For example, consider Figure 1 which shows an individual performing three different activities. The similarities in the total body movement patterns are obvious. In fact it is almost impossible to determine exactly which of many activities is being performed in each picture sequence. It might be interesting for the reader to try to identify each sequence. Is the first a striking or throwing skill? Which specific skill is being performed?

These pictures are not offered as examples of perfect "form" but rather as examples of the way one particular individual moved when performing three different skills. Figure 2 shows clearly which activities are being performed. Many other activities use this pattern, e.g., bowling, horseshoe pitching, and hockey. The last is somewhat modified owing to the fact that two hands are used to control the long implement more readily.

There are also many activities which use a similar overhand pattern (Fig. 3). Whether the student is throwing, serving a tennis ball, hitting an overhead badminton clear, smashing a tennis ball, or a badminton shuttle, he is executing essentially the same movement pattern. The purpose of each causes some adjustments, but the basic mechanics remain the same.

There is also a sidearm pattern (Fig. 4). Whether it be the basketball throw for distance, a tennis drive, badminton drive, or batting, the body movement is essentially the same.

While there are some differences in the several movement patterns involved in the various throwing and striking activities, all follow the same basic mechanical principles. This was recognized by Tittle, former quarterback for a professional football team, when he stated in an article published in *Sports Illustrated*, "The motion in passing is a lot like the motion in any throw, or even in hitting a golf ball or baseball."[2] The factors he discusses are the body position, weight transference, length of backswing and follow-through.

The subject pictured here performed these same activities while electromyographic records of the function of 68 muscles were made.* Analysis of these records indicated that there was considerable similarity in the functioning of the leg muscles while performing the underhand throw and the volleyball serve. The pattern of muscle function was the same for the badminton serve, except that the activity was considerably less since the weight transference was less for this activity which required less force. As might be anticipated, the greatest difference in muscle function during the performance of these three activities was found in the left arm since this hand was used to support and toss the volleyball and to drop the shuttle. The muscle action indicating the toss of the ball was different

(*Text continued on page 16.*)

*These electromyograms can be found in reference 3.

UNDERHAND PATTERN

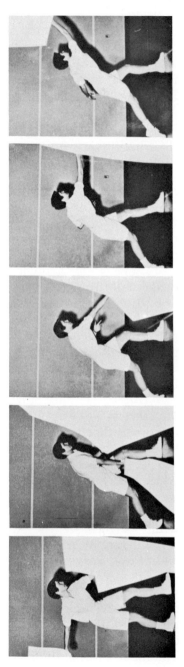

Figure 1. Sequence of photographs shows the subject performing skills associated with three activities in which the total body movement patterns are similar. Areas have been eliminated from the illustration which gives clues to the activity. Can you identify the activity in each sequence? What skill is demonstrated? (See Figure 2.)

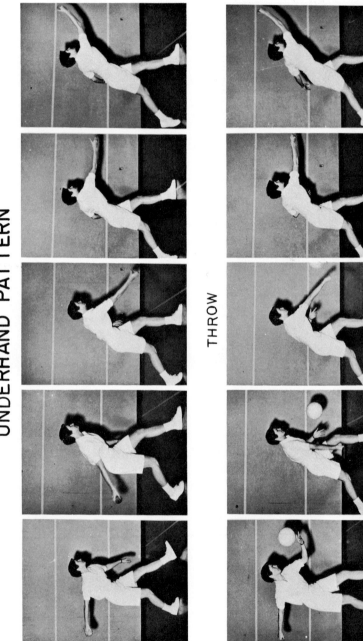

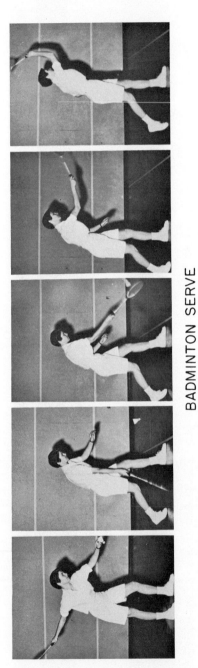

BADMINTON SERVE

Figure 2. *Photographs from Figure 1 are unmasked to show the actual skills involved. Note the almost identical positions at each stage of the skill performance.*

OVERHAND PATTERN

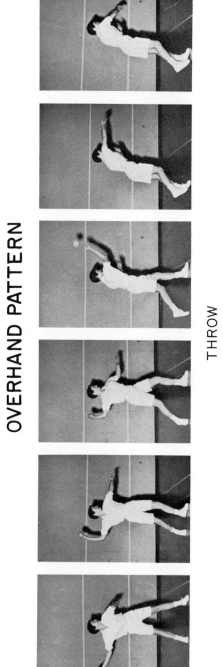

THROW

BADMINTON CLEAR

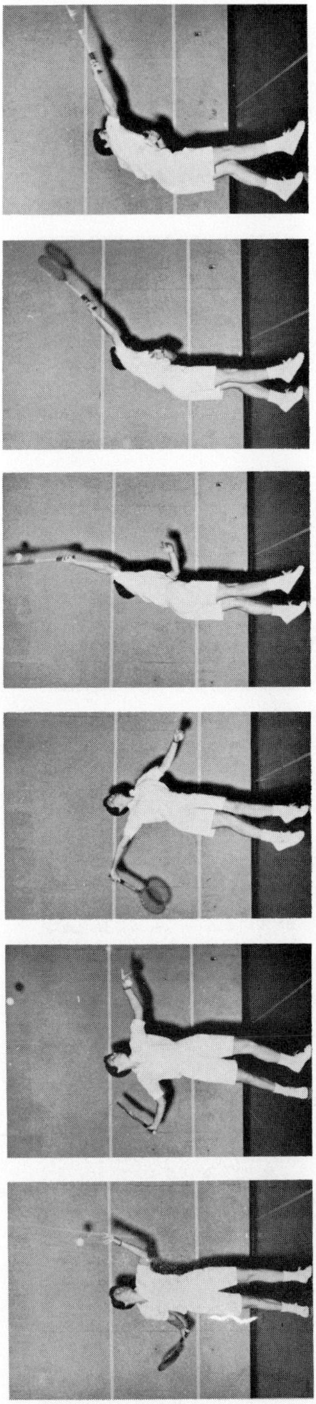

TENNIS SERVE

Figure 3. Similar patterns are seen in the execution of skills employing an overhand movement. Note the body positions immediately prior to the beginning of the forward swing and at each stage of the movement.

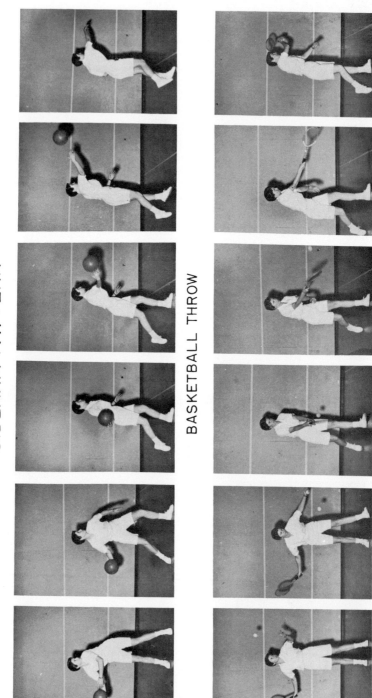

SIDEARM PATTERN

BASKETBALL THROW

TENNIS DRIVE

BATTING

Figure 4. *Some differences caused by the toss of the ball for tennis and two hands on the bat can be noted but the similarity in basic body movement is still obvious.*

from that indicating the drop of the shuttle and these were absent from the records of the throw. The right arm function was almost identical for the three activities, the one real difference is in the greater activity in wrist and finger flexors during the badminton serve and throw than in the volleyball serve.

Both leg and arm action were found to be similar in the overhand throw, badminton clear and tennis serve. There were slight differences in the functioning of the right arm muscles during the overhand throw, but the two striking activities were almost identical.

The sidearm pattern activities pictured here again appeared to be very similar. The left arm was less active during the tennis drive than the basketball throw. The arm pattern for batting was found to be more similar to the other activities than anticipated. An outstanding difference was seen in the left triceps' action which was considerably greater in batting. This, of course, was expected since the left arm was actively used in applying force.

When the leg action for the throws – underhand, overhand, sidearm – was compared, it was found that the muscle function for all three patterns was very similar. It was apparent that there was a general pattern of leg action which, with minor adjustments, this subject used when executing various throwing and striking activities *requiring considerable force*. There also appeared to be some general patterns of arm and trunk muscle function that were used for different skills with slight adjustments according to specific purpose.

Another interesting pattern is that seen in those activities which require a one foot jump for height, i.e., basketball lay-up, volleyball spike and diving (Fig. 5). Diving was not included in the electromyographic study, but the leg action for the volleyball spike and basketball lay-up was found to be almost identical. More activity in the abdominal muscles was required by the striking activity, and there was a clear difference in arm action in the two activities. Since one is a striking action which brings the arm forward-downward and the other a pushing action which moves the hand upward, this was to be anticipated. Although the action of the upper body when in the air was different, the movement pattern used to convert forward momentum to upward momentum to lift the body into the air was clearly the same.

In taking the pictures of the one foot jump it was found that this individual jumped from the left foot and raised her right knee whenever she was doing a lay-up shot in basketball or a volleyball spike. However, on the diving board she raised the left knee and took off from the right foot. When questioned about this change in body movement, she replied that when learning to dive, her instructor had insisted that she must start her steps on the right foot and lift her left knee in executing a diving hurdle. She reported that it had been extremely difficult for her to learn the running front dive. In approximately 45 minutes of practice this student was able to perform a better dive using a lift of the right knee (her normal movement pattern) than she had been able to do after some eight years of raising the left knee on the diving hurdle. How frequently is movement development hindered by a performer attempting to repeat exactly, or a teacher requiring that a student use, a stereotyped form which has perhaps been successful with someone else but may not be his normal movement?

The locomotor patterns are applicable in many different activities. Walking is fundamental to almost all. There are slight changes due to purpose. If the objective is a smooth, gliding movement of the body, the walk will be executed differently than if the purpose is to economize on energy over a long period of time. However, basically it is still the same pattern. The similarity between the crawl kick and the walking pattern is frequently overlooked. Running is used in a wide variety of activities. Whether the slide, gallop, skip, and pivot are used in the various dance activities, or in covering the tennis, badminton, or basketball courts the mechanics are the same. Twists and turns while the body is in the air are executed in the same manner in diving, gymnastics, dance and some basketball shots. The movement involved in changing from the front to the back crawl is essentially the same as that of the dance roll using the shoulder lead. If injury is to be avoided the principles involved in falling must be followed whether the individual is sliding into base, executing a dance fall, tumbling, or losing his equilibrium in skiing or any other activity.

Actually, these similarities among different activities are not surprising if the purpose of the movement is considered in terms of the required amount of force and its direction, rather than simply in terms of getting the ball over the net, into the basket, or over the plate.

In discussing the execution of a motor skill the terms "good form" and "poor form" are frequently used. One may encounter disagreement on what is good form for a particular skill. The discussion usually arises because of a confusion of

(Text continued on page 20.)

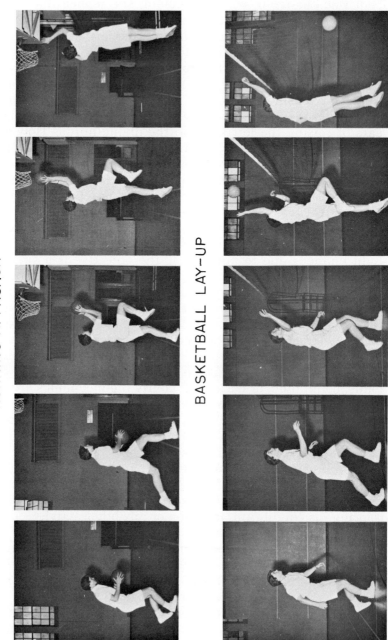

ONE FOOT JUMP—HEIGHT
RUNNING APPROACH

BASKETBALL LAY-UP

VOLLEYBALL SPIKE

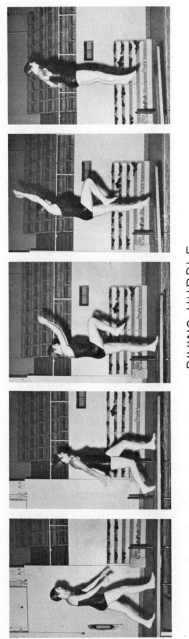

DIVING HURDLE

Figure 5. *The movement patterns used in three skills which require conversion of forward momentum to upward momentum are very similar.*

"mannerisms" with form, or the definition of form. Histori-
cally, good form has been determined by analyzing the performance of an individual, or individuals who have been
unusually successful in a particular activity. The concept of
good form has changed from time to time because of the fact
that an individual who looked different from the accepted
model demonstrated even greater success. There has been a
failure to consider the possibility that an individual may be
having success despite certain incorrect mechanics by compensation and extra expenditure of energy, *or* that an individual who uses his body well mechanically may have certain
mannerisms which, while they do not necessarily detract from
his success, are *not the reasons* for it.

The causes for the disagreement on form are generally
little mannerisms which, because they have been noted in
some highly skilled player's movement, have become a part of
the accepted picture of the form of the particular activity.
Many of the points which are so often questioned, points of
form on which there is disagreement, are simply these little
mannerisms that are independent of the basic mechanics
involved in the efficient execution of the skill. In fact, the
difference in style with which individuals execute a skill may
be due to structural differences. An unusual style in one
individual may be a necessary compensation, which in the case
of another individual would be detrimental to efficiency.
Performers and teachers "need to recognize that many somewhat different movements may be efficient and correct for a
given purpose, depending upon the individual doing the performing."[4] In discussing skiing technique Hutter stated that
"style is the highly personal application of technique. And
technique . . . is the natural, logical and most economic application of mechanics and use of physical laws in any given skiing
situation."[5]

In summarizing literature dealing with motor learning
Hellebrandt stated, "There are many ways in which the same
goal can be reached, and man unconsciously picks and chooses
among the gamut of those available, easing the burden of
fatigue . . . , and thus extending the range and sensitivity of
his movement vocabulary. The physical therapist, shop fore-
man, physical educator or coach may wish to impose upon the
human subject some precise and specific technique of movement, but an infinitely wise living machine . . . makes its own
autonomous adjustments. Instead of suppressing these, we
would do well to study them."[6]

One person looking at the picture of the underhand pattern (page 10) criticized the "form" of the volleyball serve because it was his belief that the ball should not be tossed on the service. Actually, the only thing that is important to the success of the service is that the ball be contacted with the correct amount of force on the correct spot so that the force is through the center of gravity in the direction that the ball is to go. If the individual tosses the ball and is successful in contacting the ball properly, why should anyone insist that the ball be held? Obviously, when the ball is held the problem of timing of toss and contact is not involved. Therefore, it may be expedient to suggest to the beginner that the ball be held. However, this does not mean that it is incorrect to toss the ball. Mechanically it is the point of contact that is important. It is necessary to understand the difference between those principles that are basic and must be followed if efficient movement is to result, and the little extras that are determined by individual differences or preferences.

Time and energy should be spent in learning the basic mechanics that are essential; the individual's mannerisms will eventually develop and little individual differences — so long as they do not interfere with the mechanics — will not be important. Good form is not a set pattern but rather the movement, or movements, which accomplish the purpose with the least expenditure of energy. Metheny stated that form in all activities is based on an understanding of two fundamental principles, "(1) how to conserve energy by proper use of the body and its parts, and (2) how to expend energy intelligently and efficiently to accomplish a given purpose."[7] It is only through such understanding that relationships between various movements of the body and between various activities can be seen. Just as two sentences which express different ideas use many of the same words, so also do movement tasks which accomplish different specific purposes use many of the same basic neuromuscular patterns.

In 1956, Huelster[8] stated that, owing to the structure of the human body and its muscular function, there are elements of movement common to all specialized techniques. Examination of the pictures of the four patterns presented certainly indicates that there are many common elements upon which the learning of future skills can be based. The principles of balance, force production, motion and leverage are identical regardless of the activity. Common elements would be much more apparent if learning were approached from the standpoint of several questions. What is the purpose of this movement (or activity)? Purpose should be considered, not only in the very specific terms of hitting the tennis ball over the net, but in the broader terms of force production — whether a maximum production of force or controlled force is needed. How can this be accomplished with the least strain and least expenditure of energy? Why is this method more effective (in terms of really basic physical laws)?

Such an approach should aid in the realization that each activity is not a completely new pattern of movement but is largely familiar, although some specific adjustments may be necessitated by the purpose of the specific activity. It should clearly indicate that no activity demands a stereotyped pattern of movement but rather that its effectiveness is determined by its mechanics, degree of energy expenditure, and rhythmic quality. H'Doubler has stated that ". . . all purposeful activities such as the activities of play and work expressed in pushing, pulling, striking, hauling, throwing or their associated expressions in the technique of sports, or their abstractions in the creative movements of dance, have their forms set by the laws of body mechanics and the symmetries of physical movement."[9]

Movement is an essential in everyone's life and is influenced not only by body build but also by personality traits. An individual's movements have certain characteristics by which he can be recognized by those who know him well even when his face is not distinguishable. Some persons' movements are large and expansive, while those of others are small and restricted. The movements of some are always very direct and those of others indirect. Some individuals are habitually quick in moving while others move more slowly. Within the framework set up by the neuromuscular equipment, body build and personality of the individual, the physical laws operate.

There are mechanical principles that govern all movement and determine what the body can and cannot do. These principles are the same regardless of the type of activity, whether dance, sports, everyday tasks, or work tasks. The purposes and motivations may be different but all use the same tool (the body) and the same medium (movement), and body movement is governed by physical laws. If these basic principles are understood, knowledge important to all skills can be learned through any specific activity. It is interesting to note that as long ago as 1914 Watts stated, "When once these principles are understood, they may be applied, not only to define exercises, but to all sports, as also to the unconscious everyday movement of life, with a certainty of finding a more complete order of activity, a stronger current of force, a new power of control."[10]

It must be recognized that an understanding of human movement must be approached from the anatomical, physiological, neurological, and psychological as well as the mechanical basis. Since human movement takes place only as a result of neuromuscular activity, the importance of the neurophysiological aspects of movement and motor learning is obvious.

The human mechanism is endowed with certain reflexes upon which effective patterns of movement can be built. This human mechanism is the base upon which the mechanical principles are applied, and while the mechanical approach to the study of movement is vital to total understanding, the other aspects cannot be overlooked. However, one book cannot cover this vast area. This book, therefore, is limited to the understanding and application of the mechanical basis of movement.

It is the purpose of this book to help the performer and the teacher, or future teacher of physical education, understand the most fundamental mechanical principles as they relate to human movement (Part Two); to point up the mechanics involved in the skills fundamental to all activities—those used in the accomplishment of daily tasks as well as sport and dance techniques (Part Three); and to suggest applications to some of the common physical education activities (Part Four).

REFERENCES

1. Steinhaus, Arthur H.: *Toward an Understanding of Health and Physical Education*. Wm. C. Brown Company, Publishers, 1963, p. 33.
2. Tittle, Y. A.: Secrets of a Pro Quarterback. *Sports Illustrated*. 9:14–52. October 6, 1958.
3. Broer, Marion R. and Houtz, Sara Jane: *Patterns of Muscular Activity in Selected Sport Skills: An Electromyographic Study*. Springfield, Charles C Thomas, 1967.
4. Movement Group Report, *Workshop Report: Purposeful Action*. Washington, D.C., The National Association for Physical Education of College Women, 1956, p. 93.
5. Hutter, M. K.: Technique Today: An Evaluation. *Skiing*, 17:2:100, November, 1964.
6. Hellebrandt, F. A.: The Physiology of Motor Learning. *Cerebral Palsy Review*, 10:4:13, July-August, 1958.

7. Metheny, Eleanor: *Body Dynamics*. New York, McGraw-Hill Book Company, Inc., 1951, p. 5.
8. Huelster, Laura J.: Comments on the Calling We Profess. *Workshop Report: Purposeful Action*. Washington, D.C., The National Association for Physical Education of College Women, 1956, p. 14.
9. H'Doubler, Margaret N.: *Movement and Its Rhythmic Structure*. Madison, Wisconsin, Kramer Business Service, 1946, p. 8.
10. Watts, Diana: *The Renaissance of the Greek Ideal*. New York, Frederick A. Stokes Company, 1914, p. 36.

2

Prerequisites to Efficient Movement

While the bulk of this book deals with the application of the basic physical laws to movement, the base to which the physical laws are applied must be considered. There are certain physical, mental, and emotional prerequisites that must be recognized and dealt with as the need arises.

PHYSICAL PREREQUISITES

The degree to which movement can be effective may be influenced by body build, reaction time, strength, power, flexibility, endurance, and the acuity of the senses. The importance of each of these is dependent upon the movement task to be performed. For example, while reaction time is not an important factor in most tasks of the lifting, pushing and pulling, and carrying type, it is extremely important in many sports such as tennis, basketball and badminton. There are, however, sports in which reaction time does not play an important role, e.g., golf and bowling. It is important in any survival activity involving dodging and falling. This is obvious when one is crossing a street and a car suddenly bears down. Effective automobile driving depends upon a quick reaction time. Reaction time, of course, is tied in with the physical acuity of the senses and many mental abilities. Without acute senses and the ability to make quick decisions, reaction time would be slow.

Strength, on the other hand, is extremely important to many tasks of the lifting-carrying type, and assumes a less prominent role in some sport activities. However, pelvic strength and control are important in most activities. The trunk must be stabilized as a base for effective action of the extremities. Arm and shoulder girdle strength may be of concern in archery, bowling, canoeing, swimming, skiing, gymnastics, and field activities; strength of the legs is involved to some extent in almost all activities but is particularly important in basketball, fencing, riding, gymnastics, skiing, track, etc.; wrist strength is essential in tennis; finger and wrist strength in archery; etc. An understanding of the compensations students are likely to make for lack of strength is extremely important in teaching. For example, if a student persists in swinging the bowling ball in an arc around the body even though he understands the contribution of a straight swing to accuracy, in all probability he lacks the strength to control the ball when it is farther from his center of gravity. He swings it in an arc because in this way it can be kept close to his center of gravity and is, therefore, easier to control.

Or, if a student turns his right foot (if right-handed) diagonally outward, thus making the approach irregular because of the outward as well as forward push from the right foot, he may lack the strength necessary to keep the trunk erect and adjust to the added weight of the ball on the right side of the body. Therefore, he turns the right foot somewhat outward to enlarge the base on the side of the weight. In both cases the answer is not to reiterate the proper swing or the proper approach, but rather to give him an understanding of his problem, to provide a lighter ball, and to suggest exercises which will strengthen the muscles which are weak.

When in beginning tennis the right-handed student continually hits to the right, it should be determined whether he lacks the wrist strength to withstand the force of the ball against the racket and gives with the wrist thus turning the racket face to the right. This can be corrected by helping the student understand the reason his ball went to the right and that "squeezing" the racket at impact will help to stabilize the wrist. Also exercises should be suggested to strengthen the wrist muscles. It will do no good to continue to tell the student to keep the racket face straight ahead on contact, since he lacks the strength to do it. The teacher needs to understand that since the ball hits the racket far from the fulcrum (the shoulder) of the lever involved, the force of the ball against the racket is greatly magnified.

Also the student who, in hitting a tennis drive, continually draws the arm in so that the elbow is close to the side, may be compensating for lack of strength. Since, with the elbow well bent, the impact is taken at the end of a shorter lever, it can be withstood with less strength than when the student reaches for the ball with an extended arm (a longer lever). Here again, the student needs to be helped to understand his problem and be given suggestions for ways to increase strength. This last fault, that of hitting with the elbow close to the body, may also be due to a spatial judgment problem.

MENTAL PREREQUISITES

Through the years the student has built up a spatial concept of the distance that he can reach. The length of his arm is familiar to him and he can quickly judge how close to approach an object that he wishes to strike with his hand. Is it not possible that, when he is given a tennis racket that lengthens his reach by approximately 24 inches and is expected to make rapid judgments as to how close to approach the ball in order to hit with an extended arm plus racket, the habit of a lifetime is too strong, and he approaches the ball at his normal striking distance (arm length)? While swinging he finds that he is too close to the ball and draws the elbow toward the body to shorten the reach. In the long run teaching time could be saved if, when a new implement is introduced, some time were taken to help the student gain the new spatial concept. Perhaps some of these problems have arisen because it has been taken for granted that these new spatial concepts are developed immediately and automatically.

Time also needs to be spent in developing the timing concept peculiar to badminton. Again, over the years the student has developed a concept of the timing of the flight of a ball. Since the shuttle is affected more by air resistance, the flight is different and this concept of the speed with which objects fall must be adjusted if the student is to be successful in the game of badminton.

Whenever a moving object is involved, not only must one judge the speed of its movement, but also distance and height, as well as the force which will result from contact with it, must be assessed.

Rhythmic judgment—the ability to "feel" the beat, judge time duration, stress and intensity—is involved in all movement. The ability to perceive quickly and to make quick decisions adapted to the situation, to remember past movement experiences (not only the results of moving in a certain way but the *feeling* of the movements) so that they can be applied in the solution of new motor problems, and to understand the mechanics of effective movement are all important.

EMOTIONAL PREREQUISITES

Despite the physical and mental equipment of the student, teaching will not be effective unless there is a feeling of need for, or desire to learn, the particular skill involved. For example, a student being taught the serve in tennis found that when she lifted her racket forward and up with a bent arm and contacted the ball just slightly above her head, she could get the ball over the net and into the service court. When she attempted the circular backswing and a high contact she was successful less frequently. Since she had a greater feeling of success with the short swing and arched slow service which resulted, she was resistant to instruction which described the "correct form." This student was then approached from the standpoint that the purpose of the service is to put the ball into play *in such a way that it would be difficult for an opponent to return it*, the ease with which her service could be returned and the reasons for this. A demonstration of balls being dropped from the height at which she was hitting and the height to which she could reach, indicated to her the difference in the distance that the two balls had to fall, and thus the time available to get a straight ball over the net. The difference in the speed with which the racket could be moving at contact with her short backswing and the longer circular backswing were made clear to her through her own experimentation. Her response to this approach was, "This makes sense. I'll try it." Discussion of purpose followed by teaching through problem solving is an excellent method for making the student aware of the necessity for following the principles basic to the particular task and creating a realization of need and thus *a desire to learn.*

The teacher must also recognize the fact that disturbing emotional factors may block efficient movement. This is tremendously important in teaching swimming where fear of loss of support when the feet are taken off the bottom can, unless realistically dealt with, cause great retardation of learning. Fear must also be recognized in sports involving oncoming objects and body contact. In fact, simply fear of something new can be involved in most any movement situation. The pointing up of similarities to other activities and the application of known patterns and basic principles previously encountered to the new activity can go far in doing away with this fear of the unknown by showing that the "new" activity is, after all, made up of elements that are largely familiar.

ORGANIZATION OF PREREQUISITES AND CONTROLS LEADING TO EFFICIENT MOVEMENT

An attempt to chart the organization of the various prerequisites and controls that lead to efficient movement can be found in Chart 2. This chart shows clearly the importance of the nervous system to human movement. Obviously, efficient movement is impossible without its smooth functioning. In any movement all of the systems of the body are brought into play and work through the nervous system to produce balance, timing, and muscular control. These three types of control depend to varying degrees on the items listed in the chart under physical, mental, and emotional prerequisites. One of these prerequisites may be more important to one of the three controls and another, to another.

Balance control involves the ability to adjust the center of gravity effectively in relation to any base, stationary or moving. Because of the importance of the eyes and semicircular canals to balance, head orientation is fundamental to this ability. In addition, when the body is in motion, the use of the arms and legs in alternation to assist balance is involved.

The individual must be able to time the contractions of various muscle groups so that he can produce motion at the speed, in the sequence, and for the duration of time which will result in the force required by the given purpose. This *timing control* sets the rhythm of his movement. He must be able to time his movements with those of objects, whether he is to use his upper or lower extremities (or other body segment), to impart force to, or absorb force from, an object. This ability has been labeled "hand-eye" and "foot-eye" coordination.

The speed and range, and resultant force of a movement must be adapted to the purpose. The degree to which direction is controlled determines accuracy. The fixation of certain body segments is essential if other segments are to have a base for action. All of these are involved in *muscular control*. In addition, muscular control involves the ability to relax — the ability to keep muscles which can in no way contribute to the maintenance of the position or execution of the movement, from contracting. The fact that the ability to relax is as much a

(Text continued on page 32.)

CHART 2.   ORGANIZATION OF PREREQUISITES AND CONTROLS INVOLVED IN EFFICIENT MOVEMENT

Prerequisites to Efficient Movement

A. PHYSICAL

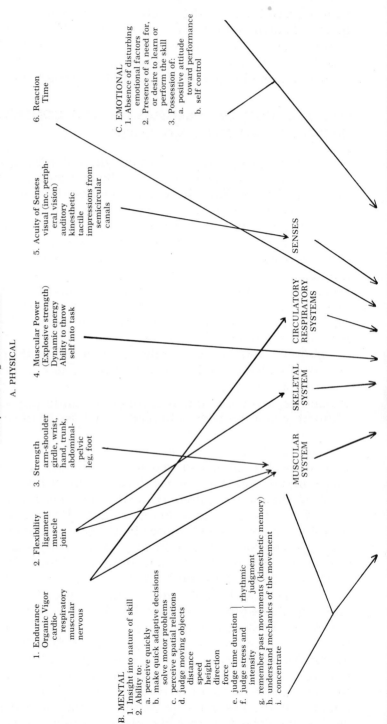

1. Endurance
   Organic Vigor
   cardio-
   respiratory
   muscular
   nervous

2. Flexibility
   ligament
   muscle
   joint

3. Strength
   arm-shoulder
   girdle, wrist,
   hand, trunk,
   abdominal-
   pelvic
   leg, foot

4. Muscular Power
   (Explosive strength)
   Dynamic energy
   Ability to throw
   self into task

5. Acuity of Senses
   visual (inc. periph-
   eral vision)
   auditory
   kinesthetic
   tactile
   impressions from
   semicircular
   canals

6. Reaction
   Time

C. EMOTIONAL
1. Absence of disturbing
   emotional factors
2. Presence of a need for,
   or desire to learn or
   perform the skill
3. Possession of:
   a. positive attitude
      toward performance
   b. self control

B. MENTAL
1. Insight into nature of skill
2. Ability to:
   a. perceive quickly
   b. make quick adaptive decisions
      solve motor problems
   c. perceive spatial relations
   d. judge moving objects
      distance
      speed
      height
      direction
      force
   e. judge time duration ⎫ rhythmic
   f. judge stress and   ⎬
      intensity   ⎭ judgment
   g. remember past movements (kinesthetic memory)
   h. understand mechanics of the movement
   i. concentrate

MUSCULAR
SYSTEM

SKELETAL
SYSTEM

CIRCULATORY
RESPIRATORY
SYSTEMS

SENSES

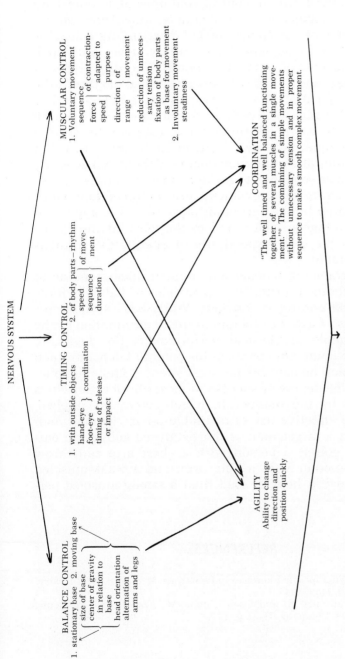

NERVOUS SYSTEM

MUSCULAR CONTROL
1. Voluntary movement
   sequence
   force $\Big\}$ of contraction- adapted to
   speed $\Big\}$ purpose
   direction $\Big\}$ of
   range $\Big\}$ movement
   reduction of unneces-
   sary tension
   fixation of body parts
   as base for movement
2. Involuntary movement
   steadiness

TIMING CONTROL
1. with outside objects
   hand-eye $\Big\}$ coordination
   foot-eye
   timing of release
   or impact
2. of body parts—rhythm
   speed $\Big\}$ of move-
   sequence $\Big\}$ ment
   duration

BALANCE CONTROL
1. stationary base 2. moving base
   size of base
   center of gravity
   in relation to
   base
   head orientation
   alternation of
   arms and legs

AGILITY
Ability to change
direction and
position quickly

COORDINATION
"The well timed and well balanced functioning
together of several muscles in a single movement."* The combining of simple movements
without unnecessary tension and in proper
sequence to make a smooth complex movement.

EFFICIENT MOVEMENT
The combining of coordinated movements to produce the force required by the
particular purpose and to apply it though the most advantageous point, in the
most advantageous direction with the least expenditure of energy.

*Kraus, Hans: Therapeutic Exercises in Pediatrics. *Medical Clinics of North
America, 31*:629, May, 1947.

motor skill as any movement, is too frequently overlooked.

Balance control, timing control, and muscular control are all mutually interrelated. For example, muscular control provides the means for control of balance; timing control is certainly involved in sequence of voluntary movement which is an important part of muscular control. The three types of control together lead to what has been termed "agility"—the ability to change direction and/or position quickly—and to "coordination." Kraus has defined coordination as "the well timed and well balanced functioning together of several muscles in a single movement."[1] It might be defined further as the combining of simple movements without unnecessary tension, in proper sequence to make a smooth complex movement. When coordinated movements are combined to produce the force required by the particular purpose and to apply it at the most advantageous point and in the most advantageous direction with the least expenditure of energy, the result is efficient movement.

The importance of teacher and student understanding of the basic mechanical principles—principles of balance, force production, and control—is obvious. While body size, shape, strength, and so forth, are factors in the determination of the success attainable in physical performance, the degree to which an individual can approach his potential depends upon the way in which he uses his physical, mental, and emotional equipment. "The degree of success in most physical activities is determined by the manner in which forces are applied. Through more effective use of available forces, a small man can outwrestle a larger man, a short-statured golfer can out-drive a taller golfer, a person with a short arm can throw farther than another with a long arm, and a weak-muscled person can move a heavier load than a strong-muscled person."[2]

REFERENCES

1. Kraus, Hans: Therapeutic Exercises in Pediatrics. *Med. Clin. North America*, 31:629, May, 1947.
2. Morehouse, Laurence E. and Cooper, John M.: *Kinesiology*. St. Louis, C. V. Mosby Company, 1950, p. 117.

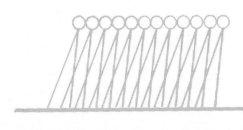

Part Two

*Basic Mechanical Principles
Underlying Efficient Movement*

3

Gravity and Buoyancy

GRAVITY

Since the force of gravity is always acting on every object, including the human body, it must be considered in the determination of any position or movement. This force is always exerted in a vertical direction downward, toward the center of the earth. It acts on all parts of an object or body in such a way that for all practical purposes it can be considered to pull on the weight center of the object, body, or body segment.[1] For this reason the center of weight of a body or object is known as the "center of gravity." Bowen and Stone[2] explain that the force of gravity acting on every particle of an object causes many forces which are parallel, and when added vectorially the resultant is a single force through the weight center of the body. This point has been described as the point about which a body balances, or as the point at which the weight of the body can be considered to be concentrated. No matter how irregular the shape of an object or body, it has a point about which it will balance. If a single force equal to the weight of the body (or in other words equal to gravity's pull) could be applied vertically upward at the body's center of gravity, the body would be supported in equilibrium, no matter how it were turned about its center of gravity.[3]

In the case of any rigid symmetrical body with uniform density, such as a ball or block, the geometrical center is also the center of gravity. It is not as easy to predict the location of the center of gravity in an irregularly shaped object. Not only is the human body irregular in shape, but also it has moving parts and therefore, its shape is constantly changing. However, a relatively simple method for determining the center of gravity of the body in its "normal" position with the arms at the sides, has been suggested.[4] A board is placed on two "knife edges," edges of two triangular blocks, one of which rests on a large block of wood and the other on a scale so that the board is horizontal. The scale is then read. The individual lies on the board with the top of his head even with the "knife edge" resting on the block. The total weight of the individual multiplied by the distance from the top of his head to his center of gravity (X – the unknown) is equal to the reading on the scale (minus the original reading) times the distance between the two "knife edges."

$$W \cdot X = L \cdot S$$

W = weight of individual
X = distance head to center of gravity
L = total length
S = scale reading (minus original reading)

In the normal standing position with the arms hanging at the sides, the center of gravity in the adult male is approximately 56 or 57 per cent of the total height from the floor and that of women, approximately 55 per cent of the height.[2, 5, 6] This will vary somewhat with body build. In general, the center of gravity in the human body can be thought of as being located in the region of the hips. However, any movement of a body part will shift the center of gravity in the direction of the movement. This is discussed more fully in Chapter 4, Equilibrium.

The shape of an object may be such that the center of gravity is actually outside the object itself. When a string with a weight and a V shaped piece of cardboard are *freely* suspended from a pin which is inserted in three different points of the cardboard (Fig. 6A,B,C), and the lines where the string crosses the cardboard in each position are drawn across the piece of cardboard, it is found that the three lines intersect in the space, *not* on the cardboard (the actual object) (Fig. 6D). The point of intersection indicates the center of gravity. The similarity of this piece of cardboard to the pike position of the body is obvious (Fig. 6E).

The body assumes many positions in which its center of gravity is outside the body itself. In general, when two parts of the body are at an angle, the center of gravity for the total is on a line which joins the centers of gravity of the two seg-

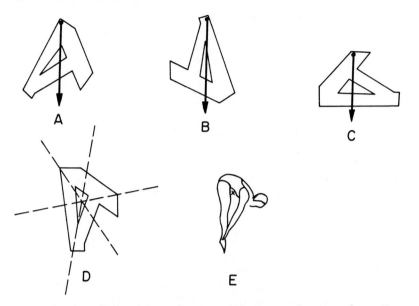

Figure 6. A, B, C, D, *Finding center of gravity of uneven shape.* E, *Comparison with pike position.*

ments.[7] When in a pike position the center of gravity of the total body lies on a line connecting the center of gravity of the trunk and arms segment with the center of gravity of the lower extremities. When the arm is flexed at the elbow, the center of gravity of the total arm lies on a line connecting the center of gravity of the forearm with the center of gravity of the upper arm.

Since the force of gravity pulls vertically toward the center of the earth, the line passing from the center of gravity downward (toward the center of the earth) is known as the "line of gravity."

Law of Falling Bodies. The law of falling bodies states that, *in the absence of air friction,* all bodies, regardless of size and weight, will fall with the same acceleration. At sea level this acceleration is 32.17 feet per second per second.[8] For purposes of calculation this can be considered to be 32 feet/sec./sec. without undue error resulting. If the distance an object has fallen is known, the time taken to fall to earth can be easily calculated by using the formula.[9]:

$$S = \tfrac{1}{2} gt^2$$

S = distance
g = acceleration of gravity
t = time

A ball will fall 8 feet in 0.71 second.

$$8 = \frac{1}{2}(32)\, t^2$$

S = 8	$8 = 16\, t^2$
g = 32	$\frac{8}{16} = t^2$
t = ?	$t = \sqrt{0.5}$
	$t = 0.71$

Or if the time in which a ball fell is known, the vertical distance which it fell can be determined. For example, if a ball hit the floor one-half second after release and was given no upward force to counteract the pull of gravity or downward force to add to the pull of gravity, one would know that it fell four feet.

S = ?	$S = \frac{1}{2}(32)(0.5)^2$
g = 32	$S = 16 \times 0.25$
t = 0.5	$S = 4$

This downward acceleration of 32 feet per second per second takes place independent of any horizontal motion. If one body falls freely from rest at the same time that another is projected horizontally *from the same height*, both will strike the ground at the same time. However, they will strike in different places. This is explained further in Chapter 9, Projectiles.

Air Resistance. Air resistance is present in all normal activities of the human body. In many activities it is so small a factor as to be negligible and need not be considered. However, in other activities it becomes an important factor. Air resistance varies with the physical characteristics of the object, its size, shape and weight per unit volume, and with its speed of movement. The larger the surface of resistance and the lighter the object per unit volume, the more it is affected by air resistance. This means that because of air resistance, a light object with a large surface area falls more slowly than a compact small object. This is the cause of the difficulty in hitting a badminton bird which is experienced by many beginners. Their past experience has led them to develop certain concepts of the speed with which a ball falls. Confronted by a much lighter object with a less compact surface area they fail to adjust to the slower drop of the bird. An understanding of the effect of the size, shape and weight of an object on air resistance and an opportunity to note the acceleration of the bird, while practicing simply hitting the bird upward many times, will do a great deal toward overcoming this difficulty.

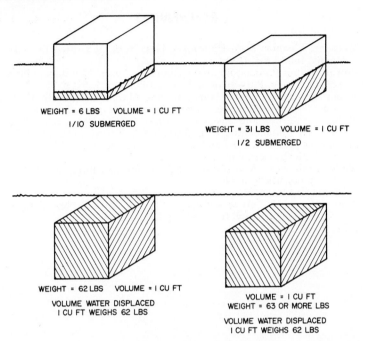

WEIGHT = 6 LBS   VOLUME = I CU FT
1/10 SUBMERGED

WEIGHT = 31 LBS   VOLUME = I CU FT
1/2 SUBMERGED

WEIGHT = 62 LBS   VOLUME = I CU FT
VOLUME WATER DISPLACED
I CU FT WEIGHS 62 LBS

VOLUME = I CU FT
WEIGHT = 63 OR MORE LBS

VOLUME WATER DISPLACED
I CU FT WEIGHS 62 LBS

Figure 7.   *Buoyancy of blocks of various weights but constant volume.*

BUOYANCY

While buoyancy does not affect all movement as does gravity, it is extremely important in all aquatic activities.

Archimedes' principle states that a body wholly or partially submerged in a fluid is buoyed up by a force equal to the weight of the displaced fluid.

This force of buoyancy, acting in an upward direction, counteracts the force of gravity to various degrees, depending upon the weight and size of the object or body which is immersed in the fluid. If an object placed in water displaces an amount of water equal in weight to the weight of the object, the object will float. If the water displaced weighs more than the object weighs, the object will float partly out of the water. It will be pushed up by the water until that part which is under the water displaces an amount of water weighing as much as the total object. If the water displaced weighs less than the object, the object will sink (Fig. 7).

REFERENCES

1. Metheny, Eleanor: *Body Dynamics*. New York, McGraw-Hill Book Company, Inc., 1951, p. 98
2. Bowen, Wilbur Pardon and Stone, Henry A.: *Applied Anatomy and Kinesiology*. 7th ed. Philadelphia, Lea and Febiger, 1953, p. 52.
3. Weber, Robert L., White, Marsh W. and Manning, Kenneth V.: *College Physics*. New York, McGraw-Hill Book Company, Inc., 1952, p. 110.
4. Williams, Marian and Lissner, Herbert R.: *Biomechanics of Human Motion*. Philadelphia, W. B. Saunders Company, 1962, p. 57.
5. Morehouse, Laurence E. and Cooper, John M.: *Kinesiology*. St. Louis, C. V. Mosby Company, 1950, p. 131.
6. Wells, Katharine: *Kinesiology*. 3rd ed. Philadelphia, W. B. Saunders Company, 1960, p. 340.
7. Williams and Lissner: *op. cit.*, p. 17.
8. White, Harvey E.: *Modern College Physics*. 3rd ed. New York, D. Van Nostrand Company, Inc., 1956, p. 35.
9. *Ibid.*, p. 38.

4

Equilibrium

In all activities, whether stationary or moving, balance is an important factor. Sometimes the purpose of a particular activity demands stability, other times instability. If the mechanical principles involved are understood maximum advantage can be taken of the forces present.

A body is balanced when its center of gravity is over its supporting base. If the line of gravity passes outside the base, the body moves downward until a new base which is directly below the center of gravity is established. It follows then, that *the nearer to the center of the base the line of gravity falls, the more stable the body.* Conversely, the nearer the line of gravity falls to the edge of the base, the more precarious is the equilibrium. One can experiment with this principle by standing with the feet slightly apart, weight centered, and asking a partner to push toward the right against the left shoulder and then, standing with the weight on the right foot, again asking the partner to push against the left shoulder. It will be noted readily that balance is more easily maintained when the weight is originally in the center of the stance because of the fact that the center of gravity has more possibility of movement before falling beyond the edge of the base, or beyond the side of the right foot.

Another factor which determines how far the center of gravity can move without falling outside the base is the size of the base. Obviously then, *the larger the base, the more*

41

stable the body. The center of gravity can move a greater distance without falling outside the base. In any activity in which stability is important the base of the body should be large enough so that the shifting of the center of gravity due to movement of the body, or body parts, will not cause the line of gravity to fall beyond the base. The principle of the large base can be easily demonstrated by standing with feet together and having a partner push against the left shoulder. If, following this, the feet are placed in a side-stride position and again the partner pushes against the left shoulder, it is obvious that balance can be maintained more easily in the side-stride position since the base is wider in this direction and the center of gravity has more opportunity to move before falling beyond its edge. There are several activities that are difficult because of the small base involved. It is this factor which constitutes a major problem in some modern dance techniques, tumbling stunts, walking a balance beam, ice skating, and toe dancing.

In making the base wider, however, several things must be considered. The first of these is the direction of the moving or opposing force. *The base should be enlarged in the direction of the moving or opposing force* to allow for a decided shift of the center of gravity without the line of gravity falling outside the base. Stability in a given direction is in proportion to the horizontal distance of the center of gravity from the edge of the base toward which a given force is being applied, or in the direction of an anticipated movement. Again, this can be easily demonstrated by standing in a side-stride position and having a partner apply force toward the right against the left shoulder and then backward against the same shoulder. If one then stands in a forward-backward stride position and has these same two forces applied, it can be easily perceived that when the force is toward the right, balance can be maintained more readily with a side-stride position and when the force is toward the back, the forward-backward stride is necessary for the maintenance of balance.

When standing or walking on a moving train the sway of the train tends to throw one sideways, and therefore balance is improved by spreading the feet sideways. However, when the train is stopping or starting a forward-backward stride is more beneficial in helping one resist the forward or backward force. This can be further demonstrated by throwing a ball as far as possible with feet together, then in a side-stride position, and finally in a forward-backward stride position. It is obvious that balance is more easily maintained in the forward-backward stride position because the base is widened in the direction of the force.

If the forward-backward stride position is taken first with the right foot forward and then with the left forward, this last experiment can point up another factor in base enlargement — the restriction of joint action. As a right-handed person throws a ball with the right foot forward, it can be noted that back-swing is definitely restricted due to the position of the hip joint. When the left foot is forward, the right hip is freed and a longer backward rotation is possible. Therefore, *any widening of the base to give greater stability should be accomplished in such a way that movement in the joints is not restricted, or strain put on any joint.* There must always be a margin for movement in all directions if injury to a joint is to be avoided in case a sudden force is contacted.

In making the base wider *another factor which must be considered is the direction of the force which is exerted by the individual against the ground.* At any time that one takes a stance wider than the hips, the legs assume a slanting position. This introduces a lateral component of force, an outward as well as a downward force. It depends upon the activity involved whether or not this is desirable. It is desirable when resisting a force from that direction provided that there is good friction between the feet and the supporting surface, the floor or the ground. On the other hand, it is definitely un-desirable if it is combined with insufficient friction between the feet and the supporting surface. For example, when standing on ice a widening of the base will not contribute to stability. In fact, it will make the feet more difficult to control as the lateral force will tend to push them out from under the body. All principles which apply to a given situation must be observed. If only some of them are observed results will not be as expected.

Whenever one body part moves away from the line of gravity in one direction, the center of gravity shifts in that direction. If this shift puts the center of gravity beyond the base, another body part must move in the opposite direction to bring the center of gravity back over the base or balance will be lost. Balance, of course, could be regained without a shift of a body part in the other direction by moving the base so that a new base is established which is under the shifting center of gravity. One can experiment with this principle simply by standing with the back to the wall, heels against the wall, and attempting to lean forward. It is im-mediately obvious that the bending of the upper body forward shifts the center of gravity beyond the forward edge of the base (the toes), and either the body falls forward or one foot is shifted forward to establish a new base which is under the forward moving center of gravity. However, if one moves a foot or so from the wall the bend can be performed with no loss of balance because the hips are free to move backward to balance the forward moving trunk.

Since various body parts are constantly moving, the center of gravity of the body is constantly shifting. If one stands in a well balanced position with the weight centered on the feet and raises both arms forward, there is an unconscious adjustment of the body backward in order to keep the center of gravity centered over the feet. By looking at an individual's profile and noting, just in front of his face, a spot on the wall beyond, and then asking him to raise both arms forward, the movement of the body backward to balance the weight of the forward arms can be perceived readily. This unconscious shifting of the body to keep the center of gravity centered over the feet can be seen also when facing an individual, noting a spot just above his head and watching the movement of his head to the left as he raises both arms to the right. Since these adjustments are made at the reflex level, they are difficult to inhibit. However, with concentration they can be resisted and then it is possible to feel the weight shift forward onto the toes when the arms are raised forward, or onto the right foot as they are raised to the right. Opposing forces are constantly at work in the body so the task of holding these in equilibrium is always present. When opposing forces acting upon a body are equal, stability is maintained. When opposing forces are not equal, stability is disturbed until additional force is available. If the requirements for additional force are too great, strain results.

External weights added to the body become part of the total body weight and affect the location of the center of gravity, displacing it in the direction of the added weight. The effect of the weight increases with its distance from the center of gravity. This involves leverage and is discussed in detail in Chapter 6. However, it should be noted that the closer to the center of gravity the weight is held, the less it changes the location of the center of gravity and the less the effort necessary to hold it. This can be demonstrated easily by holding a heavy book close to the body and then at arm's length. The more the position of the total body-plus-weight is adjusted as a unit to keep the center of gravity over the base, the less energy required to hold the weight. The balance of each body segment over the segment below is not disturbed and the body is used as a whole to counterbalance the weight.

The lower the center of gravity the more stable the body. The potential rotating force of a weight that is high increases as the weight is lifted (Chapter 6, Leverage). The higher the center of gravity, the less the object must tip before the line of gravity falls outside the base. Object "A" (Fig. 8) is weighted so that its center of gravity is low. It can, therefore, be tipped 15 degrees and the line of gravity still falls within the base. When the force which is tipping it is released, the object settles back on its original base. Object "B," however, has been weighted so that the center of gravity is high. When it is tipped to the same angle, the line of gravity falls outside the base and the object falls until it lies on its side, having established a new base which is under the center of gravity.

Some activities are more difficult because of the height of the center of gravity. Walking on stilts is one example. Another example, familiar to physical educators, is canoeing. Better balance is obtained by kneeling in the bottom of the canoe than when sitting on the seat because of the difference in height of the center of gravity. In any activity when equilibrium is precarious in the standing position, a crouching, kneeling, or sitting position should be assumed. This lowers the center of gravity and increases stability. This principle is followed when, in modern dance or conditioning exercises, the beginner is given exercises while sitting or lying on the floor. With the problem of maintaining balance minimized the student is free to concentrate on the movement which will stretch or strengthen certain given muscles. The more advanced student with better control of his balance will be able to perform the techniques in a standing position.

Forward (or backward) rotating motion increases sta-

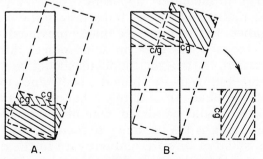

A.   B.

Figure 8. *Comparison of the stability of two objects with centers of gravity at different heights.*

bility. While the object is rotating about one axis it has great inertia to rotation about another axis. This is why, although it is extremely difficult to balance a bicycle which is still, it is easy to balance a bicycle which is in motion.

Many sensory organs are important in the maintenance of balance: the organs of the middle ear (the semicircular canals), the organs of vision, the organs of touch, and the end organs of the kinesthetic sense (the proprioceptors in the muscles, tendons, and joints). Whenever the head is rotated for any period of time, either by rolling or twirling, the fluid in the inner ear is put into motion. Because of inertia (Chapter 5) this motion of the fluid continues after the movement of the head has stopped and gives the individual a sense of continued motion although the body is actually still. When the individual attempts to make adjustments to this false sense of motion a reeling movement may result. The degree to which this can be conditioned in different individuals by training is questionable. However, it is obvious from watching a beginner the first day he attempts a forward roll, and the same student after several weeks of tumbling instruction that the training has been effective. While a beginner, after executing *one* forward roll may feel considerable dizziness and have difficulty controlling his movements, the more seasoned gymnast can execute several rolls or flips in succession and maintain control of his subsequent movements. In dance techniques involving whirling, this effect of the semicircular canals can be minimized by holding the head still momentarily between sudden turnings rather than moving it constantly in the circular motion. The organs of vision are also involved in this technique.

The importance of the eyes to balance can be demonstrated by standing on one foot with the eyes open and then closing the eyes. The difficulty of maintaining the balance with the eyes closed is immediately apparent. The eyes give a point of reference and therefore, are important in the maintenance of body balance. In the dance technique previously mentioned the dancer focuses the eyes on some object during a part of every rotation. In general, the focus should be in the direction of intended movement, since the body tends to follow the direction of the head. In walking a balance beam, running, etc., the focus should be ahead. One of the problems of the beginner in diving is his tendency to focus downward toward the board instead of upward and outward in the direction he wishes to move. Morehouse and Cooper[1] suggest that balance during movement is best maintained if focus is taken on an object that is 20 feet or more away, since the ocular muscles must make continual adjustments to keep the object in view when focus is taken on an object less than 20 feet from the individual.

The proprioceptors of the kinesthetic sense are extremely important in that when muscles* and tendons are stretched, the proprioceptors are stimulated and information as to position and movement is carried to the brain. Without this information, adjustments leading to the maintenance of balance would be impossible. The proprioceptors in the muscles, tendons, and joints of the feet and legs are important in helping to control body sway. The organs of touch are also extremely important in this function. In fact, many authorities assign to them the major role in controlling sway. The sensations of the soles of the feet are particularly important but it seems reasonable that, at the same time that the organs of touch are stimulated by the increased pressure on the balls of the feet, caused by a forward swaying of the body, the extensor muscles of the ankles and muscles of the feet are stretched stimulating the end organs of the kinesthetic sense. Both senses would, therefore, be responsible for the information received by the brain that the body is swaying forward and that a backward adjustment is necessary to maintain balance.

REFERENCES

1. Morehouse, Laurence E., and Cooper, John M.: *Kinesiology*. St. Louis, C. V. Mosby Company, 1950, p. 137.

---

*Some recent research appears to indicate that proprioceptors may not be located in muscles, but since they are located in ligaments and joints, they are stimulated when muscles are stretched or when they are contracted changing joint position.

5

Motion

Motion implies a change of place or position. It involves direction and speed. Motion of a body or object, or any part thereof, is brought about when a force of sufficient magnitude to overcome the object's inertia is applied to it. Newton formulated three Laws of Motion.

NEWTON'S LAWS OF MOTION

Newton's First Law states that *an object which is at rest or in motion will remain at rest or in motion at the same speed, in a straight line, unless acted upon by a force.* Force must be applied to set any object in motion or to change its motion, either its speed or its direction. This tendency of a body or object to remain in its present state of motion is known as *inertia*. The resistance of a body to a change in its state of motion depends upon its mass and the speed at which it is moving. The heavier the object and the faster it is moving, the more force necessary to overcome its inertia. Once the movement is started it takes less force to maintain a given speed than to change speed. It follows then, that the greater the use of momentum the less energy required. While the glide in certain swimming strokes saves considerable energy, it is important that the swimmer execute a second stroke before forward momentum from the first has been lost (due to water resistance). If the glide is maintained until momentum is lost, the energy saved by the glide will have to be used in overcoming inertia on each stroke.

The *Second Law of Motion* states that *when a body is acted upon by a force, its resulting acceleration (change in speed) is proportional to the force and inversely proportional to the mass.*

This law is expressed by the formula[1]

$$a = \frac{F}{m} \quad \text{or} \quad F = m \times a$$

In other words, given an object of a certain weight, the greater the force applied to it, the greater the speed of the object. If a force of 50 ft. lbs. were applied to a 2 pound object, the resulting acceleration would be 25 ft./sec., but if the force were doubled (100 ft. lbs.) the acceleration would also double (50 ft./sec.). Force and acceleration have a *direct* relationship.

$$a = \frac{50}{2} = 25 \text{ ft./sec.} \quad a = \frac{100}{2} = 50 \text{ ft./sec.}$$

On the other hand, given a certain force applied, the greater the weight of the object, the *less* the speed of its movement. If the force were maintained at 50 ft. lbs. but the mass of the object doubled (4 pounds), the acceleration would be *half* as great (12.5 ft./sec.). Acceleration and weight have an *inverse* relationship.

$$a = \frac{50}{4} = 12.5 \text{ ft./sec.}$$

The movement takes place in the direction of the acting force. To increase speed, force must be increased proportionately.

Newton's Third Law deals with action and reaction and states that *to every action force, there is an equal and opposite reaction force.* When the body moves, the supporting surface or other object against which it applies force develops an equal and opposite momentum. The momentum of an object is the product of its mass times its velocity.[2] This is expressed in the formula

$$M = mV \qquad \text{Momentum} = \text{mass} \cdot \text{Velocity}$$

Velocity is the distance that the object moves in a given time. Expressed as a formula this becomes[3]

$$V = \frac{S}{t} \qquad \text{Velocity} = \frac{\text{distance}}{\text{time}}$$

The effect of the equal and opposite reaction force is readily seen when the swimmer or canoe paddle pushes backward exerting a backward force against the water. The water moves backward with a certain velocity depending on the force-fulness of the stroke, and at the same time the equal and opposite force produced by the water pushing forward against the arm or canoe paddle, moves the swimmer or canoe forward. The effect of the two forces is not obvious when a runner pushes backward against the earth and the equal and opposite force produced by the earth causes him to move forward, because of the tremendous weight of the earth in relation to the weight of the runner. Since momentum is the product of mass times velocity, the velocity of the earth is infinitesimal. When one object applies force against another the mass of object one times the velocity of object one equals the mass of the second object times *its* velocity. This is expressed in the formula[4]

$$m_1 V_1 = m_2 V_2$$

It follows that the smaller the mass of one object in relation to the other, the faster will be its velocity in relation to the velocity of the other.

If a 15 pound bowling ball were traveling 20 feet per second its momentum would be 300 feet per second ($M = mV$). When it strikes a 3 pound pin which has no velocity, it will transfer some of its momentum to the pin, which being much lighter than the ball will move considerably faster than the ball was moving before impact. To calculate the exact velocity of the pin after impact, the velocity of the ball after impact must be known. For example, if the ball were still moving at 10 feet per second, its momentum would have dropped 150 feet per second.*

Loss of momentum = momentum before impact − momentum after impact
$$= 15 \times 20 \ (mV \ \text{before}) - 15 \times 10 \ (mV \ \text{after})$$
$$= 300 \ \text{ft./sec.} - 150 \ \text{ft./sec.}$$
$$= 150 \ \text{ft./sec.}$$

This momentum would have been transferred to the pin and it would fly off at a velocity of 50 feet per second.

$$\text{Momentum} = mV$$
$$\text{Momentum of pin} = m_p \times V_p$$
$$150 \ \text{ft./sec.} = 3 \times V_p$$
$$V_p = \frac{150}{3}$$
$$= 50 \ \text{ft./sec.}$$

---

*These velocities are theoretical and chosen for ease of calculation to illustrate the point.

The force of the pin on the ball would deflect the ball, but since the ball is so much heavier, the ball would be deflected much less than the pin. The lighter the ball, the more it is deflected from its original path when it strikes a pin. This is one of the reasons for using as heavy a ball as can be easily controlled.

A runner is propelled forward with a force equal and opposite to that with which he pushes backward against the ground, provided that there is sufficient friction and resistance to prevent slipping. The equal and opposite momentum is obvious when one attempts to run in sand. Since the sand is not solid and the mass of each grain in contact with the foot is so small, the grains of sand move readily (considerable velocity) in response to the runner's backward push. The forward force exerted by them against the runner is slight. Only when the grains of sand have become packed so that they become, in effect, a part of a large solid mass is enough force exerted to move the runner forward with any speed.

When the body is unsupported in the air, as it is in diving and many tumbling stunts, and a body part moves, the equal and opposite reaction of other parts of the body can be seen. This principle is, therefore, important in fancy diving, in stunts on the trampoline, and tumbling stunts executed in the air.

TYPES OF MOTION

Observation of people and objects in motion indicates that there is an almost endless variety of ways in which they move. They may move along the ground, freely through the air, or through the air while attached to another object. The body itself may move through the air while some body part is attached to an object which in turn may be still or moving,* and objects may move through the air while attached to some body part, implement or machine. They may move in a straight, curved, or angled path; they may slide, roll, swing, bounce, rotate, or sail through the air. However, when the basic characteristics of all these movements are studied, it is found that there are actually two types of motion—linear and angular— and all movement can be classified as being essentially one or the other, or a combination of the two.

Angular (also called rotatory or rotary) _motion_ is characterized by movement around an axis with all parts of the

---

*Examples of such movement are movements performed on the horizontal bar (a body segment attached to a still object) and on a trapeze (a moving object).

object moving in an arc. The spokes of a wheel, a spinning ball, a paper cutter, scissors, the legs, in fact all levers, carry out this type of motion. This motion may be a small arc or a full circle. The spokes of a wheel and a spinning ball move in a full circle, the legs in a smaller arc.

The second type of motion, *linear* (also called translatory) is characterized by the progression of the body as a whole with all parts moving the same distance, in the same direction, at a uniform rate of speed. A block pushed straight across the floor moves linearly. The human body experiences linear motion when it is carried forward on a train, in a plane, or in a car.

Many objects, including the human body, may experience linear movement of the whole by means of angular motion of some of their parts. In walking the human body experiences linear motion as a result of the angular motion of its legs. The movement of the legs that carries the body as a whole linearly is actually a series of two angular motions. The upper end of the thigh and the body attached to it rotate forward around the foot as an axis. The axis then shifts to the hip joint and the leg rotates forward around this joint (Chapter 11, Walking). In skiing downhill the skier experiences pure linear motion, but in skiing cross country his linear motion results from the angular motion of his extremities. The same is true of the child on roller skates, although the skates themselves always move linearly as a result of the angular (rotary) motion of their wheels.

A great deal of movement is not strictly linear or rotatory, but rather a combination of the two. As was noted the act of walking takes place because of the rotatory motion of the legs but the body as a whole is moved linearly. A car, a train, a bicycle, a wheelbarrow, in fact anything on wheels moves linearly as a result of angular motion of its wheels. "The angular motions of several segments of the body are frequently coordinated in such a way that a related segment will move linearly."[5] This happens in the thrust in fencing and boxing, the push shot in basketball, the shot put, and in any push or pull executed by the hands and arms. In executing a jump for height the various segments (levers) of the legs experience rotatory motion which gives upward linear motion to the body as a whole.

Many objects have a form of motion that is not strictly linear but rather curvilinear. The flight of a ball, an arrow, in fact any projectile (Chapter 9), carries out this curvilinear motion. The motion is linear at the start but gravity, air resistance, or friction act upon the object to make the motion curvilinear. It is possible for this curvilinear motion to be an actual arc, even a complete circle. Frequently circular motion is indicated as a third type of motion. It is actually a type of angular motion if all parts move in an arc about an axis, or curvilinear if the object moves as a whole in a circular path. An excellent example of this type of motion – a person riding on a merry-go-round – was noted by Wells.[6] The person is moving as a whole in a circular path. The merry-go-round itself is, of course, experiencing rotatory motion since it is turning about its axis. An ice skater in performing a figure eight experiences curvilinear motion. He moves in a curved path; he is not rotating about an axis with which he is in contact. A discus moves in a circular path during the thrower's turn, and since it is held in the hand it becomes a part of the arm-hand lever that is rotating around the moving axis of the feet. Therefore during this time it could be said to be moving angularly, although it is in a situation similar to that of the person on the merry-go-round. Once it is released it moves linearly but the path is made curvilinear by gravity.

When the body, or an object, is carried forward as a whole owing to the movement of another object, such as when an individual rides in a car, it acquires the motion of the object to which it is attached and due to inertia it tends to keep moving in that same direction and at that speed. When a car stops suddenly the individual is likely to move forward off the seat because of the linear motion (and resulting inertia) which he has developed because of movement of the car. A ball or discus held in the hand acquires the same motion as the hand and if the contact is released it continues to move with the speed the hand was moving at release until acted upon by another force.

Even though an object is made to move in a circle it has a tendency to move in a straight line. Two forces are acting on it, the force causing motion and the force holding the object to the center of the arc. A stone whirled on the end of a piece of string is itself experiencing linear motion but in this case it is attached to an axis by means of the string. Therefore, the motion, while the string is in contact with the axis, is really rotatory. However, if the string is released, contact with the axis is broken, and the force bringing about motion causes the stone to move in a linear path (made curvilinear by gravity). The force pulling toward the center of motion (toward the axis), is known as *centripetal force*. The outward pull is the equal and opposite action force and is known as *centrifugal force*.

If the centripetal force, that holding the object to its circular or curved path, is suddenly released, the equal and opposite centrifugal force is also released and the only force left to act on the object is the object's inertia. Since it tends to keep moving in the same direction and at the same speed the object will fly off in a straight line (linear motion), tangent to the arc through which it was moving at the moment of release. This centripetal force, and therefore the centrifugal force, depend on weight, speed, and the radius of curvature of the arc. The formula[7] is:

$$F_c = \frac{mv^2}{r} \text{ or Centrifugal force} = \frac{\text{mass} \times \text{velocity}^2}{\text{radius}}$$

The centrifugal force increases as the weight (mass) increases, but since it increases as the *square* of the velocity, speed is a greater factor in increasing centrifugal force than is weight. Increasing the length of the radius, however, *decreases* the centrifugal force and the shorter the radius the greater the centrifugal force. These relationships are illustrated in the following situations:

Situation	Mass of Object	Velocity	Radius
1	1 lb.	20 ft./sec.	2 ft.
2	2 lbs.	20 ft./sec.	2 ft.
3	1 lb.	40 ft./sec.	2 ft.
4	1 lb.	20 ft./sec.	1 ft.

$$F_c 1 = \frac{1 \cdot 20^2}{2} = \frac{1 \cdot 400}{2} = \frac{400}{2} = 200 \text{ ft. lbs.}$$

$$F_c 2 = \frac{2 \cdot 20^2}{2} = \frac{2 \cdot 400}{2} = \frac{800}{2} = 400 \text{ ft. lbs. (when mass doubled)}$$

$$F_c 3 = \frac{1 \cdot 40^2}{2} = \frac{1 \cdot 1600}{2} = \frac{1600}{2} = 800 \text{ ft. lbs. (when velocity doubled)}$$

$$F_c 4 = \frac{1 \cdot 20^2}{1} = \frac{1 \cdot 400}{1} = \frac{400}{1} = 400 \text{ ft. lbs. (when radius halved)}$$

Since the linear velocity of an object moving in an arc equals the rotatory velocity times the length of the radius of the arc,[7, 8] the inverse relationship of the length of radius is again apparent when rotatory velocity is considered.

$$\text{Lin. V} = \text{Rot. V} \times \text{radius} \text{ or } \text{Rot. V}^* = \frac{\text{Lin. V}}{\text{radius}}$$

---

*Rotatory velocity expressed in radians per second.

Therefore, the longer the radius, the less the rotatory velocity and the shorter the radius, the higher the rotatory velocity.

This relationship of rotatory velocity to length of radius can be demonstrated effectively by attaching a string to a small weight and putting the other end of the string through a hole bored in a piece of wood. Moving the wood in a small horizontal circle gives force which moves the weight in a circle, since it is held by the string. If, while the same amount of force is being applied to move the wood at the same speed, the string is suddenly pulled up so that the distance from the point where it crosses the wood to the weight (radius of the weight's circle) is shortened, the increase in speed of the weight can be seen clearly. The skater draws his arms to his body for a fast turn and extends them to slow the turn. A diver in a tucked position rotates more rapidly than one in a pike or lay out position. LaDue and Norman[9] point out that to be completely correct the length of the radius of rotation is the distance from the center of rotation to the center of gravity of the mass away from the center of rotation. In other words, in twisting and twirling the true radius of rotation is not the distance from the center of rotation to the fingertips, but rather the distance to a point somewhere in the general location of the elbow which would be the center of gravity of the part of the body to that side of the center of rotation. In the case of a somersault the radius would extend to a point closer to the knees than the toes. However, the radius of rotation decreases as the extremities are brought in close to the body. Centripetal and centrifugal force are present in all motions of the various parts of the body, since all parts move around some joint. Muscles must, therefore, control the tendency of the end of the lever to move in a straight line — they must stabilize the bones at the joints.

The factors which determine the type of motion that will result when force is applied are the point at which the force is applied and the pathway of movement available to the object or body. If force is applied through the center of gravity of the object, and the object is free to move in the direction in which the force is applied, linear motion will result. Force applied uniformly against an entire side of an object, or equal forces applied equidistant from the center of gravity, can be considered to be the same as a single force applied through the center of gravity, since the forces on all sides of the center of gravity are balanced. If force is applied away from the center of gravity of the object, the object will rotate. This, of course, is the way spin is put on a ball. If an object is not free to move linearly – one end is held in place or meets interference – the object will rotate whether or not the force is applied through the center of gravity. For example, if one were pushing a large carton on wheels across a clear surface and the force were applied through the center of gravity, it would move linearly in the direction of the force. However, if the left wheel contacted a stick, rock or other obstacle that interfered with its forward movement, the carton would begin to turn to the left even with a centered force. Friction commonly causes rotary motion to result even though force is applied through the center of gravity. If friction is such that the base of an object does not move readily, force applied through the center of gravity will cause the object to tip. Since the top is freely movable but friction interferes with the movement of the bottom, the force is more effective in moving the top than the bottom and the object tips. Since, by definition, a lever has a fixed point, rotary motion always results when force is applied at ANY POINT on a lever.

FACTORS MODIFYING MOTION

There are several factors which modify motion. These may be a help or a hindrance depending upon the situation. The first of these is *friction*. Friction is the force which opposes the motion of one object across the surface of another object. It is caused by the roughness of the two surfaces, and therefore varies with the material of the two surfaces. It is expressed as a coefficient of friction. This coefficient of friction between two objects can be found by placing one object on the second and slowly tilting the second until the first begins to slide downward. The tangent of the angle of the surface of the second object with the horizontal at the instant the first object *begins to slide* gives the coefficient of friction between the two objects. This can be figured by dividing the height to which one end of the second object had been lifted when the first began to slide, by the distance from the angle to the point directly below the end of the lifted object.[10]

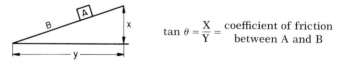

$$\tan \theta = \frac{X}{Y} = \begin{array}{l}\text{coefficient of friction} \\ \text{between A and B}\end{array}$$

Figure 9.   *Figuring coefficient of friction.*

If the surface had been raised 2 inches (X) when A began to slide down B and the distance from the angle to the point below the end of object B was 6 inches (Y), the tangent of the angle formed (θ) would be:

$$\frac{2}{6} = .3333$$

which would be the coefficient of friction between A and B.

The coefficient of friction is independent of area of surface in contact[11] and is dependent only on the total downward force[12] (weight plus any additional force pushing the object against the surface) and the type of surface (or surfaces) involved. In other words, whether the base of a 50 pound object is four square feet or eight square feet, the friction between it and any given surface is the same. When the WEIGHT is changed *or* the MATERIAL of the object's base *or* the surface on which the object rests is changed, the friction is different. Friction increases proportionally with weight, i.e., the greater the weight of the object to be moved, the greater the friction to be overcome. It also increases and decreases according to the coefficient of friction of the materials of which the two surfaces are made. If some downward force is added to the weight of the object, friction is increased proportionally. If one pushes a heavy piece of furniture with the hands toward its top edge, the force applied is downward as well as forward. The downward component is not only wasted as far as forward momentum is concerned, but adds to the task by increasing the friction to be overcome. The frictional force depends not only on the material of the surfaces in contact but also on their condition. The friction of skis on snow changes drastically with different snow conditions. To offset this the skier changes the condition of the ski surface by applying various types of wax.

Sliding friction is many times greater than rolling friction. Therefore, whenever possible a heavy object is put on wheels. "The harder a rolling wheel or ball, and the harder the surface over which it rolls, the less is the force of rolling friction."[13] This is obvious in the longer roll of a golf ball on a dry, hard fairway over that of a ball with similar momentum on a fair way of thick grass. It is obvious when one attempts to push a wheelbarrow through loose dirt or sand instead of over a hard surface.

Friction is a help to man in the performance of tasks necessitating the application of a diagonally forward and upward force to (or through) the human body — tasks in which he must push downward and backward against the supporting surface. Without it the runner, broad jumper, thrower, or pusher could not exert maximum force without danger of slipping, because the backward component of his diagonal force would have no force to resist it and push back against him. On the other hand, friction hinders the movement of any object being pushed or pulled as well as a rolling ball.

The second factor that modifies motion is *air resistance*. Without air resistance a sailboat could not move, an airplane could not fly. On the other hand air resistance can be a great hindrance to movement. Unless it is a tailwind, the golfer or the runner finds that air resistance hinders movement considerably. Badminton, because the light weight and lack of compactness of the shuttle make it so responsive to air pressure, is extremely difficult to play outdoors unless the air is unusually still.

A third factor modifying motion is *water resistance*. Water resistance is somewhat different from the other factors mentioned in that it both assists and hinders movement at the same time. It is essential to the propulsion of the body, or boat, through the water and at the same time it hinders the progress of the same body or boat. Since backward force against the water causes an equal and opposite force which sends the body forward, and since the broader the surface pushing against the water, the greater the water resistance, the problem is to present the broadest surface possible when applying force in the direction opposite to the direction of desired movement, and the smallest possible surface in the direction of the desired movement. Thus, the blade of the paddle is moved backward flat against the water but it is feathered (edge forward) as it is moved forward. The swimmer pushes back against the water with the full arm but the arm is either taken out of the water, or bent and kept close to the body as it moves forward on recovery.

Finally, the fourth factor which modifies motion is *gravity*. While this force must be considered in all movement, it has been discussed in Chapter 3 and, therefore, is not included here.

The magnitude of the applied force relative to the magnitude of the resistance is the all-important factor causing motion.[14] In all movement tasks one needs to understand the methods for taking advantage of these forces when they contribute to the movement, and for minimizing them when they hamper the movement.

REFERENCES

1. White, Harvey E.: *Modern College Physics*. 3rd ed. New York, D. Van Nostrand Company, Inc., 1956, p. 42.
2. *Ibid.*, p. 46.
3. *Ibid.*, p. 18.
4. Weber, Robert L., White, Marsh W., and Manning, Kenneth V.: *College Physics*. New York, McGraw-Hill Book Company, Inc., 1952, p. 133.
5. Wells, Katharine F.: *Kinesiology*. 3rd ed. Philadelphia, W. B. Saunders Company, 1960, p. 296.
6. Wells, Katharine F.: *Kinesiology*. 2nd ed. Philadelphia, W. B. Saunders Company, 1955, p. 304.
7. Weber, Robert L., White, Marsh W., and Manning, Kenneth V.: *College Physics*. New York, McGraw-Hill Book Company, Inc., 1952, p. 147.
8. White, Harvey E.: *Modern College Physics*. 3rd ed. New York, D. Van Nostrand Company, Inc., 1956, pp. 115–116.
9. LaDue, Frank, and Norman, Jim: *This is Trampolining*. Cedar Rapids, Iowa, Torch Press, 1956, pp. 73–74.
10. Weber, Robert L., White, Marsh W., and Manning, Kenneth V.: *College Physics*. New York, McGraw-Hill Book Company, Inc., 1952, p. 74.
11. *Ibid.*, p. 71.
12. White, Harvey E.: *Modern College Physics*. 3rd ed. New York, D. Van Nostrand Company, Inc., 1956, p. 87.
13. *Ibid.*, p. 90.
14. Wells, Katharine F.: *Kinesiology*. 3rd ed. Philadelphia, W. B. Saunders Company, 1960, p. 294.

6

Leverage

Levers are used many times a day, in the kitchen, the garden, the workshop, and on the sportsfield. When a knife is used to lift a lid, a bottle opener to pry off the top of a bottle, a nutcracker to crack the shell of a nut, scissors to cut cloth, the head of a hammer to pull out a nail, a wheelbarrow to transport a load, a crowbar to lift a heavy rock, or any bone of the body is moved, leverage is involved.

A lever is a rigid bar which revolves around a fixed point called a fulcrum, or axis. It has two important functions.

FUNCTIONS OF LEVERS

A lever is used to *gain a mechanical advantage* so that a small force exerted over a great distance is converted into a *larger force* operating over a lesser distance, or *speed* is gained. Speed and range of motion are linked together. If two levers move through an angle of 40 degrees at the same velocity (Fig. 10) the tip of the longer lever (AC), travels much farther than the tip of the shorter lever (AB), and because it covers this longer distance (CE) in the same time that the shorter lever covers the shorter distance (BD), it must travel faster. When a lever moves about its axis the distance that all points on the lever move is proportional to their distance from the axis. If a point is twice as far from the axis, it will move twice as far and, therefore, twice as fast.

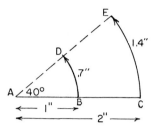

Figure 10. *Relationship of length of lever to speed and range of movement.*

TYPES OF LEVERS

Levers are of three types according to the relationship of the fixed point (the axis) to the points of application of force and resistance. When the axis (or fulcrum) is located between the resistance and the force, the lever is of the first class. The *first class lever* may have force and resistance arms that are equal (i.e., the force and resistance are equidistant from the axis), the force arm may be longer than the resistance arm (the force farther than is the resistance from the axis) in which case the lever favors force, or the resistance arm may be longer (the force closer than is the resistance to the axis) in which case the lever favors speed (Fig. 11). This lever may favor speed or force depending upon the relative lengths of the force and resistance arms. Some examples of this type of lever are the crowbar, scissors, arm extension at the elbow, the head on the neck, and extension of the foot when it is not bearing weight.

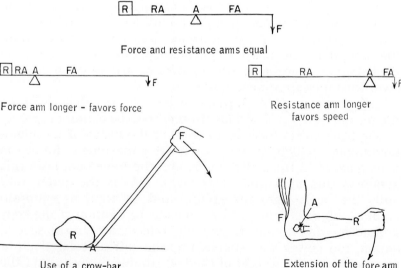

Figure 11. *First class levers. A = axis (fulcrum); F = force; R = resistance; FA = force arm (distance from force to axis); RA = resistance arm (distance from resistance to axis).*

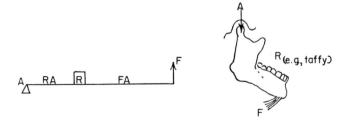

Figure 12.   *Second class levers—favor force.*

The *second class lever* always has a force arm which is longer than the resistance arm, since the resistance is located between the axis and the point of application of the force. Therefore, it favors force. This force advantage is gained at the expense of speed and range of motion (Fig. 12). Examples of this class lever are found in the wheelbarrow, the nutcracker, and a door when opened by use of the knob.

There are very few levers of the second class in the human body. Cates[1] describes the opening of the jaw as the action of a lever of this class (Fig. 12). Many textbooks, in analyzing the mechanics of rising onto the toes, have indicated that the action is that of a second class lever with the fulcrum at the toes, the weight of the body falling on the instep, and the force applied at the insertion of the Achilles tendon on the heel. In 1919, Rogers[2] analyzed it as the action of a first class lever with the fulcrum at the ankle joint, the weight of the body falling over the toes, and the force applied at the insertion of the Achilles tendon. In experimentation he found that the force exerted by the calf muscles was much greater than the weight of the body. He explained this as being due to the relatively shorter length of the force arm of the first class lever (distance from heel to ankle).

However, in 1950, Karpovich[3] pointed out that rising on the toes involves two actions. In the first, the center of gravity of the body shifts forward in front of the heads of the meta-tarsal bones which are the axis for this movement. Since the resistance is in front of the axis and the force behind it, this action is that of a first class lever. This is the action that pulls the heels from the ground and, in order to maintain equilibrium, it is followed by a backward rotation of the body around the ankle joint. Karpovich stated that, "In the second action, the power was supplied by the calf muscles; load or resistance, by the weight of the body minus the weight of the feet; and the fulcrum, by the talotibial joint. This system when the subject stood normally belonged to the first class lever also, but when the body began to lean forward, and the attachment of the calf muscles on the leg shifted in front of the fulcrum, it became a third class lever."[4] Since this second action actually involves a backward rotation of the body around the ankle joint as the axis with the calf muscles supplying the force to pull the body backward, it would seem that the body becomes the lever, rather than the foot. The weight of the body concentrated at the center of gravity is the resistance, and since the calf muscles act on the body between the ankle joint (the axis) and this resistance, this action is that of a third class lever.

This explanation is not in opposition to the experimental evidence offered by Rogers. The difference lies in the interpretation of the evidence. Rogers assumed that the contraction of the calf muscles was responsible for the elevation of the heel. This assumption makes the foot the lever as he described. Karpovich found experimentally that the heel lift actually is caused by the body lean and that the calf muscles act to pull

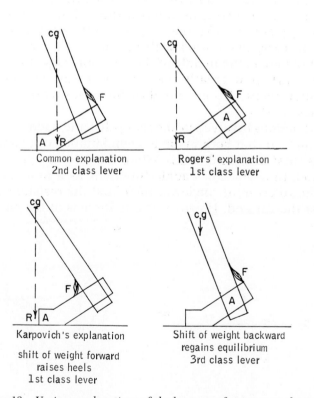

Figure 13. *Various explanations of the leverage of rising onto the toes.*

the body weight backward in order to restore equilibrium. Essentially the body becomes a third class lever. In a third class lever force always exceeds resistance because the force arm is shorter. Therefore, to move the body backward the calf muscles would have to exert more force than the weight of the body. The various explanations are diagramed in Figure 13.

In the *third class lever* the force acts at a point between the axis and the resistance and, therefore, the resistance arm is always longer than the force arm (Fig. 14). This type of lever favors range of motion and speed at the expense of force. Flexion of the lower arm and extension of the lower leg are examples of this class lever. In fact, the human body is essentially a system of third class levers.

There are many levers which fall into different classes depending upon the way in which they are used. A door is a second class lever when opened or closed by means of force applied at the knob, and therefore it takes little force to produce the movement. The resistance (the center of gravity of the door) is between the point of application of force (the knob) and the axis (the hinges). However, when the door is closed by a mechanical device it becomes a third class lever since the force is applied between the hinges and the center of the door (Fig. 15). Experimentation with pushing open a door by pressure at the knob, the middle of the door, and close to the hinges shows clearly how greatly the force necessary to produce the same movement of the same door increases as the force arm becomes shorter.

The actions involved in shoveling dirt and paddling a canoe are similar in that both involve a combination of two leverage actions (first and third class). When the force is applied by the top hand, the shovel or paddle functions as a first class lever with the fulcrum at the lower hand and the resistance acting against the far end. However, some force is at the same time

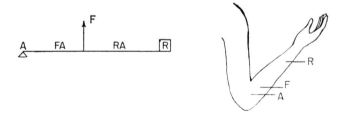

Figure 14. *Third class levers favor speed and range of motion.*

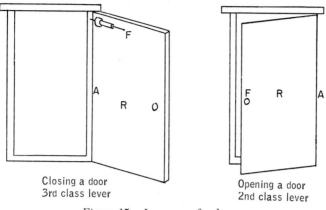

Closing a door
3rd class lever

Opening a door
2nd class lever

Figure 15. *Leverage of a door.*

applied by the lower hand and this results in third class leverage since the fulcrum for this force is the upper hand and this
force is, therefore, applied between the fulcrum and the
resistance.

PRINCIPLE OF LEVERS

The term "moment of force" is used to describe the effective force producing rotatory motion. The moment of force is
determined by multiplying the magnitude of the force by the
perpendicular distance between the point at which the force
is applied and the fulcrum (length of the force arm).[5] When a
lever is in equilibrium, the moment producing clockwise force
(force times the length of force arm) is equal to the moment
producing counterclockwise force (resistance times the length
of the resistance arm).[6]

$$F \cdot FA = R \cdot RA$$

Any additional force will produce motion.

The reaction of a lever is in proportion to its length.
Even a slight movement at the end of a long lever causes
considerable reaction at the other end. This is the principle
applied by a tightrope walker carrying a very long pole. The
longer the force arm, the greater the moment of force about
the axis.

If a 1500 pound weight is to be lifted by an application of
150 pounds of force, the lever will need to have a mechanical
advantage of 1500 divided by 150 or 10. In other words, the
force arm will have to be ten times as long as the resistance

arm if this weight is to be lifted with this amount of force.*

$$Since\ F \cdot FA = R \cdot RA$$
$$150 \cdot FA = 1500 \cdot RA$$
$$FA = \frac{1500}{150} \cdot RA$$
$$FA = 10\ RA$$

The longer the force arm the less energy it takes to balance the lever, and the longer the weight or resistance arm the more force necessary to balance it. However, the longer the weight arm the greater the range and speed of motion. Obviously then, for strength tasks a lever with a long force arm in relation to the weight arm should be used, and when movements requiring range or speed of motion and involving relatively light weights are desired the resistance arm should be lengthened.

LEVERS OF THE HUMAN BODY

In the human body the lever is the bone, the fulcrum is the joint at which the movement takes place, and the force is supplied by the contraction of the muscles innervated by the nerves and applied at the point where the muscles insert on the bone. Since muscles pull at an angle and the effective force arm is the *perpendicular* distance from the point of force application to the axis, the length of the force arm for a muscle *cannot* be determined by measuring the distance from the point of insertion to the joint. The *perpendicular* distance from the muscle to the joint must be determined (Chapter 7, p. 76). The resistance is the weight of the body part plus any added weight, and it is applied at the center of gravity of the body part plus the added weight. For example, if the forearm is being raised the elbow is the axis, the force is supplied by the flexor muscles at their point of insertion on the forearm, and the resistance is the weight of the forearm applied at its center of gravity. However, if a book were held in the hand, the resistance would then become the weight of the forearm PLUS the weight of the book and would be applied considerably farther from the elbow since the center of gravity of the forearm PLUS the book would be at this point. The

---

*Efficiency can be calculated by the length of the lever arm only when friction is not involved.

direction of resistance is straight downward (pull of gravity) *unless* the body is in the water, moving through strong air resistance, or contacting some other outside force.

With few exceptions, the levers of the body are of the third class. They have a shorter force than resistance arm since the muscles insert close to the joint and the weight is concentrated farther from the joint. The human body, therefore, favors speed and range of motion at the expense of force.

On the whole, the levers of the human body are long and therefore, the distal ends can move rapidly. Therefore "wide movements of the body can be made with speed, but at the expense of large muscle forces."[7] The human body does easily those tasks which involve fast movement with light objects, throwing a ball, for example. When heavy work is demanded the human body must use some type of machine such as a crowbar to gain a force advantage. Sport instruments lengthen the levers of the body still further and greatly increase the speed of the object imparting force, but their use also adds greatly to the muscular effort required. A relatively small difference in the weight of a piece of sports equipment (since this weight is so far from the axis) makes a considerable difference in the demand made on the muscles that are involved in moving it. Therefore, it is important that each individual use equipment suited to *his* strength.

Leverage of the human body rarely, if ever, involves a single body part (a simple lever). Instead movement results from a system of levers functioning together. Even when movement of a single lever does take place, many other parts of the body must be immobilized. When the force produced by the human system of levers is dependent upon speed at the extremity, the levers function in sequence, each coming into action at the time that the one before has reached its maximum speed. However, when many levers are brought into a heavier task, such as pushing, they function simultaneously (Chapter 7, Force).

REFERENCES

1. Cates, H. A. and Basmajian, J. V.: *Primary Anatomy.* 3rd ed. Baltimore, Williams and Wilkins Company, 1955, p. 108.
2. Rogers, James Frederick: The Leverage of the Foot. *Anat. Rec.,* 16:317-318, 1919.
3. Karpovich, Peter V.: Mechanics of Rising on the Toes. Abstract of a Paper presented at the National Convention of the American Association for Health, Physical Education and Recreation, Dallas, Texas, April 18, 1950.

4. *Ibid.*, p. 2.
5. Weber, Robert L., White, Marsh W. and Manning, Kenneth V.: *College Physics*. New York, McGraw-Hill Book Company, Inc., 1952, pp. 107–108.
6. White, Harvey E.: *Modern College Physics*. 3rd ed. New York, D. Van Nostrand Company, Inc., 1956, p. 141.
7. Williams, Marian and Lissner, Herbert R.: *Biomechanics of Human Motion*. Philadelphia, W. B. Saunders Company, 1962, p. 61.

7

Force

In Chapter 5 the fact that motion results only when sufficient force to overcome the object's inertia is applied, was
discussed. It follows that energy expended to move a body or
change its motion, either its direction or speed, is a force
applied. Essentially this energy is expended as either a push or
a pull. The major types of force that cause the human body to
move are the internal force produced by the body itself, an
external force applied by another person, an animal, a machine, the wind, etc., and the downward pull of gravity.

PRODUCTION AND APPLICATION OF FORCE

Whether the body is producing force to move itself, or to
resist or react to an external force, the force must be supplied
by muscles innervated by nerves. Since muscles exert force
by shortening, the force exerted by them is a pull. In applying
force, whether to move the body or some object, the objective
of the movement must be considered. It is necessary to consider whether the desired outcome calls for a maximum production of force available in the body or a controlled application of force. An all-out effort, and therefore maximum force,
is required if the purpose is to throw as far or as fast as possible,
or to jump as far or as high as possible. On the other hand,
many a putt has been missed in golf because too much force
was used, and many a catch has been fumbled because the ball
came to the receiver from a short distance too forcefully. In

applying force one must consider the amount of force to be applied (its magnitude), the direction of its application, the point of application, and the distance over which it is applied.

Magnitude of Force. The first point concerning magnitude has already been stated, that is, that the force must be sufficient to overcome the inertia of the object if movement is to result. The greater an object's mass, or any resistive forces such as friction and the surrounding media of air or water, the greater its inertia and the more force necessary to move it.

The amount of force produced depends upon the magnitude of the propelling force and its duration. The magnitude of the force in turn depends on the mass and speed of the object imparting the force. The greater the mass of the object imparting the force and the faster that it is moving, the greater the force imparted, all other things being equal. As was stated earlier (Chapter 5) momentum depends upon mass and velocity. A slowly moving object can have great momentum if it is very heavy (train, truck, etc.). A small object can have great momentum because of the speed with which it is moving (bullet, arrow, golf ball, etc.). Velocity is the product of acceleration times the time over which the acceleration takes place. This is expressed in the formula[1]:

$$V = at \qquad \text{Velocity} = \text{acceleration} \cdot \text{time}$$

Thus, the greater the distance, and thus the time over which an object is accelerated, the greater the velocity and therefore, the greater the momentum possible; the longer the force is applied to the object, the greater the force imparted, all other things being equal.

The greatest total force is attainable when all of the forces that can contribute to the desired outcome are employed at their maximum and in sequence. All body parts that can contribute to the desired movement should be used if maximum force is the objective. The fewer *noncontributing* muscles that are contracted, the less the energy wasted. It must be remembered that muscles can contribute to a movement while not being *directly* involved in its production. They may be carrying out the extremely important task of a restraining or holding action which involves considerable tension within the muscle.[2] A movement is efficient when opposing muscle groups work in harmony. If both groups contract with the same amount of force at the same time no movement results, only tension and fixation. If they do not work in harmony, jerky or uncontrolled movement results. Frequently, difficulty in learning a skill arises because of a generalized contraction caused by an emotional disturbance such as fear of the water, fear of any unknown, or feelings of frustration. The tension of the beginning swimmer is well known. In such cases contraction of muscles which *in no way contribute* to the desired movement wastes energy and interferes with the production of the movement. On the other hand, difficulty in producing effective movement may result from the student's failure to stabilize certain body segments so that they can become a base for the segment which must move. A crawl stroke is not effective unless the trunk and shoulder girdle are fixed as a base upon which the arms can act. Nor can the breast stroke be effective if the pelvis is not fixed so that it is a solid base for leg action. In throwing a baseball, the feet against the floor must provide a base for leg action, the pelvis, for trunk action and the trunk, for shoulder and arm action.

The body may produce a great deal of force but unless there is a firm base for the action, this force is not effective. Thus, the effectiveness of a force produced by the body is dependent upon the fixation of the origins of the muscles involved, by other muscles, in order to give a firm base on which to act, and upon the interaction between the body and the supporting surface. For example, in pushing, the scapulae must be held against the ribs if the push is to be effective against the object and not simply push the scapulae out away from the ribs. There must be sufficient friction between the feet and the ground so that the feet do not slide backward, or the force will be effective in pushing the body backward rather than the object forward.

Strong tasks require the body to resist considerable equal and opposite force. To resist such force there must be effective fixation through many body segments. If one were to attempt to push an automobile, it would be useless to approach the car on the run and attempt to push it when contact was made. Rather the whole body is set in the position for maximum forward pushing force (Chapter 16) and then the force is applied. Less energy is required to carry out a heavy task when the muscles that are to perform the given work get set before contacting the load.[3] For an individual with weak wrists, even contacting the fast moving tennis ball at the end of the long lever becomes a heavy task and therefore, it is wise for this individual to set the wrist muscles before starting the swing.

The body, being a system of third class levers (Chapter 6), can be an effective instrument for the production of speed of relatively light objects. Obviously, the faster the muscular contraction the faster the end of the lever will move and therefore, speed of muscular contraction is an important factor in the amount of force produced in all relatively light tasks, those in which force depends largely on speed (for example, throwing, striking, running, jumping).

On the other hand, the slower the muscular contraction, the less the energy required.[4] For relatively light speed tasks such as throwing a ball, fast muscular contraction is needed since force is dependent on speed; while for strong tasks a slow, steady maximum contraction is needed. When the body wishes to produce the considerable amount of force required to move a very heavy object, it is wise to make use of tools that give a force advantage.

When several muscle groups are cooperating in the production of force for a given purpose, the total effective force is the sum of the forces produced by all groups if all are applied in the same direction and in the proper sequence. When forces are added successively, each should be applied when the one before has reached its peak (*is moving with its greatest velocity and least acceleration*).[5] If maximum force is to be produced in relatively light tasks in which the force is largely dependent upon speed (for example, throwing and striking skills), the contractions should be sequential, starting at a fixed point and moving through the body reaching the extremity last. Each part should be brought into the movement when the part below has reached its maximum speed. However, in heavy tasks such as pushing, the forces are applied simultaneously. The total effective force is limited by the weakest force of the group.

Obviously, more force is available from strong than from weak muscles. When a task demanding a good deal of force is involved, the stronger the muscles called into play, the more efficient the action and the less the muscular strain. To avoid strain the strongest muscles that are available to the particular task to be performed should be used. All muscles are not equal in potential maximum force and, therefore, are not equally adapted to the task of supplying force. The magnitude of muscular force is directly proportional to the number and size of the muscle fibers contracting.[6] This is referred to as the cross section of the muscle. Strength of a muscle group can be increased by use, but to increase strength a muscle must be overloaded, either the intensity of contraction or its duration (or both) must be greater than is normal for the muscle. As was pointed out in Chapter 2, many of the difficulties which are encountered in the performance of sport skills are due to lack of strength. The student may understand the mechanics of the skill but if he lacks the strength to carry them out no amount of discussion of his incorrect movement will be of help to him. Exercises to condition the weak muscles are essential.

The more fully a muscle is stretched the greater its potential force. As it shortens, its force diminishes. Zoethout and Tuttle[7] stated that in an active muscle the amount of energy liberated during contraction increases as the initial length of the muscle increases.

When the internal resistance of a muscle is decreased before the maximum task is undertaken, less energy is required to carry out the task. This points to the importance of the use of some method for warming up the muscles to be involved. The internal resistance can be reduced by submaximal contractions and by warming the muscles with hot water, methods which gradually increase circulation through the muscle. There has been some argument in the literature concerning the importance of warm-ups. While it may be possible to produce maximum force without previous warm-up, the muscular soreness which results is familiar to all. Until more evidence to the contrary is available, it seems reasonable that increasing circulation gradually before making an all-out muscular effort is advisable.

Direction of Application of Force. Unless hindered by some other force such as gravity, off-center friction, or an obstacle in the pathway, an object will move in the direction of the force applied to it. When the human body applies force to move itself, the direction of the force is along the line from the point of force application through the center of gravity of the body. Thus in walking, running or jumping the direction of the force applied by the push-off of the toes is determined by the relationship of the center of gravity to the toes at the moment of take-off. Since in order to move itself, the body is dependent upon the reaction force from an outside medium (ground, water, another object), the force produced by the body must be applied in the direction opposite to the desired movement.

When an object is acted upon by two forces, the movement is in the direction of the resultant of the two forces. This can be illustrated diagrammatically by drawing lines in the directions that the two forces are acting, the length of the lines being dependent upon the relative magnitude of the two forces. If lines parallel to the other force are constructed at the end of each force line, the point of intersection indicates both the direction and magnitude of the resultant, or the actual force

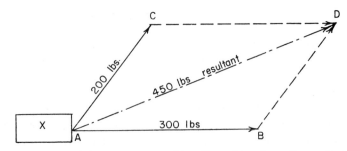

Figure 16. *Actual force acting on object* X *resulting from the application of forces* AB *and* AC.

acting on the object. If forces AB and AC were acting on object X in Figure 16, X would move in the direction AD. The magnitude of this resultant force is indicated by the relative length of the line AD and is not the arithmetical sum of the two forces acting. When a ball with spin bounces on the floor two forces are involved, the rebound force and the spin force. The ball will react according to the resultant of these two forces (Chapter 8).

It follows that a diagonal force applied to an object is, in effect, the resultant of two forces. If a diagonally downward and forward force is applied to an object resting on the floor, the exerted force is divided into a downward component and a forward component. The floor, exerting upward force against the object, prevents its moving in the exact direction in which the force is applied and it moves in the only direction in which it is free to move, forward. The downward component is effective only in increasing friction (p. 57) and thus hinders the forward movement. When force is applied in a diagonally upward-forward direction, as when pulling an object with a rope, the force exerted again is essentially two forces, one in the direction of desired movement (forward) and the other upward (against gravity and therefore reducing friction) (Fig. 17). In general, the more nearly the force is applied in the direction of the desired motion the more effective the force since less force is wasted. However, in many situations the

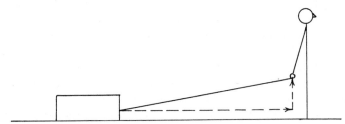

Figure 17. *Two components of a diagonal force.*

second component of a diagonal force may be useful either in counteracting some other force acting on the object or in accomplishing the specific purpose. Whether or not an upward force is desirable depends upon the amount of friction to be overcome. The greater the friction the more upward component of force desirable.

In considering muscular force the angle between the muscle's line of pull and the axis of the bone to be moved determines the angle at which the force is applied. This is not constant as it is when pulling an object such as a sled, because the pull of the muscle results in rotation of the bone which constantly changes the angle of pull (Fig. 18). The more nearly the angle of pull approaches 90 degrees, the more effective the contraction since at any other time the force is broken down into two components. Whenever the angle of pull is less than 90 degrees only a portion of the force is effective in producing the desired movement of the bone. Much of it pulls the bone

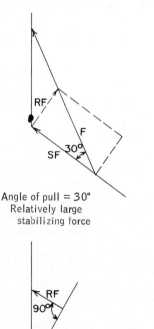

Angle of pull = 30°
Relatively large
stabilizing force

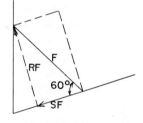

Angle of pull = 60°
Rotating force larger in
relation to stabilizing
force

Angle of pull = 90°
All force rotating

Angle of pull = 110°
Some dislocating force

Figure 18. *Relative magnitude of stabilizing (or dislocating) force and rotating force for various angles of muscle pull.*

back into the joint against the other bone and acts as a stabilizing force. Since extensor muscles cross the outside of a joint, their pull is in line with the axis of the bone or, depending on the bony structure over and around which they pass, at a very slight angle. This means that they exert considerable stabilizing (or compressing) force.

This has been termed by Cates[8] as the "internal work" of the muscle as opposed to the "external work," that which accomplishes the movement of the bone. He states that, "As the angle of pull departs from a right angle, internal work . . . begins to be performed and, to that extent the power to do external work . . . is lost."[9] When the angle of pull is greater than 90 degrees a small dislocating force pulling the bone away from the joint, is present. This occurs rarely in the body and as Figure 18 indicates, it happens when the muscle has shortened to such an extent that there is little force remaining. Also other muscles assisting in the movement help to stabilize the joint.[10] "When several muscles act together to produce a single movement, they act at different points and at different angles. In this way they help to steady and guide the segment throughout the movement."[11]

It must be remembered that the effective force arm is the *perpendicular* distance from the point of force application to the fulcrum. Therefore, the length of the force arm for a muscle is not the distance from the point of insertion to the joint, but rather the perpendicular distance from the muscle to the joint. It is only when the angle of pull equals 90 degrees that the force arm is the distance from insertion to joint. Figure 19 indicates the increase in length of the force arm (FA) as the angle of pull of the muscle approaches 90 degrees.

Point of Application of Force.   If linear motion is desired, the more nearly through the center of gravity the force is applied the less the force required to move a given object. When force is applied through the center of gravity and the object is free to move, linear motion results. If, however, the object is not free to move, if there is a great deal of friction or an obstacle in its path, rotatory motion results. If one point is fixed, it rotates around the fixed point no matter where the force is applied. The farther from the center of gravity the force is applied the more the object tends to rotate (turn or tip). When force is applied toward one end of an object the total object will move in the direction of the force, *but at the same time* it will rotate. In other words, unless there is considerable friction or some other obstacle to motion, both ends will move but the end nearest the point of force application will move forward

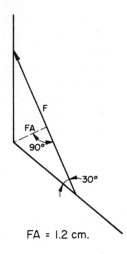

FA = 1.2 cm.

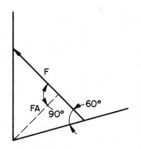

FA = 2.2 cm.

FA = 2.5 cm.

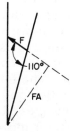

FA = 2.3 cm.

Figure 19. *Variation in length of actual force arm* (FA) *with different angles of pull.*

faster. An object tends to rotate if force is applied above or below or on either side of the center of gravity instead of through the center of gravity. The farther from the center of gravity the force is applied, the less force necessary to rotate the object.

Distance Over Which Force is Applied.—Inasmuch as force depends upon mass and acceleration

$$F = m \cdot a \text{ (Newton's Second Law, p. 49)}$$

and acceleration is the velocity divided by time

$$V = at \text{ (p. 70)} \qquad \text{or} \qquad a = V/t$$

it follows that the velocity of an object of a given mass (m) depends upon both the amount of force and the length of time that it is applied.

$$F = m \cdot V/t \qquad \text{or} \qquad F \cdot t = m \cdot V$$

Since the amount of force depends upon the duration of the force as well as its magnitude, more force can be applied to an object when it is applied over a longer distance. If a ball is kept in contact with the racket for a short time, more force is applied to the ball than if it hits and immediately leaves the racket. However, the greater the distance over which the force is applied, the greater the amount of work done. Work is determined by multiplying the force by the distance over which it is applied.[12]

$$W = F \cdot S$$

W = work
F = force
S = distance

Here again the type of task must be considered. If the purpose is to apply as much force as possible in a relatively light task such as hitting a tennis ball, the force would be applied as long as possible. If, however, the purpose is to lift a heavy load with as little strain as possible one would lower the body only as far as necessary to contact the load.

Summary.   The following points summarize the discussion of the production and application of force.

1. Force must be of sufficient magnitude to overcome inertia if movement is to result.
2. The greater the mass of the object imparting the force and the faster it is moving, the greater the force imparted.
3. The greater the time and the distance over which acceleration can be developed, the greater the momentum possible.
4. The longer the force is applied to an object, the greater the force imparted.
5. The more contributing muscles used, the more force obtainable.
6. The fewer noncontributing muscles used, the less energy wasted.
7. The stronger the muscles called into play for a task demanding a good deal of force, the more efficient the action and the less the muscular strain.
8. The faster the muscular contraction the greater the speed at the end of the moving lever and the greater force produced, the slower the speed of contraction, the less the energy required.
9. In relatively light tasks in which force is largely dependent upon speed, the more sequential the movement, the more force obtainable.

10. The more the muscles that are to perform a given task get set before contacting the load, the more they can resist the equal and opposite force and the less the energy required to carry out a heavy task.
11. The effectiveness of a force produced by the body is dependent upon the fixation of the origins of the muscles involved (by other body muscles) to give a firm base on which to act, and upon the interaction between the body and the supporting surface.
12. The more fully a muscle is stretched the greater the force that it can exert.
13. An object acted upon by two forces moves in the direction of the resultant of the two forces.
14. A diagonal force applied to an object is, in effect, the resultant of the two forces.
15. The more nearly the muscle's angle of pull approaches 90 degrees, the more effective the contraction.
16. If linear motion is desired, the more nearly through the center of gravity the force is applied, the less force required to move a given object.
17. The farther from the center of gravity the force is applied, the less force necessary to rotate the object.
18. If one point of an object is fixed, it will rotate regardless of where the force is applied.
19. The greater the distance over which the force is applied, the greater the amount of work done.

ABSORPTION OF FORCE

In a great many movement tasks the individual is concerned not only with the efficient production and application of force, but also with the stopping of momentum or receiving of force. The problem of force absorption involves the maintenance of equilibrium while receiving the impetus, or momentum, of a moving object without injury or rebound resulting. Injury and rebound can only be avoided by the reduction of the shock of impact. The force of impact depends upon the weight of the moving object (objects) and the speed with which it (they) is (are) moving.

The human body must be able to absorb effectively the force created by its own momentum as well as the force of many other moving objects. This force that must be received may be in a horizontal direction as when an individual is running, skating, skiing, or performing a series of forward rolls, and wants to stop; or when he wants to stop an object that is rolling or sliding. It may be in a vertical direction as when an individual drops from a pole vault, falls from a wall and lands on the ground; or when he attempts to catch some object dropping straight down through the air. In this case, because of the acceleration of gravity, the momentum of the individual or object, and therefore the force to be received, increases rapidly with the distance that he, or the object, falls.

The force that must be received is frequently a combination of the two, i.e., the object or individual is moving through space at an angle and two forces are, in effect, operating (a horizontal and vertical component). This is the situation when catching a thrown or batted ball, or when landing from a broad jump, a dive over obstacles, a fall or jump from a moving object. If an individual jumps from a moving bus the friction between the ground and feet reduces the momentum of the feet sharply, but the forward momentum acquired from the motion of the bus throws the body forward and he falls forward and downward. If a cantering horse suddenly shies and turns to the left, the forward momentum of the rider, unless he has a firm seat, throws him straight ahead out of the saddle. If the momentum of skis is suddenly decreased due to a spot of deep soft snow, the skier must have excellent control of his weight to avoid falling forward.

In all of these cases as soon as the individual loses the support of the object which has been moving him, gravity and momentum due to inertia take over and both vertical and horizontal forces are involved. Whenever gravity is involved, that is in any movement which is not purely horizontal, kinetic energy—energy due to motion—increases rapidly as the height from which the individual or object falls, increases. This is due to the acceleration of gravity.

Regardless of whether the problem involves absorption of force created by the momentum of the human body itself or by the momentum of some object, of whether the force is horizontal, vertical or a combination of the two, the same principles must be applied if injury or rebound is to be avoided.

The more sudden the loss of kinetic energy the more likely is injury or rebound to occur. Conversely, the more gradual the reduction of this force, the less likely is injury or rebound to occur. This means that force must be absorbed, or spent, gradually. This can be done by *increasing the distance and the time over which the force is absorbed*. One method for accomplishing this is to provide a partially nonresistive surface for the impact.

A given amount of force must be absorbed and if the area is small more force must be taken per unit area than if it is large. For example, if 100 foot-pounds of force is received by one square inch of surface all of the force acts against this small area. If however, this same force is received by 20 square inches of surface, each square inch receives only five foot-pounds of force since the force is then distributed over the larger area. *The greater the area over which the force is taken, the less force per unit area.*

Since a force applied at any point other than through the center of gravity tends to rotate the body, equilibrium is a problem that must be considered in any force absorption task. The nearer to the center of gravity the force is received and the more nearly the center of gravity is kept over the center of the base, the more readily stability can be maintained.

The above applications of the principles of force absorption apply whenever the surface is resistive to any degree, i.e., the surface does not part and allow the body or moving object to move through it. However, absorption of the force involved when the body meets a nonresistive surface (the particles of the surface do part, e.g., water) presents a different problem and the application of the principles in this situation is discussed on pages 161–162.

The force absorption tasks most frequently faced by the human body involve landing from a fall, landing from a jump, and catching. The application of the above principles to these tasks is discussed in Chapters 13, 14 and 18.

REFERENCES

1. White, Harvey E.: *Modern College Physics.* 3rd ed. New York, D. Van Nostrand Company, Inc., 1956, p. 26.
2. Crouch, James E.: *Functional Human Anatomy.* Philadelphia, Lea and Febiger, 1965, p. 205.
3. Lee, Mabel and Wagner, Miriam M.: *Fundamentals of Body Mechanics and Conditioning.* Philadelphia, W. B. Saunders Company, 1949. p. 148.
4. *Ibid.,* p. 146.
5. Bunn, John W.: *Scientific Principles of Coaching.* New York, Prentice-Hall, Inc., 1955, p. 67.
6. Wells, Katharine F.: *Kinesiology.* 3rd ed. Philadelphia, W. B. Saunders Company, 1960, p. 306.
7. Zoethout, William D. and Tuttle, W. W.: *Textbook of Physiology.* St. Louis, C. V. Mosby Company, 1952, p. 103.
8. Cates, H. A. and Basmajian, J. V.: *Primary Anatomy.* 3rd ed. Baltimore, Williams and Wilkins Company, 1955, p. 107.
9. *Ibid.,* p. 107.
10. Wells, Katharine F.: *Kinesiology.* 3rd ed. Philadelphia, W. B. Saunders Company, 1960, p. 311.
11. *Ibid.,* p. 315.
12. White, Harvey E.: *Modern College Physics.* 3rd ed. New York, D. Van Nostrand Company, Inc., 1956, p. 124.

8

Angle of Rebound and Spin

ANGLE OF REBOUND

When a moving object meets a resistance greater than its own momentum it will rebound from that resistance. The force of the rebound depends on the magnitude of the resistance (firmness of the surface), the momentum of the object itself, and its degree of restitution (elasticity, i.e., its ability to retake its shape after being flattened by the force of impact). Ordinarily a ball will rebound at an angle equal to that at which it strikes the surface.[1] When a ball approaches the floor from directly above, the entire bottom of the ball is depressed equally making the force of rebound the same from all parts of the bottom of the ball and it bounces straight upward. However, when a ball approaches at an angle to the floor, the back of the bottom of the ball is depressed more than the front,* and the rebound force throws the ball forward and upward. The angle at which it strikes determines how far back on the bottom of the ball the greatest depression comes and therefore, how much the rebound will be forward. The smaller the angle of approach the farther back will be the area of greatest depression and the more forward will be the rebound (Fig. 20).

*Front of the ball is considered to be that part toward the direction of movement.

82

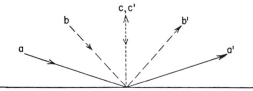

Figure 20. *Rebound of balls approaching surface at various angles.*

The normal angle of rebound is altered by the degree of restitution (or elasticity) of the ball. If the ball is soft and does not instantly resume its original shape, some of the force is absorbed and the rebound is lower than would be expected normally. Also, if the surface struck gives as the ball strikes, the rebound is similarly affected. A soft basketball or an old tennis ball cannot be expected to rebound in the same way as a fully inflated basketball or a new tennis ball; the rebound is both lower and shorter because less force is applied against the ball. When a ball hits a tennis racket with loose strings the rebound is not as fast and the angle is modified since some of the force is dissipated in pushing the strings backward.

Another factor that modifies the normal angle of rebound is spin.

SPIN

A ball may spin (turn) around an axis which passes through the center of the ball horizontal to the ground (horizontal axis) or an axis that is vertical to the ground (vertical axis).

When a ball is spinning around a *horizontal* axis in such a way that the *top* of the ball is *moving forward* (in the same direction the ball is moving), the ball is said to have *top spin* or *forward spin*. If the top of the ball is *moving backward* (away from the direction of flight), it is said to have *back spin*.

Top spin can be demonstrated by placing a ball on the desk or floor and moving the top forward and downward (away from the individual causing the movement and in the direction of flight if the ball were moving). If the top of the ball is moved backward and downward, back spin is demonstrated.

When a ball is spinning around a *vertical* axis so that the *front* of the ball (the side facing the direction of flight) is moving to the right the ball is said to have *right spin* and when the front is moving left, *left spin*.

Frequently individuals are confused as to which is right, and which is left, spin around a vertical axis. Placing one

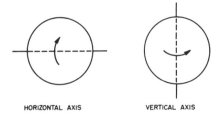

HORIZONTAL AXIS   VERTICAL AXIS

Figure 21.   *Balls spinning around horizontal and vertical axes.*

hand on top of the ball and twisting the hand rapidly to the right starts the ball spinning to the right. The ball spins in the same direction that the hands of a clock would move if the clock were lying flat on the desk (clockwise). This can also be accomplished by placing the flat hand along the right side of the ball and quickly drawing the hand backward. It can be noted that in both cases the *front of the ball* (the side away from the person giving the force and toward the direction of flight) moves toward the right while the back of the ball (the side toward the person) moves to the left. If the hand on top of the ball twists to the left, the ball is given left spin (counter-clockwise). The *front* of the ball moves toward the left.

Spin is further complicated by the fact that it is possible to turn the ball to the right and left around a horizontal axis which is parallel to the direction of flight. (The horizontal axis for forward and back spin is at right angles to the line of flight.) Movement around this "parallel" horizontal axis can be demonstrated by placing the hand on top of a ball and moving the top to the right and downward (right spin) and then to the left and downward (left spin). Actually this type of spin is used little.

When a ball moving at a high velocity is spinning about its axis, pressure is built up on one side and reduced on the other, owing to the fact that the surface of the ball tends to drag a little air along with it. On the side where the air resistance to forward motion is in opposition to that of the air moving around the ball, a high pressure area is built up. On the opposite side of the ball the two forces are in the same direction and the velocity of the moving air is increased causing a low pressure area.[2] The ball tends to move toward the side where the pressure is least. Since with forward (top) spin, the pressure is built up on the top of the ball and reduced under the ball, the ball tends to drop more rapidly than normal. With back spin the pressure is built up under the ball and reduced above the ball causing it to tend to remain in the air longer (or even rise) since this pressure overcomes some of gravity's pull (Fig. 22).

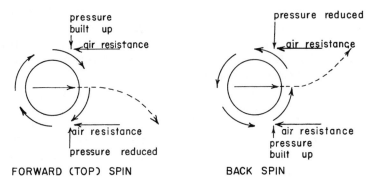

Figure 22. *Effect of forward and back spin on path of ball (looking at side of ball).*

When a ball is spinning to the right around a *vertical* axis, the pressure is built up on the left curving the flight to the right, and when spinning to the left the pressure is built up on the right curving the flight to the left (Fig. 23). Right and left spin around a *horizontal* axis are rarely encountered. However, a diagonally right (and top) spin is imparted by the American twist serve in tennis (see p. 281). Since this type of spin builds air resistance toward the top of the ball on the side toward which the top is spinning (right if spinning right) the ball curves toward the opposite direction (right spin curves ball to left) *when spinning around a horizontal axis.*

Because a head wind increases air resistance to the flight of the ball it increases the change in the path of a spinning ball.

The effect of spin on a fast moving ball is perceived late in the flight since the linear velocity of the ball is great in relation to the spin force. The effect of spin on a slower moving ball

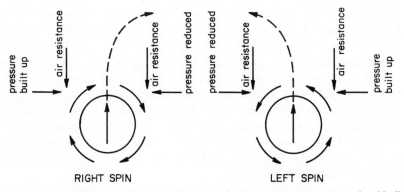

Figure 23. *Effect of left and right spin around a vertical axis on path of ball (looking down on ball).*

is seen earlier in its flight as the linear velocity is less in relation to the force caused by the pressure resulting from the spin. Spin has more effect in curving the flight of a light than of a heavy ball because the greater momentum of the heavy ball makes it less responsive to air pressure.

Hicks reported that a ball with no spin at all may curve if its seams are in unequal positions on the two sides. "As air moves around an object, eddies begin to form. At the point where these eddies form, a surface irregularity can, surprisingly 'smooth out' the air flow and minimize the drag effect of this turbulence. This is known as tripping the boundary layer."[3] This means that if a ball can be thrown with no spin at all but so oriented to the air stream "that its seams trip the boundary layer on one side and not on the other," there is more drag on one side and the ball curves. Hicks reported a study which indicated that a ball with no spin but with its seams oriented to trip the boundary layer of air on one side and not on the other curved more than a ball with spin.

Terrell[4] became interested in the strange action of a ball with little or no spin and questioned Dr. Corrsin of Johns Hopkins University who offered the following "educated guess." He theorized that, because a ball is a blunt rather than a streamlined object, the flow of air around it is always irregular. Generally the flow is relatively smooth on the top and sides of the ball, but once the air stream reaches the back of the sphere it becomes confused. Instead of adhering smoothly to the surface of the ball it breaks away, some of it whirling back into space, some of it being sucked in close behind the ball to form a turbulent wake. "This is much like the wake behind a boat, a whirling vortex of eddies and current and agitated air."[5]

He stated further that the point at which the smooth stream of air breaks away from the ball is called the separation point and that the separation line around the back of the ball is formed by these countless separation points. Because of many factors such as the seams of the ball, imperfections of the spherical shape, and gusts of wind, this separation line is erratic rather than straight. The swirling eddies cause unbalanced sideways pressures which eventually cause the ball to change direction and this change in direction cannot be predicted. In fact, the direction of a ball may change more than once. Because spin smoothes out the air flow and causes the separation points to occur farther back it has a stabilizing effect on the flight of a ball.

Spin also affects the roll of a ball when it lands. Since the top of a forward spinning ball is moving forward the *bottom* must move *backward*, and therefore a ball with forward spin pushes backward against the ground. The equal and opposite force of the ground against the ball is forward and this force is added to the forward momentum of the ball causing the ball to roll father than it would normally. The top of a back spinning ball is moving backward and thus the *bottom* is moving *forward* and so a ball with back spin pushes forward against the ground, the ground pushes backward against the ball and this force being in opposition to the forward momentum of the ball, reduces the length of the roll.

Spin, like any other rotatory motion is caused by an off center application of force. The force that puts the ball in motion may be applied off center in many ways. These methods are discussed in the chapters dealing with throwing and striking. However, a forward moving ball that is not put in motion with spin acquires spin as it rebounds from a surface, and a ball put in motion with back spin may have the direction of its spin reversed by contact with a surface. A ball moving forward with little or no spin rebounds from the floor with forward spin caused by friction. As the ball strikes the floor friction applies a restraining force to the bottom of the ball. Since this is an off center force restraining the movement of the bottom of the ball only, the top of the ball moves faster than the bottom and top spin results. A ball spinning forward as it approaches the floor spins faster as it rebounds. When a ball with back spin strikes the floor, if the force of friction is greater than the spin force, the spin is either stopped or reversed, that is, the ball rebounds with no spin or with some forward spin.

If the free motion of the object is interfered with by friction or the presence of some obstacle, rotatory motion results despite the fact that the force is imparted through the center of gravity. When putting in golf, even though the force is applied through the center of gravity of the ball in a forward direction, the ball *rolls* forward because of the friction between the ball and the ground. The same thing is true of the bowling ball.

EFFECT OF SPIN ON ANGLE OF REBOUND

A spinning ball exerts a push against the floor and the rebound is, therefore, the resultant of the normal rebound force and the spin force. A ball with top spin pushes backward against the floor. The equal and opposite force of the floor against the ball is, therefore, forward. The resultant force causes a bounce that is at a lower angle than normal. A ball with back spin pushes in a forward direction against the floor, the floor pushes backward against the ball and the resultant of the normal rebound force and this spin force is at an angle that is higher than the normal bounce.

A ball with forward (top) spin approaching the floor from directly above (90-degree angle) bounces forward rather than straight upward as does the ball with no spin. The path of the ball is the resultant of the normal rebound force which is upward and the reaction force caused by the spin which is forward (Fig. 24). If the ball is spinning very fast, the magnitude of the force caused by the spin is greater and the resultant is, therefore, more forward (Fig. 25). If the ball has back spin it will bounce backward rather than straight up (Fig. 24).

Right or left spin about its *vertical axis* as the ball approaches the floor from directly above (90-degree angle) does not affect the rebound. Since the entire bottom of the ball is depressed, the friction against the forward part of the ball is the same as that against the back part of the ball. If a ball is spinning to the right, the forward part exerts a force against the floor to the right and the back part exerts a force against the floor to the left (Fig. 26). These two forces, being in direct opposition, neutralize each other and the ball bounces straight upward. The spin will be either stopped or reversed depending

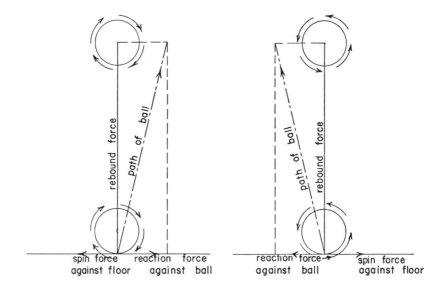

| spin force | reaction force | reaction force | spin force |
| against floor | against ball | against ball | against floor |

FORWARD (TOP) SPIN   BACK SPIN

Figure 24. *Effect of top spin and back spin on bounce of ball approaching floor at ninety-degree angle (looking at side of ball).*

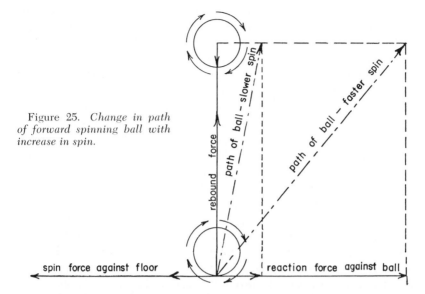

Figure 25. *Change in path of forward spinning ball with increase in spin.*

upon the force of impact and speed of spin. If the forces are not great the spin will be stopped, but if the ball is spinning with considerable speed the equal and opposite force of the floor on the ball will reverse the spin.

If the ball is spinning left or right around its *horizontal axis*, the rebound is in the direction of the spin. The *bottom* of a right spinning ball is moving to the left and therefore exerts a force against the floor to the left. The equal and opposite force of the floor against the ball is to the right and the ball bounces to the right.

When a ball with top spin approaches the floor at an angle, the reaction force of the floor against the ball caused by the spin is in the same direction as the horizontal component of the rebound force and therefore the rebound is longer as well as at a lower angle. Because *the angle is lower*, it is said to rebound lower. Actually, as can be seen in the diagrams, the ball will reach the *same height* as a ball with equal forward force and no spin, but it will be farther forward. Because of the friction

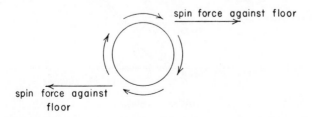

Figure 26. *Looking down on ball with right spin approaching floor at ninety-degree angle.*

involved in the contact with the surface, the bottom of the ball is momentarily stopped while the forward momentum of the ball carries the top forward. Therefore, the ball's top spin is increased. However, in the case of back spin, this reaction force caused by the ball's spin is in direct opposition to the horizontal component of the rebound force and thus the length of the rebound is reduced and the angle of rebound increased (Fig. 27). Since the friction of impact and forward momentum of the ball act together to cause a rebounding ball to spin forward and this is in opposition to the direction of the ball's spin as it approached the surface, the back spin is stopped, or if the forward momentum is great in relation to the speed of the back spin, the spin is reversed.

Some discussion has arisen because experienced tennis players find that balls coming to them with very fast top spin bounce higher than those projected in the same trajectory without spin. This appears to be in contradiction to the above discussion. However, it must be noted that a ball with very fast top spin will drop through the air more quickly and therefore, will approach the surface at a greater angle than would

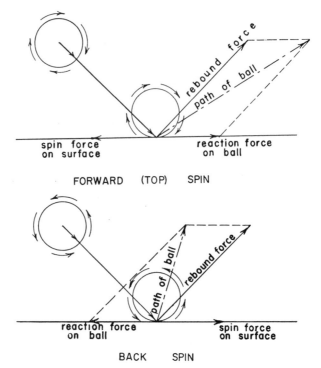

Figure 27. *Effect of top spin and back spin on bounce of ball approaching floor at an angle.*

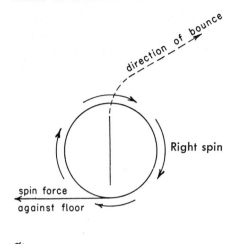

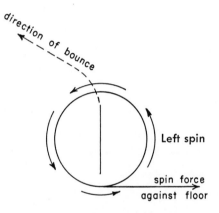

Figure 28. *Direction of bounce of right and left spinning balls approaching floor at an angle (looking down on top of ball spinning around a vertical axis and at the back of ball spinning right or left around a horizontal axis).*

be anticipated for its projected flight. This results in a greater angle of rebound and although the spin force reduces this to some degree, the ball, having a *faster* and longer bounce, still may appear to bounce higher than a ball projected on the same path with no spin.

Right and left spin do not alter the height of the bounce, but a ball with right spin approaching the floor *at an angle* other than 90 degrees regardless of which axis it is spinning around, bounces to the right and one with left spin bounces to the left. Since, when a ball approaches the floor at an angle, the *back* of the ball is depressed more than the forward part, the *direction of spin of the back of the ball determines the direction of the rebound.* The back of a ball spinning to the right around its vertical axis is turning left (Fig. 27.) and therefore, pushes against the floor toward the left. The reaction force against the ball is to the right. Since the *back of a ball* spinning to the left around its vertical axis is turning right, it exerts force against the floor to the right, the reaction force is to the left and the ball rebounds left. A ball spinning to the left or right about its *horizontal axis* also bounces in the direction of its spin since the entire bottom of the ball is moving in the direction opposite to the spin. (The bottom of a right spinning ball moves to the left.) Again, friction stops the right or left spin and the forward momentum of the ball causes it to rebound with top spin.

Some texts have stated that spin causes the greatest deviation from the normal rebound when a ball approaches a surface at right angles and that the smaller the angle of approach

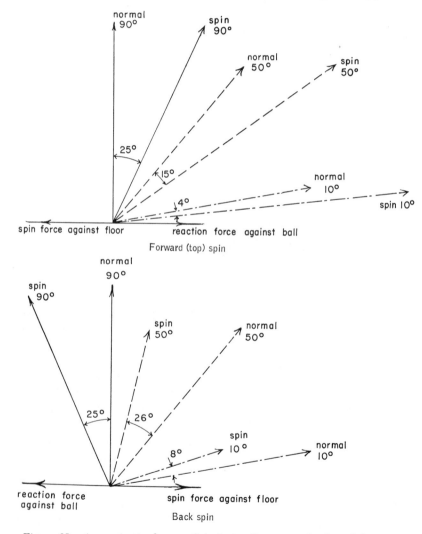

Figure 29.   *Approximate degree of deviation from normal rebound for various angles of approach to floor and a given spin.*

the less is the deviation caused by the spin. This is true when top spin is being considered, and holds, in general, for back spin. However, in the case of back spin, when the angle of approach is between 90 degrees and approximately 50 degrees, the deviation from normal is slightly greater than when the angle of approach is 90 degrees (Fig. 29). This statement is not true for balls with right and left spin about a vertical axis since, as was previously explained, these spins have no effect on a ball approaching the floor at 90 degrees.

A discussion of rebound from vertical surfaces such as basketball backboards, tennis rackets, clubs and bats is included in Chapter 19 which deals with striking.

SUMMARY

Unless some factor such as spin, degree of restitution of the ball, or hardness of the surface struck is involved, a ball will rebound at an angle equal to that at which it strikes the surface. A ball with back spin stays in the air longer or rises; its roll is shortened; its bounce is more upward and shorter than normal. A ball with forward spin drops; its roll is lengthened; its bounce is longer and at a lower angle than normal. A ball with clockwise spin (right) around a vertical axis curves to the right and bounces to the right unless it approaches the floor at a 90-degree angle in which case the rebound is unaffected; the height of its bounce is not affected. A ball with counterclockwise (left) spin around a vertical axis curves to the left and bounces to the left; the height of its bounce is also unaffected.

REFERENCES

1. Bowen, Wilbur Pardon and Stone, Henry A.: *Applied Anatomy and Kinesiology.* 7th ed. Philadelphia, Lea and Febiger, 1953, p. 369.
2. White, Harvey E.: *Modern College Physics.* 3rd ed. New York, D. Van Nostrand Company, Inc., 1956, p. 257.
3. Hicks, Clifford B.: The Strange Forces of the Air. *Popular Mechanics Magazine, 111*:6:127, June, 1959.
4. Terrell, Roy.: Nobody Hits It. *Sports Illustrated, 10*:26:14-19, June 29, 1959.
5. *Ibid.,* p. 18.

$$9$$

Projectiles

Actually all of the physical laws governing projectiles have already been discussed. However, since so many sport activities deal with projectiles it seems expedient to gather together in one discussion these physical laws as they relate to this topic.

A projectile is defined as any object which is given an initial velocity and then allowed to move under the influence of gravity. This means that the body itself is a projectile in any jump or dive and, therefore, its path through the air is determined by these laws in the same way as that of a thrown or struck object.

Force to project an object into space is supplied in many ways. It may be applied by a person directly to an object. This is the case when the object is held by a body part, or an implement held by the body (such as the crosse for lacrosse) and is moved through the air rapidly and then released (throwing). A direct application of force is also made when the object is momentarily contacted by a moving body part or by an implement held or attached to the body (striking), and when the body projects itself. Force is applied indirectly to a projectile when the person moves some part of another object which in turn applies the force to the object to be projected. By using an elastic type object such as a slingshot, an individual indirectly applies force to a projectile. An archer's bow acts in the same way. The individual applies force which puts the bow into a position to supply force. The bow when bent has potential energy (energy because of its position) and this energy of the bow when released is transformed into kinetic energy (energy due to motion). A gun is a mechanical device by which an individual applies force indirectly to the bullet. The individual pulls the trigger and the firing pin applies the force which results in the movement of the bullet.

A projectile undergoes linear motion made curvilinear by the force of gravity which acts on it throughout its flight. Air resistance is also an important factor in the movement of a projectile since it, too, modifies its flight, but for the sake of simplicity air resistance will be ignored in this first discussion.

AIR RESISTANCE NEGLECTED

There are two forces acting on any projectile, the projecting force and gravity[*] and with the exception of a straight upward or straight downward projection, a horizontal component is involved in the projecting force. The downward force produced by gravity causes an acceleration which is the same as that of a freely falling body (32 ft./sec./sec.— Chapter 3) and is independent of any horizontal force. As has been previously stated, if one object falls freely from rest at the same time that another is projected *horizontally from the same height,* both will strike the ground at the same time. However, they will strike in different places. The one that falls freely will strike directly under its point of release and the one projected forward will go as far out as the forward force can carry it in the time it takes gravity to pull it to earth from the height at which it was released. In other words, if these two balls were released at a height of eight feet, they would both hit the ground 0.71 second later ($S = \frac{1}{2}gt^2$, Chapter 3, page 37). If one of them was given sufficient forward force to result in an average velocity of 60 feet per second it would hit 42.6 feet out from the one released with no forward momentum (Fig. 30). The distance which an object that is projected horizontally will travel can be calculated by multiplying the velocity by the time.[1]

$$S = V \cdot t$$
$$S = 60 \times 0.71$$
$$S = 42.6 \text{ ft.}$$

_____

[*]An object which is simply released without force is a free falling object rather than a projectile.

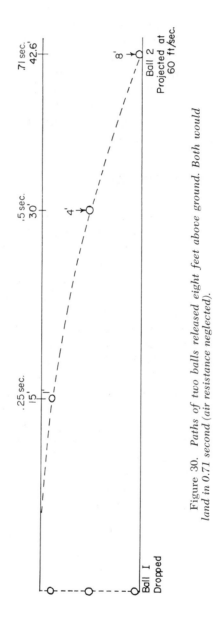

Figure 30. *Paths of two balls released eight feet above ground. Both would land in 0.71 second (air resistance neglected).*

The time it takes an object to hit the ground can be altered only when the projecting force is applied either diagonally upward (some force upward opposing gravity) or diagonally downward (some force downward and therefore added to gravity's force).

When an object is projected straight upward, directly in opposition to the force of gravity, its speed gradually diminishes until the force with which it was projected is neutralized by the pull of gravity. At this point it comes to rest and immediately begins to fall back toward the earth and as it falls it accelerates. When it reaches the point at which it was projected, its speed will be equal to the speed at which it was originally projected, i.e., the deceleration of the upward flight is equal to the acceleration of the downward flight, or the upward motion is the same as the downward motion in reverse. The height to which the object will climb depends upon the speed with which it is projected. This relationship is expressed in the formula[2]:

$$V^2 = 2gS \qquad \text{or} \qquad S = \frac{V^2}{2g} \quad \text{or}$$

$$\text{height of projection} = \frac{\text{projecting velocity squared}}{2 \times \text{acceleration of gravity}}$$

If an object is given an initial force that is strictly horizontal, the vertical force which is caused by the pull of gravity brings about acceleration in a vertical direction (downward) throughout the flight. If it is given a diagonally upward initial force, it is, in effect, given two forces, one vertical and the other horizontal. The vertical force is decelerated by the pull of gravity as the object climbs to the high point in its path, which is the point at which the vertical component of the projecting force is neutralized by gravity, and it is accelerated as it drops from the high point. The time required to reach the highest point equals the time it takes to fall back downward *to the height at which the object was originally projected.* Also, when it reaches the height of the point at which it was projected, its velocity is the same as the vertical velocity at which it was projected.

The distance that a projectile travels depends upon its initial *speed* and the *angle* at which it is projected. The lower the angle of projection the greater the horizontal component in relation to the vertical component of the projecting force (Fig. 31). Therefore, when an object is projected at a low angle

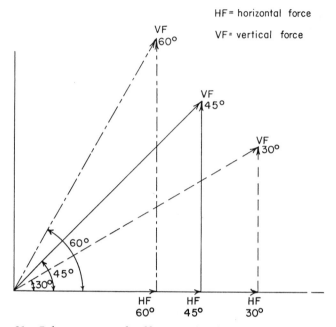

Figure 31. *Relative magnitude of horizontal and vertical components of a given force applied at various angles.*

the horizontal velocity resulting from a given projecting force is relatively high but the vertical force is low and therefore does little to resist gravity's pull. As a result, the object does not stay in the air long enough to cover much distance. If the angle of projection is large, the vertical component of the projecting force is larger and thus keeps the object in the air longer, but since the horizontal component is relatively small, the distance covered is small. Since the horizontal and vertical components of a force applied at a 45-degree angle are equal, *in the absence of air resistance,* the greatest distance is obtained when an object is projected at this angle (Fig. 32).

Since the projecting force applied to an object which is thrown or struck, is in the direction tangent to the arc through which the throwing or striking part (or implement) is moving at the moment of release or impact, the arc and the point on that arc at which the object is released or struck, determine the angle at which the initial force is applied. Methods for controlling this angle are discussed in the chapters dealing with throwing and striking (Chapters 18 and 19).

In several tumbling stunts, as in diving — in fact in any jump — the body itself becomes a projectile and responds to the laws governing projectiles. Since the path of a projectile is determined by its initial speed and angle of projection, the path

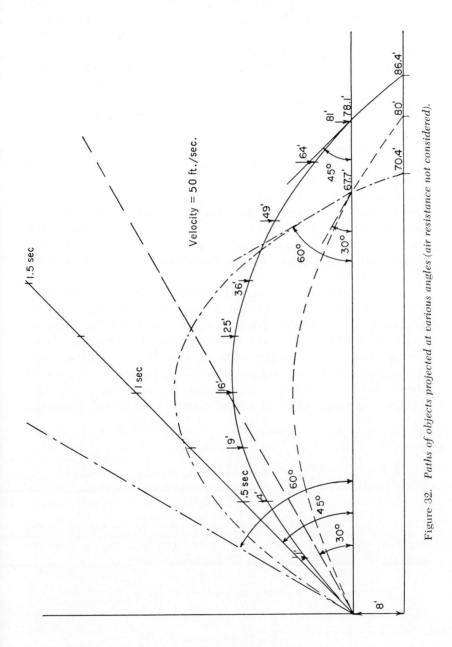

Figure 32. *Paths of objects projected at various angles (air resistance not considered).*

of the *center of gravity of the body* is determined at take-off. Various movements of body parts while in the air can change the relationship of the various parts about the center of gravity and alter the point where the center of gravity of the body is located, but the path of the center of gravity cannot be altered. LaDue and Norman explain this by stating "If the performer is in the air, free of support, no movement will raise or lower his center of gravity, but it may raise or lower his body around the center of gravity."[3] Lanoue[4] stated that the path of the center of gravity of the diver is a regular parabola which is dependent upon the mass of the body, the take-off velocity, and the take-off angle.

An object approaches the ground at approximately the same angle as that at which it was projected. If projected from the ground the angles are equal. If projected from above the ground they are equal at the line of projection extended but because gravity is still acting, the path from this point to the ground is not a completely straight line but curved somewhat downward and the angle with the ground is, therefore, very slightly larger.

Any variation from the 45-degree angle of projection, whether it is above or below 45 degrees, will result in the same loss of distance at the point straight out from the point of application of force (Fig 32). If two objects are projected from the ground with the same velocity, one at a 30-degree angle (15 degrees below 45) and one at a 60-degree angle (15 degrees above 45) both will hit the ground at the same point. The distance a projectile will travel can be calculated from the formula:[5]

$$R = \frac{V^2}{g} \sin 2\theta$$

R = range (distance)
V = velocity
g = acceleration of gravity (32 ft./sec.)
θ = angle of projection

If three objects traveling 50 ft./sec. are projected at 30 degrees, 60 degrees and 45 degrees, they will travel approximately 68 feet, 68 feet, and 78 feet respectively.

30-degree angle of projection: $\theta = 30°$, $2\theta = 60°$, $\sin 60° = 0.866$

$$R = \frac{50^2}{32} \times 0.866$$
$$R = 78.125 \times 0.866$$
$$R = 67.656 \text{ ft.}$$

60-degree angle of projection: $\theta = 60°$, $2\theta = 120°$, sin $120° = 0.866$

$$R = \frac{50^2}{32} \times 0.866$$
$$R = 78.125 \times 0.866$$
$$R = 67.656 \text{ ft.}$$

45-degree angle of projection: $\theta = 45°$, $2\theta = 90°$, sin $90° = 1.000$

$$R = \frac{50^2}{32} \times 1.000$$
$$R = 78.125 \times 1.000$$
$$R = 78.125 \text{ ft.}$$

However, when two objects are projected at some point above the ground, the one projected at an angle of 30 degrees will gain some distance advantage by the time the two reach the ground because the one projected at 60 degrees drops at a more acute angle than the one projected at 30 degrees. Figure 32 illustrates this point. Since in throwing, the ball is released some feet above the ground, when throwing for distance it is better to throw at an angle less than 45 degress than at the same angle above 45 degrees because some advantage in distance will be gained. If the ball is caught at approximately the height it was projected there will be no distance advantage but time will be gained.

To gain maximum distance is not always the purpose of projection. Frequently speed is the essential factor and if an object is to reach its destination as fast as possible, the angle of projection should be as small as possible to carry the distance necessary. Obviously the faster the velocity, the lower the angle can be for a given distance. *The optimum angle of projection, then depends upon the particular purpose involved.*

AIR RESISTANCE CONSIDERED

Up to this point in the discussion the influence of air resistance has been ignored. In many of the activities it is not of great importance because the object is a ball which does not move at a great speed. However, it must be remembered that air resistance varies with the physical characteristics of the object (its weight, size and shape), the speed with which it is moving, and any motions of the object in a direction other than the direction of flight. The lighter the object and the larger its surface area, the more it is affected by air resistance. Thus a shuttlecock is affected more than a tennis ball. Since air resist-

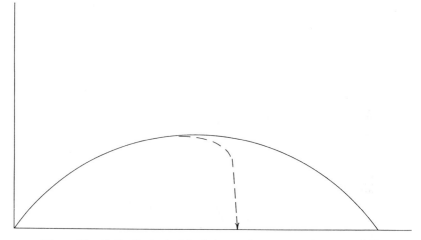

Figure 33.   *Path of a typical badminton shot compared to a parabola.*

ance increases rapidly as speed increases,[6] it is a considerable factor in the flight of high speed projectiles. While a ball may be thrown for distance most effectively at an angle of approximately 45 degrees, a golf ball, because of its great speed, must be projected at a much lower angle. The horizontal component must be enlarged to offset the tremendous air pressure which is built up. When a football spins end-over-end, or an arrow quivers the air resistance is increased by the additional motion and greater surface area, and the flight is retarded more than it would be if these movements were not present.

The horizontal force of a projectile is decelerated throughout its flight by air resistance. Because of this a projectile does not follow the true parabolic path diagrammed in Figure 32. The greater the air resistance the more the flight departs from that of a true parabola. The path of a shuttlecock which has been hit a forceful blow departs markedly from the parabolic path. Because of its light weight, shape and speed, air resistance builds up to the extent that the horizontal force is overcome long before gravity has pulled the shuttle to the ground. When the horizontal force has been dissipated the only force left to act is the force of gravity and the shuttle falls straight down from that point (Fig. 33).

SUMMARY

There are three forces that act on any projectile: gravity, air resistance, and the initial force which put it in motion. Therefore, a projectile carries out two independent motions, a horizontal motion which is gradually decreased by air resistance and a vertical downward motion which is accelerated by the force of gravity.

The distance that a projectile travles depends upon its initial speed and the angle at which it is projected. When air resistance is not a factor the optimum angle of projection for maximum distance is 45 degrees. As air resistance becomes a greater factor this angle is lowered to increase the horizontal component of the projecting force. If the purpose of projection is speed rather than distance, the angle should be as low as possible to carry the required distance. The greater the speed of projection the lower the angle can be for a given distance.

The lighter the object, the larger its surface area, the greater its speed and the more it is moving in any direction other than the direction of flight, the greater the air resistance.

If air resistance were neglected, a projectile would follow a parabolic path. If projected from the ground it would land at the same angle and the same speed as that at which it was projected. The greater the air resistance the more the path of flight departs from the path of a true parabola.

REFERENCES

1. White, Harvey E.: *Modern College Physics.* 3rd ed. New York, D. Van Nostrand Company, Inc., 1956, p. 20.
2. *Ibid.,* pp. 37-38.
3. LaDue, Frank and Norman, Jim: *This is Trampolining.* Cedar Rapids, Iowa, Torch Press, 1956, p. 69.
4. Lanoue, Frederick Richard: Mechanics of Fancy Diving. Unpublished master's thesis, Springfield College, 1936, p. 52.
5. White, Harvey E.: *Modern College Physics.* 3rd ed. New York, D. Van Nostrand Company, Inc., 1956, p. 110.
6. Rasch, Philip J. and Burke, Roger K.: *Kinesiology and Applied Anatomy.* Philadelphia, Lea and Febiger, 1959, p. 123.

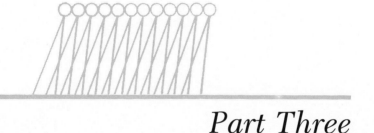

Part Three

Application of the Basic Mechanical Principles to Fundamental Physical Skills

10

Standing

Because everyone learns to stand as an infant, many individuals have assumed that there is no necessity for teaching this skill. It has also been argued that no one stands still for any length of time, that dynamic, not static, posture is of importance.

It is certainly true that individuals move more than they stand still. Hellebrandt concluded that even standing is not static but rather that it is "movement upon a stationary base."[1] She found that individuals are constantly swaying and thus the center of gravity is constantly moving. This involuntary swaying, she found, was important in that it aided the return of venous blood and assured adequate circulation in the brain.[2] Her experiment indicated that this sway was so accurately balanced that the average center of weight always fell close to the geometric center of the base.[3]

The stretch reflex apparently is responsible for the balanced control which keeps the center of gravity within the limits of the base of support of the body.[4] This stretch reflex plays an important role in the maintenance of the upright position. When the extensor muscles, those muscles which resist the tendency for the pull of gravity to flex certain joints of the body, are stretched they are reflexly stimulated to increase tonus and thus hold the joints in extension. In the lower extremity this reflex is also elicited by pressure against the sole of the foot. The tonic neck and labyrinthine reflexes also aid in maintaining the upright position in that they cause reactions of the body in response to positions of the head.

However, these reflexes operate regardless of the particular upright position assumed by the individual. Since the body is made up of many segments joined together at the joints by muscles and ligaments, there are a great many positions that it can assume. Also there are many variations in body build which influence position and individual differences must be considered. As the child grows he develops a habit of aligning his body segments in a certain way. While it is true that he does not maintain any one position for an appreciable period of time, a characteristic pattern is observable. The habitual position is usually influenced to a great degree by the models that are observed most frequently as he is growing up and the importance that he attaches to those models. Observation of any typical college group today indicates that the majority of students have not been fortunate in the models most readily available to them. It is only necessary to open a fashion magazine to understand one reason for many of the inefficient and aesthetically displeasing postures of young girls today. Unfortunately, good models have not always been offered during instruction dealing with movement. Too frequently the teacher has been a model of inefficient and uninspiring habitual posture.

While it is certainly necessary that an individual possess a certain level of strength, flexibility, kinesthetic perception, and kinesthetic memory to be able, at will, to assume and maintain a well balanced position, these factors are not the primary cause of the poor positions of the majority of the individuals. There will be some whose muscular strength and/or flexibility, due to such factors as illness, injury, and long term extreme positions at a joint, have fallen below the minimal level necessary. However, for the great majority, the most important factors are an understanding of an efficient position,[5] the kinesthetic perception of it, and last, but by no means least, a sincere desire to reeducate the muscles and nervous system so that this position is assumed habitually. The understanding and kinesthetic perception can be taught in a relatively short time. Besides helping the student to solve these problems the teacher must also provide an inspiring model. To make the learning carry over into everyday life the teacher must motivate the student to *want to* develop a new habitual pattern. Habits are formed only with constant repetition over a long period of time and the student must understand that only through patience and persistent application will the gaining of the knowledge of the mechanics of standing become a valuable learning experience.

VALUES OF A WELL ALIGNED POSITION

Most people, men and women alike, are interested in the way they look and the impression they make on others. The knowledge that one looks well adds materially to self-confidence. The first impression of an individual is visual and, therefore, position is an important factor in the impression one individual makes on another. A drooping posture is associated by the observer with an unenthusiastic and listless personality. Clothes are made for a balanced figure and do not hang evenly on a body which zigzags.

Reason indicates that a well aligned position should require less energy than a poorly balanced one. Electromyographic records of the muscle function of a young adult female[6] did show less activity in thigh and lower leg muscles when standing in a well balanced position, than when standing with the pelvis tilted either forward or backward. On the other hand, Tepper, Hellebrandt and Brogdon[1, 7] found that the metabolic cost of standing was slight, although there was considerable variation among individuals. A study by Mc Cormick[8] has borne this out and has indicated that the *metabolic cost* of the well aligned position was somewhat greater than that of the position known as the typical "fatigue posture" — a position with hips forward, upper back rounded, trunk inclined backward, and head forward. In this position all segments have been allowed to sag to the point where bone and ligament structure prohibit further movement. It is the position which, in the minds of people, has become associated with fatigue.

In this position gravity exerts considerable rotatory force on each of the weight bearing segments. Wells has characterized this position as one of "hanging on the ligaments."[9] With the ligaments and muscles considerably stretched, a great deal of adjustment is necessary before the body is in a position to move efficiently. While it is probable that this position requires no more energy than a well aligned position, it is a position which can cause pain due to stress (stretch and pressure), and it is *not* a position from which one is able to move with dispatch, and some of the joints, for example the knees, are in a position which leaves no margin of safety, since they are at the extreme position possible in one direction. Also the depression of the body segments seems to be reflected in the lack of alertness of the mind. One neither gives the impression of being alert and animated, "ready to go," nor does one feel this way. Further research dealing with the metabolic cost of various standing positions for individuals for whom a well aligned position is habitual and for whom it is not, as well as study of the industrial output and energy requirement of individuals with various habitual postures would prove interesting.

Although the metabolic cost of standing has been found to be slight,[1, 7, 8] the effect of various positions on the efficiency of movement, and the psychological and aesthetic values are important considerations. In addition, the fact that faulty body mechanics (in standing) can cause painful conditions "has become a well established concept in the field of Orthopedic Surgery, and is one of the basic concepts in the relatively new field of Physical Medicine."[10] Pain is caused by pressure from some firm structure (bone, cartilage, taut muscle, etc.) on any part of a nerve or by tension (stretch or strain) of a structure (muscle, tendon, ligament) which contains nerve endings.[11] Basic to an understanding of pain caused by faulty positions is "the concept that the accumulative effects of constant or repeated small stresses over a long period of time can give rise to the same difficulties as a sudden severe stress."[10] Wells[9] stated that the skeletal structure should be architecturally and mechanically sound so there is a minimum of strain on the weight bearing joints. These joints must be so aligned that friction is minimized, tension of opposing ligaments balanced, and pressures within the joint equalized.

Study is needed to determine the psychological implications of position and movement. It is certainly obvious that position is expressive of mental attitude. The question that needs to be investigated is the extent to which mental attitude can be influenced by changes in patterns of position and movement.

BASIC PRINCIPLES OF AN EFFICIENT STANDING POSITION

Although individuals move much more than they stand, many of the basic principles that apply to the great variety of positions necessitated by voluntary movement can be more readily explained in a discussion of static posture.

Since an efficient position for any task is that which makes the best adaptation of the particular body structure to the mechanical problems involved in the task, the "correct" position will vary to some extent depending upon body structure.

However, despite differences in body structure there are certain principles which all can apply, but application of them cannot be expected to produce individuals who look alike.

Since the body is made up of segments, assuming an upright position can be likened to building a man of blocks (Fig. 34). So long as the blocks are centered one above the other the man of blocks will stand. However, if one block is moved so that its center of gravity is not over the block below, the man of blocks will fall. The human body does not fall apart as do the blocks because its various segments are held together by muscles and ligaments. However, when a body part is out of line with the part below, gravity tends to pull the part downward, the bones of the joint are out of line, pressure is exerted unevenly, and the tension of opposing ligaments is unbalanced. Since the more nearly the center of gravity of an object is centered over its base the more stable the object, total body balance is maintained with a minimum of strain when each part is centered over the part below.

Good posture might be defined as that position in which the center of gravity of each body segment is centered over its supporting base (the segment immediately below). In this position the force of gravity is used to advantage as much as possible in keeping the alignment in the weight bearing joints. The line of gravity of each segment is an extension of the line of gravity of the segments above and below and thus gravity actually helps to maintain the position of various segments since it pulls each downward evenly onto the one below.

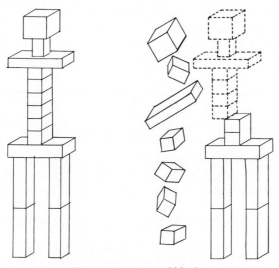

Figure 34. *Man of blocks.*

The more nearly vertical the long axis of every segment, the greater the stabilizing effect of gravity. Whenever one body part moves out of line, the center of gravity of the total body shifts in the direction of movement of that segment and another segment must be displaced in the opposite direction to bring the center of gravity of the body back over the base, or the base must move. The greater the angle of inclination of the total body or any segment of the body from the vertical, the greater the muscular effort necessary to hold it.

When standing, balance must be maintained in both the anteroposterior (forward-backward) plane and the lateral (sideways) plane. When the segments are aligned one above the other the line of gravity as seen from the side, passes from the mastoid bone or just behind the tip of the ear through the tip of the shoulder, the middle of the hip,* the front of the knee, and falls in front of the ankle over the center of the feet (Fig. 35, A). Brunnstrom[13] stated that the line of gravity falls through the center of the base, and Hellebrandt[14] placed it at an average of five centimeters in front of the ankle in young women. Thus the body can sway forward and backward without the line of gravity falling beyond the heels or the toes. Since the body weight falls forward of the center of the knee and in front of the ankle, gravity is always exerting some forward rotatory force on the body as a whole. Joseph stated that "there is general agreement that the extent of swaying is such that the line of weight almost always remains in front of the ankle joints. . ."[15] However, if the line of gravity fell *through* the ankle joints removing this rotatory force, "the margin of posterior stability would be the short horizontal distance between the ankles and the points of heel contact with the ground."[16] Falling as it does over the center of the foot, the distance from the line of gravity to the posterior edge of the base of support is increased.

Morton stated that since the direction of structural unbalance which results is forward, the muscular strain needed to maintain the erect posture is imposed entirely on the large and powerful calf muscles, while the weaker anterior group is released from any counter-balancing tension. He also pointed out that this anteriorly unbalanced position "comprises a highly important phase in the initiation of forward movement of the body."[17]

In the lateral plane the line of gravity falls from the center

---

*The line of gravity actually passes somewhat posterior to the hip *joint*.[12] However, this would put it approximately through the center of the mass of the hip as one views it from the side.

of the head through the spinal column, the center of the hips and falls over the center of the base (from side to side). This gives a margin of safety in balance as the body sways sideways.

Position of Feet. This position of the body is most easily

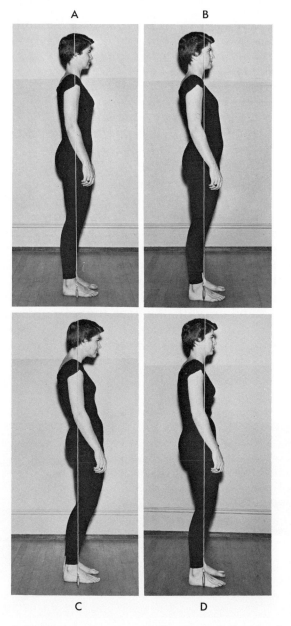

Figure 35.   A, *Well balanced position.* B, *Hips forward, shoulders back — strains lower back.* C,D, *Zigzag positions that lead to strain on all joints.*

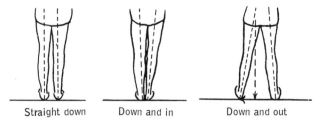

Straight down   Down and in   Down and out

Figure 36. *Direction of forces exerted against floor by individuals with feet in various positions.*

maintained if the feet are a few inches apart as they are when the legs are vertical (straight down from the hips). This gives as large a base as possible without introducing a diagonal force against the ground. When the feet are together the base is smaller and the force is exerted down and slightly inward. When they are farther apart than the width of the hips the force is exerted diagonally outward (Fig. 36). If the toes are straight ahead the weight falls on the heels, the outer borders of the feet, and the metatarsal bones. If the toes are turned outward the weight of the body falls on the inner borders of the feet—on the arches (Fig. 37). This can be readily demonstrated by standing with the feet turned outward and consciously relaxing the muscles of the ankles and feet. The rolling inward of the ankles is immediately apparant.

Since the outer border of the foot is flat and the inner border forms an arch, their functions differ. The flat outer

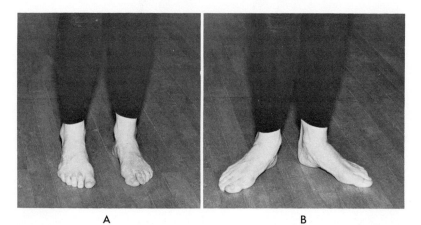

A   B

Figure 37. A, *Weight on outer border of feet.* B, *Weight on weak arch.*

border is well designed to support weight, while the arch is extremely important in the absorption of force and thus the reduction of the jar to the body at every step. If, all of the time that an individual stands, the weight of the body falls diagonally across this arch, as it does when the toes are turned outward, the bones are pushed together, nerves may be pinched, and eventually the arch may be flattened and its function lost. The position of the toes ahead is also important in that it places the feet in a position from which they can exert force directly backward when forward movement is desired. This is discussed in Chapter 11, Walking.

Position of Knees. When the knees are hyperextended (pushed backward as far as possible) the bones of the knee joint are forced together. Should any backward force be exerted against them there would be no margin of safety. They would be forced beyond their normal limit and injury would be likely. This position of the knee tends to cause the pelvis to be tilted forward and the tension of the position is likely to be reflected in general tension of the body. If the knees are bent the bones of the thigh and the lower leg are placed in a diagonal relationship to each other and the force of gravity acts to pull them closer together and the body closer to the ground. Since in this position the long axes of the leg bones have departed from the vertical relationship it takes more muscular force to hold the position. The most efficient and safest position of the knees, then, is neither bent nor hyperextended but "easy," leaving some margin for backward movement.

Position of Pelvis. Since the pelvis is the link between the entire upper structure of the body and the legs, any shifting of its position necessitates considerable readjustment in all body parts above and below. When the pelvic girdle is tilted forward* the knees are hyperextended, the lower back arched, and the abdominal muscles stretched. Habitual assumption of this position leads to weakened abdominal muscles as well as to lower back strain. The other extreme, that is the pelvis tilted backward with the hips tucked under, results in the lower back being flattened and the knees somewhat bent. Both positions make it extremely difficult to maintain a good position of the upper trunk. Neither extreme is desirable. The pelvic girdle should be held in a balanced position between the two extremes. Many individuals stand with the pelvis tipped forward and the well balanced position may be more easily under-

---

*When the pelvis tilts *forward,* the iliac crest moves forward and slightly downward.

stood by them if described by the phrase "pelvis tucked *very slightly* under." Because it does link the supporting segments of the body (the legs) to the body above (the trunk, neck, and head), control of this segment of the body is an extremely important factor in the assumption and maintenance of a well aligned position. Ability to control the pelvic girdle at will has been found to be a considerable factor in the ability of college women to improve their body alignment.[5]

Position of Shoulder Girdle.   The shoulder girdle should be balanced above the hips with the two shoulders level and pointing directly out to the sides. If the left shoulder is carried higher than the right, the dorsal (upper) spine is curved to the left. This causes the vertebrae to be tilted and uneven pressures in the joints result. The muscles on the left side of the spine are stretched while those on the right are shortened. In the level position the pull on the two sides of the spine is equalized and the spine remains in its normal straight position. If the tips of the shoulders are carried forward the rib cage is depressed, the upper back rounded, the muscles and ligaments across the back of the shoulder girdle are stretched, and the anterior muscles are shortened. Throwing the shoulders backward results in a flattening of the normal dorsal (upper back) curve, an increase in the lumbar (lower back) curve as well as tenseness throughout the body. When the tips of the shoulders point straight to each side the weight of the arms is balanced, neither pulling forward nor backward on the shoulder girdle. When the shoulders are "hunched" muscles are tense and energy is wasted. The muscles soon become fatigued and strain results. The shoulders should be relaxed, not pulled upward, forward, or backward.

Position of Head.   Since the head is heavy and is attached to the rest of the body by a relatively small flexible segment (the neck) it is important that it be well balanced above the shoulders. When the chin is dropped the line of vision is downward instead of forward and, as when the chin is thrust forward, the head is overbalanced forward causing strain on the muscles of the back of the neck and shoulders. The chin should, therefore, be carried level and drawn back as far as possible without tension.

Some individuals tend to "cock" (bend and slightly rotate) the head to one side. This not only causes tension in the shoulder and neck muscles, but also presents a vision problem since it places the eyes at different heights. This position is normally caused by a habitual sitting (to work) posture and is discussed in Chapter 15, Sitting.

SUGGESTIONS FOR GAINING A CONCEPT OF AN EFFICIENT STANDING POSITION

A kinesthetic awareness of this position can be gained by experimentation with the various positions possible for each segment. If extreme positions are assumed, the effects on other parts of the body noted, and *conscious attention directed* to the feeling of strain in various areas, the contrast of the feeling accompanying the intermediate, well balanced position is obvious.

Starting with experimentation with the feet together, wide apart, a few inches apart, with the toes in, then out, and then straight ahead, accompanied by student discussion of the effect of each position, a well aligned position of the body can be built upward just as a man of blocks is built.

Pushing the knees backward as far as possible and then bending them illustrates quickly the interaction of knees and pelvic girdle and the resulting effects on the whole body. Standing even for a minute with the knees bent is usually long enough to demonstrate the strain on the leg muscles caused by this knee position.

In experimenting with the extreme positions of the pelvic girdle, placing one hand on the lower back and attempting to hollow the back as much as possible may aid in giving the feeling for tilting the pelvis forward. If the hand is then moved down onto the hips and the other hand is placed on the abdomen, a feeling for pulling up with the abdominal muscles and down with the hip muscles which results in the backward tilting of the pelvis, is experienced. Following the perception of these two positions, with the hands in this same position, an intermediate (balanced) position of the pelvis can be ascertained more readily.

As each extreme position is assumed the effects upon other parts of the body can be consciously observed. A student experiencing difficulty in tilting the pelvis forward and backward in the upright position may be able to arch and then flatten the lower back while lying on the floor and then, having experienced the motion, he may be able to carry it over to the standing position. Sometimes it is necessary for the student to feel this movement in another person by placing one hand on the abdomen and the other on the hips of an individual as he moves his pelvis from one extreme position to the other and then back to the intermediate position. Since the ability to control the pelvic girdle is so important in assuming and maintaining a well aligned position, it is worthwhile to take time to gain this control.

Observation has indicated that a high percentage of the girls and young women of today stand with their hips forward and shoulders back of the line of gravity of the body. This position causes strain particularly in the region of the lower back. A slight straight backward adjustment of the pelvic region and forward adjustment of the shoulder region straightens the body line so that the shoulders are directly over the hips and the strain on muscles, ligaments, and joints is reduced. Since the adjustment required by most individuals is slight it is sometimes difficult to feel (kinesthetically). Exaggerating the pelvis-forward-shoulders-back position and then moving the pelvis backward as the upper trunk and shoulder region move forward may help in gaining a concept of the straight body line. Sometimes this adjustment can be perceived more easily if one hand is placed on the abdomen and the other on the back as near the shoulder blades as possible and the lower hand is pushed somewhat backward while the upper hand is brought forward.

A long mirror in which the individual can see himself in profile is an aid in developing the new concept. An individual who has stood habitually in the position with the shoulders back of the hips feels as if he is overbalanced forward when his body is aligned with the shoulders directly above the hips. This is undoubtedly due to the important function of the head in balance. Standing habitually in this position which keeps the head back, the individual develops the concept of balance with the head back. When the upper trunk, and with it the head, is moved forward a *readjustment of concept is necessary.* This does not happen immediately and it is important that the student realize that he will, for a time, because of the shift of the head position, feel slightly overbalanced forward even though he is actually standing in a well balanced position.

Experimentation with the shoulder region should include tilting the shoulder girdle to the left and right, pulling the shoulder tips forward and backward as far as possible, and hunching and relaxing the shoulders. To experience the extreme forward and backward positions of the tips of the shoulders, the tips are rolled forward as far as possible and then, by drawing the inner borders of the shoulder blades toward each other, they are pulled back as far as possible. In this way a feeling for control of the shoulders without reactions in other parts of the body can be gained. The shoulders can then be adjusted so that they point directly to each side. A feeling for relaxed shoulders can probably be gained most rapidly by hunching them upward as far as possible and then allowing them to drop. A circular motion of the shoulder may also be useful in relaxing these muscles.

The difference between moving the chin up and down and forward and backward needs to be consciously experienced. The up-and-down motion is familiar and easy. If, following this movement, the chin, while being held level, is thrust forward as far as possible, and then, using the muscles at the back of the neck, it is drawn straight backward as far as possible, when the tension is released the head will be left in a well balanced position.

CHANGE OF POSITION

While the position described is mechanically the most efficient, it must be remembered that a change of position is always restful, and therefore, when it becomes necessary to stand for any period of time various positions are, and should be, assumed. The more the various segments of the body can be kept in good alignment, the better. However, a poor position if assumed for *a short period of time only,* will not be harmful. For example, the typical position of standing with the weight on one foot and the upper body "hung up" on the supporting hip causes a high hip on the supporting side, a low shoulder on that same side and a curve in the spine to the opposite side (Fig. 38). This position causes stress in joints and strain in muscles and ligaments, and if assumed habitually a mis-

Figure 38.   A, *Well balanced position—straight spine.* B, *Weight on one foot. "Hung on one hip"—curved spine.*

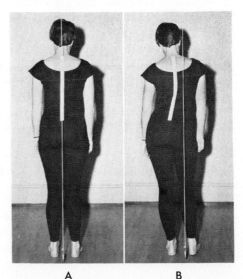

A   B

shapen body results. However, it rests the muscles of one leg and if taken for a matter of moments, and both legs are used alternately, no great harm is caused. It is important that these positions that upset the total body alignment be used *for change only* and that the well aligned position be the basic position of the body not only when standing but also during activity as well.

EFFECT OF HEELS ON STANDING POSITION

Since heels on shoes elevate the heel of the foot, the body is thrown forward. In order to keep the center of gravity of the body over the feet the body must be adjusted backward. If this adjustment is made from the ankles the relative alignment of the various segments of the body is not disturbed. The only change is at the ankle joint where the angle between the leg and the foot is enlarged. If much of the backward adjustment of the body is made from the waist, as is frequently the case, the alignment of the entire body is disturbed and many joints are put into a position of strain. Strain is felt particularly in the lower back region. The position of the foot in shoes with heels causes the calf muscles to be shortened and the anterior muscles to be stretched. Constant wearing of high heels can result in inability to place the heel of the foot on the ground.

As a result of electromyographic studies of standing, Joseph[18] reported that wearing high heels appears to result in increased activity in the muscles of the leg and hip, and that instability was indicated by relatively large bursts of activity in both the anterior and posterior muscle groups.

Kendall[19] stated that, because of the forward shift of the weight, the proportion of the weight borne on the balls of the feet increases directly with the height of the heels and there-fore, continuous wearing of high heels results is anterior foot strain. In addition, high heels tend to cause the feet to slip forward into the toes of the shoes and when this happens the toes, being wedged into too small a space, are subjected to considerable deforming pressure.

EFFECT OF PREGNANCY ON STANDING POSITION

In pregnancy the center of gravity of the body is displaced forward and again a backward adjustment of the body is necessary in order to maintain balance. Because of the added weight it is even more important that the adjustment be made from the ankles than it is in the case of high heels mentioned above. It is simply a matter of counterbalancing the additional weight which is in the front of the body with the body weight as a unit. If the adjustment is made from the waist the strain on the lower back is increased because of the added weight and lower back pain is likely to result.

EFFECT OF THE HEIGHT OF KITCHEN SINK AND COUNTER AND IRONING BOARD ON STANDING POSITION

Since the height of a kitchen sink or counter affects the standing position, it is an important factor in the fatigue experienced by women at the end of the day. The sink should be of such a height that the individual who will be using it can, when standing in a well balanced position, place her hands flat in the bottom. If it is lower, her trunk must be bent forward all the time she is working at the sink. Thus the lower back muscles are called on constantly to support the weight of the trunk against gravity's pull. In order to avoid this same waste of energy while working at the kitchen counter, the counter should be a few inches (approximately 5 inches) below elbow height. A small space which allows the toes to project under cabinets below the counter makes it possible to stand close to the task and thus maintain the normal, well balanced position while working.

It is wise to use an adjustable ironing board so that it can be set at a height that makes possible a well balanced standing position with the elbow bent sufficiently to allow free hand movement while applying downward force. Since the height of the iron (plus its handle) raises the hand above the ironing board by some 4-5 inches, the ironing board needs to be somewhat lower than a kitchen counter. However, since a downward force is needed, it should be only 2-3 inches lower.

SUMMARY

Without some conscious learning experience a high percentage of individuals do not naturally stand in a well aligned position. The characteristic posture of an individual is an important factor in the impression he makes on others, in his own feelings of well being and self confidence, and in the efficiency of his movements.

An efficient position is one in which the various body segments are balanced above each other so that there is a minimum of friction and uneven pressure in the weight bearing joints and strain on muscles and ligaments, as well as a margin of safety in every joint so that an unexpected force will not push the joint beyond its normal limits and thus cause injury.

This position is most easily maintained if the feet are a few inches apart (not wider than the hips) and the toes straight ahead, the knees "easy," the pelvis in a balanced position, the shoulders directly above the hips with the tips level and pointing directly out to the sides, and the head balanced above the shoulders with the chin level. To allow for normal body sway without loss of balance, the weight should fall near the center of the base, i.e., between the feet and in front of the ankles.

The knowledge of a well aligned position and the kinesthetic perception of it are only the first steps in acquiring an efficient habitual posture. A desire to make this a part of one's personality which is strong enough to lead to persistent practice is essential for the formation of the new habit.

REFERENCES

1. Tepper, Rubye H. and Hellebrandt, Frances A.: The Influence of the Upright Posture on Metabolic Rate. *American Journal of Physiology, 122*:563, 1938.
2. Hellebrandt, Frances A. and Brogdon, Elizabeth: The Hydrostatic Effect of Gravity on the Circulation in Supported, Unsupported and Suspended Positions. *American Journal of Physiology, 123*:95–96, 1938.
3. Tepper, Rubye H. and Hellebrandt, Frances A.: The Influence of the Upright Posture on Metabolic Rate. *American Journal of Physiology, 122*:567, 1938.
4. Hellebrandt, Frances A.: Standing, a Geotropic Reflex, The Mechanism of the Asynchronous Rotation of Motor Units. *American Journal of Physiology, 121*:471–474, 1938.
5. Broer, Marion R.: A Study of Factors Influencing the Ability to Improve Antero-Posterior Posture. Unpublished master's thesis, University of Wisconsin, 1936.
6. Broer, Marion R. and Houtz, Sara Jane: *Patterns of Muscular Activity in Selected Sport Skills: An Electromyographic Study.* Springfield, Charles C Thomas, 1967.
7. Hellebrandt, F. A., Brogdon, Elizabeth and Tepper, Rubye: Posture and Its Cost. *American Journal of Physiology, 129*:773–781, 1940.
8. McCormick, H. G.: *The Metabolic Cost of Maintaining a Standing Position with Special Reference to Body Alignment.* New York, King's Crown Press, 1942.
9. Wells, Katharine F.: *Kinesiology.* 3rd ed. Philadelphia, W. B. Saunders Company, 1960, p. 366.
10. Kendall, Henry Otis, Kendall, Florence P. and Boynton, Dorothy A.: *Posture and Pain.* Baltimore, Williams and Wilkins Company, 1952, p. 104.
11. *Ibid.,* p. 105.
12. *Ibid.,* p. 10.

13. Brunnstrom, Signe: Center of Gravity Line in Relation to Ankle Joint in Erect Standing, Application to Posture Training and to Artificial Legs. *Physical Therapy Review,* 34:114, March, 1954.
14. Hellebrandt, Frances A., Tepper, Rubye H., Braun, Genevieve L. and Elliott, Margaret C.: The Location of the Cardinal Anatomical Orientation Planes Passing through the Center of Gravity of Young Adult Women. *American Journal of Physiology, 121*:468, 1938.
15. Joseph, J.: *Man's Posture, Electromyographic Studies.* Springfield, Ill., Charles C Thomas, Publisher, 1960, p. 16.
16. Morton, J. Dudley and Fuller, Dudley Dean: *Human Locomotion and Body Form.* Baltimore, Williams and Wilkins Company, 1952, p. 49.
17. *Ibid.*, p. 50.
18. Joseph, J.: *Man's Posture, Electromyographic Studies.* Springfield, Ill., Charles C Thomas, Publisher, 1960, pp. 52, 56.
19. Kendall, Henry Otis, Kendall, Florence P. and Boynton, Dorothy A.: *Posture and Pain.* Baltimore, Williams and Wilkins Company, 1952, p. 192.

11

Walking

In standing the main concern is stability. However, stability does not always contribute to the individual's particular purpose. The act of walking is a matter of disturbing the mechanical equilibrium of the body, pushing the body forward, and forming successive new bases by moving the legs forward alternately. Walking is possible because friction between the foot and the supporting surface keeps the foot from slipping backward, and the downward-backward force applied against the surface by the extension of the leg and foot causes an equal and opposite forward-upward force that moves the body forward. Since the body as a whole moves forward, walking can be described as linear motion. However, this linear motion of the body is brought about by two rotatory motions of the legs. As the body weight moves forward, the upper end of the leg lever moves forward about the foot as an axis. This is followed by a swinging forward of the foot to establish a new base and in this movement, the distal end of the leg moves about the hip as the axis (Fig. 39).

As in standing there are certain basic physiological reactions which occur without conscious attention. "... the initial lifting of a foot from the ground is accompanied by a flexion at all joints in the extremity. With the resulting lengthening of the extensor muscles, stretch reflexes are initiated which operate to inhibit flexors and excite extensors. This brings about an extension at joints as the foot is thrust to the ground.

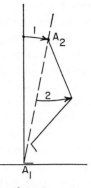

Figure 39. *Double rotary movement involved in walking.*

1 Center of gravity moves
about foot (A$_1$)
2 Leg moves about hip (A$_2$)

A supporting reaction is present in the opposite extremity until the latter begins this process. Thus, the alternating reactions progress as walking, and do so more or less automatically, though, of course, the pattern may be modified or interrupted at will."[1]

The general body position for walking is the same as that for standing, the only difference being that the center of gravity of the body is moved forward so that gravity helps overcome the inertia of the body and force can be applied in the direction of desired movement.

In the act of walking each leg alternates between a supporting and a swinging phase. During a part of the supportive phase the leg exerts force to propel the body forward, but during a part of the time it exerts force that resists the forward movement of the body. Since the foot strikes the ground *ahead of the body* there is a *forward* component of force in the thrust of the foot against the ground (Fig. 40). This results in a backward counterpressure of the ground against the foot

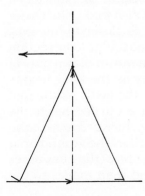

Figure 40. *Horizontal and vertical components of resistive force.*

which checks the forward momentum of the body. This resistive force makes it possible to stop the forward movement of the body at any point in the walking sequence. Without this force, inertia would cause the trunk to continue moving forward beyond the base. The resistive force is present from the time the foot first strikes the ground until the center of gravity of the body has moved forward to the point above the supporting foot. Elftman[2] found that the horizontal component of the resistive force reaches its maximum at about the time the ball of the foot touches the ground and then decreases, at first rapidly and then slowly, to become zero after the heel begins to rise and before the opposite foot touches the ground. As soon as the center of gravity of the body has moved forward of the supporting foot, the thrust against the ground caused by the extension of the hip, knee, and ankle has a backward component and, therefore, the counterpressure of the ground pushes the body forward. As the heel rises, this backward horizontal component of force increases rapidly reaching its maximum as the ball of the foot is leaving the ground and becomes zero as the foot leaves the ground.[2] This backward horizontal component of the propelling force must exceed the forward horizontal component of the resistive force if progressive motion is to result. The vertical component of the force supports the body against the pull of gravity. The farther back the weight of the body is at the time that the propelling leg is extended, the greater the vertical component in relation to the horizontal component of the force. If this vertical component is too large in proportion to the force exerted by gravity and the horizontal component, a bouncing walk results.

As soon as the leg has exerted its backward push against the ground the swinging phase of the walk begins. This starts with flexion at the hip joint which is followed by flexion of the knee and ankle. This flexion of all the joints of the leg shortens the lever so that it clears the ground despite the shortened distance from the hips to the ground and also makes its easier to move the leg weight since the weight is closer to the axis. The swinging motion is initiated by muscular contraction (flexion of hip), but both gravity and momentum play a part in its continuance. The hip continues to flex as the knee begins to extend after the foot has passed under the body. As the foot approaches the ground, the hip extensors act to decelerate the forward movement. Since the foot reaches forward to take the weight and the ankle is flexed, the heel strikes the ground first. The weight is immediately spread over the foot (the heel, outer side of the foot, and the metatarsals) and then moves to the toes and the final push for the next step is applied. This "rolling" of the weight across the foot from heel to toe reduces the shock of impact by providing for gradual force absorption. There is a period of double support in every step. By the time that the break in heel contact has been made so that the weight stress has shifted to the metatarsals, particularly the first metatarsal and digit and the second metatarsal, the larger part of the body weight has been received by the opposite foot.[3] The slower the walk, the more the overlap of the supportive phases of the two feet.

The force exerted by the foot against the surface as the heel strikes the ground and as the toes push off is greater than the body weight due to the momentum of the body at heel strike (force = mass × momentum) and the thrust of plantar flexion at push off.[4] Because of this force at heel strike, the small heels on some women's dress shoes will snap if the wearer attempts to walk normally, i.e., heel to toe. Therefore, these small high heels cause a flat-footed gait which requires shorter steps and leads to jarring of the body, since all the force must be absorbed suddenly rather than gradually as the weight rolls across the foot from heel to toe.

In walking, as in any motion, the inertia of the body must be overcome. This is accomplished by the force exerted by the pushing foot assisted by the pull of gravity which is effective when the weight of the body is shifted forward. Walking is essentially a series of episodes in which balance is lost and then regained. The center of gravity is moved forward disturbing the stability of the body and as gravity acts to pull the body forward and downward, the back foot pushes backward and downward causing a reaction force against the body forward and upward. The back foot is then lifted and moved forward so that a new base is formed under the forward moving center of gravity.

The forward movement of the center of gravity increases the forward component of the counter pressure of the ground against the pushing foot and thus force is applied more in the direction of the desired movement. The more forward the center of gravity the greater the forward component of the pushing force. Thus the speed of a walk is determined not only by the magnitude of the pushing force which in turn depends upon the force exerted by the foot *and* the resistance of the ground, but also by the direction of its application. The effect of the angle of inclination of the body on the speed of the gait can be experienced by walking with the weight well back (exaggerated) while exerting considerable force in the push of the foot against the floor and then, *keeping the same pushing force*, shifting the weight forward. The additional speed with which the body moves forward is immediately apparent. This demonstration also points up the bouncing walk which results from keeping the weight back.

Speed of walking can also be increased by lengthening the stride. However, when the stride is lengthened the up-and-down motion of the body is increased (Fig. 41) unless the supporting knee is kept somewhat flexed as the center of gravity passes forward over it. Metheny[5] suggested lengthening the stride with no additional energy expenditure by relaxing the supporting knee and allowing it to bend slightly so that the hips are brought closer to the ground and the heel strikes farther in front of the body. This puts the back leg in position to exert its force more diagonally forward and increases the forward component, thus making the force exerted more effective for forward movement.

When walking against a high wind, the body leans well forward into the wind to increase the forward component of the

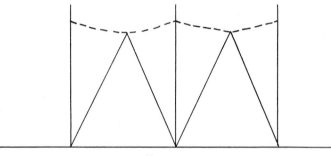

Shorter stride

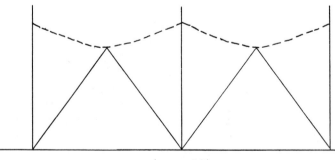

Longer stride

Figure 41. *Vertical variations of center of gravity resulting from different lengths of stride.*

pushing force. The greater the forward lean, the greater the horizontal component. The amount of lean must vary with the force of the wind. Since the farther forward one leans the more effective is gravity's pull on the body, the body must not be angled beyond the point at which the pull of gravity is balanced by the resistance of the wind. Since wind is likely to blow in gusts it is dangerous to move the center of gravity too far forward even though the push is more effective, because a sudden reduction in the force of the wind would leave the body overbalanced forward and a fall would be likely.

Any movement of the center of gravity forward is accomplished most effectively when the segments of the body are maintained in their same relative alignment, and the body as a whole shifted forward from the ankles. Frequently, individuals who are attempting to hurry lean forward from the hips. This places strain on the smaller muscles of the back which must hold the trunk up against gravity's pull, and although it does move the center of gravity forward somewhat, it does not move it as far forward as does a shift of the entire body from the ankles. Walking rapidly while leaning forward from the hips and then, keeping the same push off, bringing the hips forward (and shoulders back somewhat) to make the body a straight line which leans forward from the ankles, demonstrates that the latter is more effective since the body moves faster with the same force.

The stability of the body in walking, as in standing, is directly related to the size of the base of support. Therefore, the lateral distance between the feet is a factor in balance. It is also a factor in the direction in which the pushing force is applied. In standing, the base involves both feet with the line of gravity falling between them (center of the base) and therefore, the position of the feet a few inches apart (width of the hips) gives greater stability. However, in walking the base shifts from one foot to the other and, in order to maintain stability, the center of gravity of the body must shift to a position over the supporting foot. If the feet are moved straight forward from their stable standing position (walk with feet apart) the weight must be shifted a considerable distance from side to side at every step. This can be easily demonstrated in the standing position with the feet a few inches apart by picking up the left foot and then placing it on the floor and picking up the right foot. The sideways movement of the entire body which results is immediately apparent. Thus walking with the feet apart causes a "duck walk," one in which the body sways from side to side. This is the type of walk normally used by a baby learning to walk. He spreads his feet because his balance is precarious. He also uses his arms to help maintain his balance in the same way that a tightrope walker uses a long pole.

The sideways swaying can be eliminated by placing each foot directly under the center of gravity at each step. This is accomplished by walking a line, placing one foot directly in front of the other. However, this method of walking decreases the width of the base during the period of double support and thus reduces the stability of the body and additional energy must be expended to move each foot out and around the other at every step.

The most effective position of the feet, then, is that in which they are moved in toward the center so that the sideways shift of weight is kept to a minimum and still each foot can move directly forward (Fig. 42). When the inner borders of the feet are placed along a line the base is wider than when the feet are placed one in front of the other, the feet can move directly forward and the movement of the center of gravity from side to side is slight. In fact, if the pelvis is stabilized the leg can be swung through with little or no movement of the center of gravity to the side. Experimentation with the three positions of the feet with the attention consciously directed

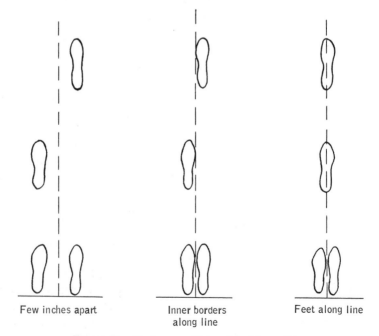

Few inches apart   Inner borders   Feet along line
                          along line

Figure 42.   *Various positions of feet in walking.*

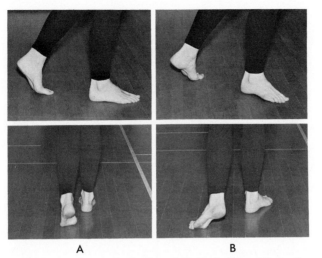

Figure 43. A, *Push straight backward.* B, *Push diagonally backward.*

to the reaction of the body, the feeling of stability, and the ease of foot movement in each, clearly points up the advantages of walking with the inner borders of the feet along a line.

When walking with the toes pointing ahead, the force is exerted in the desired direction of movement. If the feet are placed on the ground with the toes turned either out or in, the push is exerted diagonally backward-outward (away from the center of the base), sending the body forward and inward (Fig. 43). Since the right foot pushes diagonally right and back, the body moves forward and to the left in response to the force exerted by it. The push of the left foot sends the body forward and to the right (Fig. 44). Thus, energy is wasted and a zigzag walk results. The toe-out position causes outward force because the push is made with the *inner border of the great toe* and the first metatarsal (Fig. 44). In the toe-in position the force is exerted by more of the toes. As in standing, the toe-out position of the feet causes the weight to fall on the inner borders of the feet putting stress on the arch, and since the push off is exerted by the inner border of the great toe and first metatarsal, the force passes diagonally across the arch adding further stress. When the toes point approximately straight ahead all force is directed backward and is, therefore, useful in causing movement of the body in the desired direction (forward). Also, the force passes straight backward through the arch of the foot.

The arms swing easily in opposition to the legs. This motion is reflexly controlled and when an individual has difficulty with this coordination, tension or voluntary effort is interfering

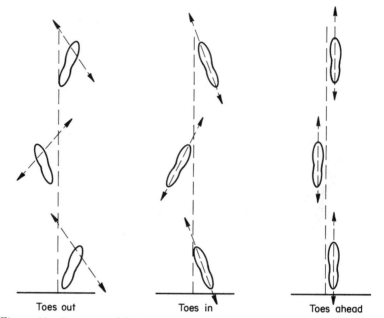

Toes out   Toes in   Toes ahead

Figure 44. *Direction of force application resulting from various foot positions.*

with the normal response. The tendency of the trunk to rotate
due to the off center application of force by the foot is counteracted by the swing of the arms. The push off by the left foot
causes an off center force which tends to rotate the pelvis and
trunk to the right, but the simultaneous forward movement of
the right arm, tending to rotate the shoulders and trunk to the
left, balances this force and thus reduces the lateral rotation of
the trunk. Because of the way that the arms hang naturally,
this arm swing is not directly forward but diagonally forward,
being somewhat across the body.

　　If one stands with the arms hanging naturally at the sides
and simply bends the elbows, the fact that the hands do not
point directly forward but rather that the lower arms are in
front of the body, is apparent. Outward rotation at the shoulder
is necessary to place the arms in such a position that the hands
point directly forward. In ordinary walking the arm swing is
largely the product of inertia and gravity acting on the weight
of the arm.[6] When the gait becomes faster, voluntary swinging
of the arms helps to carry the upper trunk forward. Any bending of the arm at the elbow shortens the lever and thus makes
faster movement of the arm easier.

　　Occasionally, one sees exaggerated hip rotation used to
produce momentum as an aid in swinging the leg forward.
While this can be an effective procedure for someone handi-

capped by loss of function of the hip flexors, it is not efficient for a normal individual. Development of a feeling for stabilizing the pelvis and moving the knee straight forward helps in overcoming this tendency. Lack of stabilization which holds the pelvis *level* produces a "hip switch" in which the hip of the swinging leg drops sharply and the knee of the supporting leg tends to hyperextend. A heavy and aesthetically displeasing walk results. A heavy lumbering walk also results when an individual "collapses" through the abdomen and trunk (allows the upper body to settle down into the pelvis). This individual is also likely to stand (and walk) with his weight back toward his heels. Getting a feeling of "lift" through the trunk and moving the weight forward will lighten the walk.

Since the forward movement of the body is effected by the horizontal component of the diagonal pushing force, friction is essential for the counterpressure of the surface to be transferred to the body. If there were little or no friction the backward component of the pushing force would simply move the foot backward across the surface. The greater the horizontal component in relation to the vertical component of the pushing force, the greater the dependence on friction for efficient locomotion since more of the force is applied backward, or in the direction to most effectively overcome friction. The more vertical the application of force the smaller the component which is in direct opposition to friction and the more effective the friction. Therefore, the less the friction, the less the force of the foot against the ground can be directed backward, and the more the weight must be kept above the base. Shortening the step keeps the center of gravity more vertically above the base and thus reduces the backward component of force.

When walking on ice short steps, which keep the horizontal component of force to a minimum and the center of gravity more directly over the base, should be used. Wells[7] pointed out that an appreciation of the horizontal component of the force of locomotion should make individuals aware of certain dangers in the home. Wet floors and scatter rugs should be approached at a slower pace and with shorter steps which keep the center of gravity more vertically above the base so that the horizontal component is lessened. This same problem is involved whenever friction between the foot and the counteracting surface is slight.

If the surface lacks solidity, such as soft snow, mud, sand, and the like, it gives with the push of the foot against it (see p. 51), and offers too little resistance to supply effective counterpressure. Since much of the force is dissipated in pushing the foot and the snow or sand backward more force must be exerted to achieve forward progress. When walking on the beach it is important to remember that fatigue sets in sooner than when walking on normal hard ground so that the distance to be walked up the beach will be gauged accordingly.

WALKING BACKWARD

When walking backward the center of gravity is not shifted in the direction of movement as it is in walking forward. Instead a foot is lifted and placed securely a short distance back before the weight is shifted. This is because there is little base behind the ankle. Because of the greater strength of the calf muscles over that of the anterior leg muscles, the length of the foot in front of the ankle, and the fact that the toes are in an excellent position to push the body backward if the center of gravity should move so far forward that balance is endangered, in walking forward the center of gravity can be shifted forward safely and thus advantage can be taken of the force of gravity and the more direct angle of push. However, in shifting the center of gravity backward balance is likely to be lost unless a new base is prepared before the shift is made. Therefore, short steps must be taken when walking backward.

WALKING ON INCLINES

When the surface supporting the body is not level the pull of gravity is no longer perpendicular to the surface. In order to keep the center of gravity of the body above the feet (its base) the angle of the body with the feet must be adjusted (Fig. 45). If the surface slopes upward the line of gravity of a body forming the normal angle with the feet falls well behind the base. To bring the center of gravity over the base, the body must lean forward. Similarly a downward incline causes the line of gravity to fall forward of the base, and a backward adjustment is necessary to bring it back over the base. The steeper the angle of the incline the greater the adjustment of the body necessary. This adjustment should be made from the ankles so that the basic, well aligned position of the body can be maintained. When the forward adjustment is made from the hips the strong gluteal muscles are brought into play giving additional muscular strength. However, the back muscles must then strain to hold the upper body up against the pull of gravity unless there is a railing on which the hand can be placed so that the weight of the upper body can be supported by the arm, or unless a cane is used. Also, the aesthetic value of

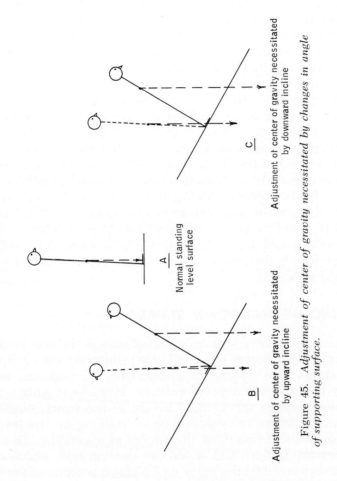

Adjustment of center of gravity necessitated by upward incline

A
Normal standing level surface

B

Adjustment of center of gravity necessitated by downward incline

C

Figure 45. *Adjustment of center of gravity necessitated by changes in angle of supporting surface.*

leaning from the ankles as opposed to leaning from the hips cannot be overlooked.

When the backward adjustment, which is necessary in walking down an incline, is made from the waist, strain is put upon the lower back.

When walking uphill the forward lean from the ankles also makes it possible to apply the force as much as possible in the direction of desired movement which is upward and forward. In walking down an incline the problem becomes one of resisting the pull of gravity in order to control momentum. The backward lean makes it possible to apply force forward and downward in the direction to oppose gravity. Actually, walking down an incline becomes a matter of controlled resistance to gravity's pull. Because of this it takes less energy to run than to walk down a hill since is is easier to move the feet forward rapidly than to resist the pull of gravity at every step. This becomes more true as the incline becomes steeper.

On steep grades there is a tendency for the foot to slip because it is applying force downward as well as backward, or forward in the case of walking down grade, and gravity is also pulling downward. The downward component of the force is added to gravity's pull. Cross bars on the supporting surface reduce the possibility of slipping since they present a surface against which the foot can push more nearly straight backward (or forward).

WALKING UP AND DOWN STAIRS

The chief problem in walking upstairs is the conservation of energy while that of descending is principally safety. Karpovich[8] stated that it takes approximately 15 times as much energy to walk up a flight of ordinary stairs as to walk a level distance equal to the vertical height of the stairs. While descending requires more energy than walking on the level, it takes only about one-third the energy of ascending. To avoid unnecessary fatigue and strain the general body position for both tasks should be the same well aligned position of the body segments as described for standing.

When walking upstairs the center of gravity should be shifted forward so that the push with the back leg is in a diagonally forward and upward direction (Fig. 46). This forward inclination should be from the ankles keeping the body segments in their same relative alignment. Leaning forward from the hips throws unnecessary strain on the muscles of the lower back. As in walking up an incline, the bend from the hips

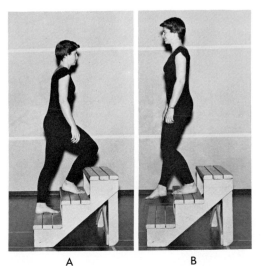

A   B

Figure 46.   A, *Weight forward. Push in direction of desired movement.* B, *Weight held back for safety.*

enables the strong gluteal muscles to work to good advantage and therefore makes more force available. Older people may need this additional muscular power but should then use the railing so that some of the weight of the upper trunk can be supported on the hand. The back leg pushes the weight up and forward over the front leg, and while this leg lifts the body and pushes the weight forward, the back leg is lifted and placed on the next step under the upward-forward moving center of gravity. Thus, a smooth ascent results from the coordination of the forces produced *by both legs* at every step, the back leg pushing the center of gravity over the forward leg so that it is in an advantageous position to add its force to that of the back leg by pushing upward.

If the foot is placed flat on the step energy does not have to be expended to hold the heel up against the pull of gravity. This can be easily demonstrated by standing for a few seconds with the ball of one foot on a step and then placing the foot flat on the step. The extra energy required to stand on the ball of the foot over that required to stand on the entire foot is obvious. Balance is also a problem due to the small base afforded by the ball of the foot. However, if the step is so narrow that placing the entire foot on it puts the toes close to the riser so that the foot must be raised straight upward, and then moved forward to be placed on the next step instead of moved diagonally forward and upward, the energy saved may be wasted in the additional movement necessary (Fig. 47). When placing the foot flat on a narrow tread there is also a danger of catching

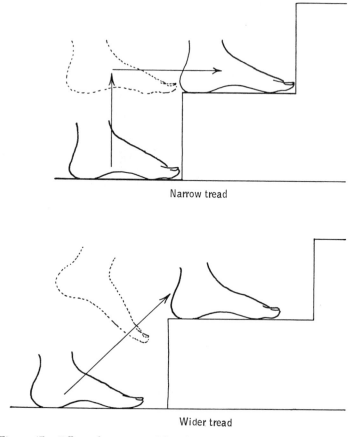

Narrow tread

Wider tread

Figure 47.   *Effect of various widths of stair treads on movement of foot.*

the toes on the lip of the step and many stairs are constructed with a slight extension of each step over its riser.

In descending stairs the center of gravity is kept back over the center of the base because of the danger of falling down the stairs if it should move beyond the toes. Safety makes it essential that the general principle concerning the placement of the center of gravity in line with the direction of movement be ignored. Actually walking down stairs is a matter of controlled "giving in" to gravity (lengthening contraction of the extensors). It involves control of the rate at which gravity pulls the body down. The weight is lowered to the next step by giving with the supporting knee. Since the center of gravity is over the supporting foot, any push exerted by that leg moves the body upward and it then has to be lowered through a greater distance. Energy is wasted in pushing up and the individual bounces down the stairs. Added force due to the dropping of the body from the additional height must be absorbed. The ball of the swinging foot makes the first contact with the step below and the heel comes down immediately.

EFFORT REQUIRED TO WALK UP INCLINE AND FLIGHT OF STAIRS

In general, it requires more effort to climb a given height on stairs than on an incline. Walking upstairs involves lifting the body weight a certain height at every step until the desired height is reached. The effort expended can be calculated by the formula for work ($W = F \cdot S$), which means that the weight of the body is multiplied by the distance (height) that it is lifted. The effort expended in walking up an inclined plane multiplied by the length of the incline is equal to the weight lifted multiplied by the distance that it is lifted. Therefore, because the length of an inclined plane exceeds its height, it has a theoretical mechanical advantage of the ratio of these two distances.

$$\text{force} \times \text{length of incline} = \text{weight} \times \text{height of incline}[9]$$
$$\frac{\text{Force}}{\text{Weight}} = \frac{\text{height}}{\text{length}}$$

If a stairway is ten feet deep and ten feet high an inclined plane covering the same distance would be approximately 14 feet long. (The square of the hypotenuse of a right triangle is equal to the sum of the squares of the other two sides.) (Fig. 48.)

$$X^2 = 10^2 + 10^2$$
$$X^2 = 200$$
$$X = 14.14 \text{ ft.}$$

If an individual weighing 140 pounds were to walk up this stairway he would have to exert 1400 foot-pounds of force in order to lift his weight ten feet.

$$W = F \cdot S$$
$$W = 140 \cdot 10$$
$$W = 1400 \text{ ft. lbs.}$$

Since the mechanical advantage of an inclined plane is equal to the ratio of the height to the length, this incline would have a mechanical advantage of $\frac{1}{1.4}$ which means that for every 140 pounds to be lifted only 100 pounds of force is needed.

$$\frac{\text{Force}}{\text{Weight}} = \frac{\text{height}}{\text{length}}$$

$$\frac{\text{Force}}{\text{Weight}} = \frac{10}{14}$$

$$\frac{\text{Force}}{140} = \frac{1}{1.4}$$

$$\text{Force} = \frac{140}{1.4} = 100$$

However, the general principle that less effort is required to climb an incline does not hold if the incline is so steep that the foot slips backward. On an incline the propelling force is exerted backward *and downward,* some of the force (the downward component) is added to gravity's pull and, if the incline is very steep, this causes the foot to slip backward. In this case less of the force exerted by the individual is effective in moving the body forward since effort is wasted in moving the foot backward.

SUMMARY

In walking, the inertia of the body can be overcome most efficiently by moving the center of gravity forward so that the force of gravity assists the movement, and the pushing force exerted by the counterpressure of the ground against the foot, is applied at an angle which results in a larger horizontal component and is, therefore, more advantageous for forward movement. The general alignment of the body segments follows the same principles as discussed in the preceding chapter on standing.

There is a short period of double support in every step and each step has two principal phases, supportive and swinging. The supportive phase consists of two parts, one propels the body forward and the other resists the forward movement. Because of the forward diagonal position of the leg, backward force which resists the forward movement of the body is applied from the moment the foot strikes the ground until the center of gravity of the body is above the supporting foot. The propelling force exerted by the pushing foot must exceed this resistive force for movement to result.

The most efficient position of the feet is that of the toes pointing ahead and the inner borders of the feet falling along a line.

The easy, relaxed arm swing in opposition to the swing of the legs serves to reduce the trunk rotation and helps to carry the upper body forward.

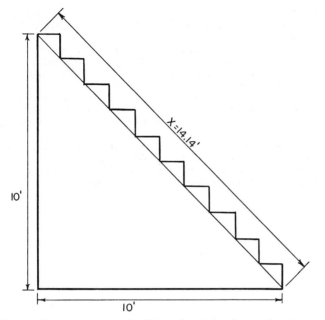

Figure 48. *Comparison of a flight of stairs and an inclined plane.*

The speed of the walk can be increased by increasing the force exerted against the ground, moving the center of gravity of the body farther forward and lengthening the stride.

Because balance is more precarious when walking backward, the foot must be moved back to prepare a new base before the center of gravity of the body moves to any extent.

When walking up an incline or stairs the force exerted by the legs and feet is made more effective by moving the center of gravity of the body forward so that the force is applied in the desired direction of movement. Since safety is the major factor in descending stairs the weight is kept back over the center of the supporting foot. On an incline the body must lean backward from the ankles to keep the center of gravity over the base. The body weight is lowered most efficiently by a controlled "giving in" to gravity.

REFERENCES

1. Gardner, Ernest: *Fundamentals of Neurology.* Philadelphia, W. B. Saunders Company, 1947, p. 227.
2. Elftman, Herbert: The Force Exerted by the Ground in Walking. *Ant. Z. Angew. Physiol.,* 10:489, 1939.

3. Morton, Dudley J., and Fuller, Dudley Dean: *Human Locomotion and Body Form.* Baltimore, Williams and Wilkins Company, 1952, pp. 83–84.
4. Williams, Marian, and Lissner, Herbert R.: *Biomechanics of Human Motion.* Philadelphia, W. B. Saunders Company, 1962, p. 122.
5. Metheny, Eleanor: *Body Dynamics.* New York, McGraw-Hill Book Company, Inc., 1951, p. 146.
6. Morton, Dudley J., and Fuller, Dudley Dean: *Human Locomotion and Body Form.* Baltimore, Williams and Wilkins Company, 1952, p. 242.
7. Wells, Katharine F.: *Kinesiology.* 3rd ed. Philadelphia, W. B. Saunders Company, 1960, p. 494.
8. Karpovich, Peter V.: *Physiology of Muscular Activity.* 5th ed. Philadelphia, W. B. Saunders Company, 1959, p. 99.
9. Flitter, Hessel Howard: *An Introduction to Physics and Nursing.* 2nd ed. St. Louis, C. V. Mosby Company, 1954, p. 65.

$$12$$

Running

Running is an important skill. Besides being used in a high percentage of sport activities, it, like walking though to a lesser degree, is used in everyday life. In general, the mechanics of running are the same as those of walking. In some ways running is easier than walking. Babies frequently run before they walk. A baby normally stands with feet apart to give a wide base and thus stability in the lateral plane, but having very small feet which give a short base forward and backward, the center of gravity is likely to pass the forward margin of the base. By moving his feet forward rapidly he may be able to maintain an upright position until he reaches a person or a piece of furniture which will support him. Also, because of the reduction or elimination of the resistive phase which is a considerable factor in the walk, a slow run takes less energy than a fast walk. This is easily demonstrated by walking a short distance as fast as possible and suddenly breaking into a jogging run. The relief from the strain caused by the resistive force of the walk is immediately apparent.

Running differs from walking in that the period of double support is eliminated and a period of no support, between the time that the back foot exerts its force and is lifted from the ground and the forward foot strikes the ground, is added. More force is supplied by the extensor muscles of the driving leg and foot giving both more forward momentum and more upward momentum. The latter is important in keeping the body in the air long enough to make full use of the forward component of the driving force. The leg swings forward and starts back just before contact, and therefore the foot strikes the ground almost under the center of gravity of the body eliminating or considerably reducing the resistive force. In fact, the supportive phase is almost entirely propulsive. The greater the speed, the more they are concurrent.

Because the foot contacts the ground under the center of gravity of the body, the first contact is made with the ball of the foot instead of the heel and the heel may or may not be lowered to the ground as the body passes over the foot. In a slow run the heel usually does come into contact with the ground, but this does not happen in a fast run. Since the force of the push off is greater and the body is actually suspended momentarily in the air, the force which must be absorbed on contact with the ground is greater than in walking. Landing on the ball of the foot makes it possible to absorb this force more readily without a jar by giving with the ankle, knee, and hip. The additional give in the knee puts this joint in an advantageous position to exert more propulsive force. Making the first contact with the heel when running causes the center of gravity to be behind the contact foot and a resistive force is applied to the body as in walking. This also makes it impossible to give with the ankle joint and thus the force is absorbed less gradually and the body experiences a greater jar.

The angle of the body is more forward than in walking but, as in walking, the forward lean should be from the ankles so that the trunk is kept in line with the driving leg. This forward angle reduces the air pressure against the body and puts the center of gravity more ahead of the driving foot enlarging the forward component of the propulsive force. Also, the forward angle, combined with additional bending of the supporting knee as the body passes over it, reduces the up and down bobbing of the body which would occur with the greater propulsive force if the angle of the body were more upright. The faster the run the more forward the angle of the body.

Since the body is moving forward faster in the run, the legs must swing faster in order to form a base under the moving center of gravity. As the leg swings forward the knee is bent considerably more than in the walk so that the weight is brought closer to the hip. Since the lever is shortened by bending the knee, the leg can be moved forward faster with less effort.

As in walking, the arm swing must be coordinated with that of the legs in order to balance the rotatory effect of the leg swing on the trunk. Since the legs are moving faster, the arms must move faster also. In order to move them rapidly with as little effort as possible they too are shortened by bending the elbows. The swing is somewhat across in front of the body as in walking. It seems reasonable, however, that when maximum speed is desired, the swing should be somewhat less diagonal so that the force can be more directly backward and forward. The energy used in the outward rotation of the arms at the shoulders necessary to point the hands more forward, is expended for the purpose of adding to the forward component of the force of the swing. Observation of pictures of Olympic runners indicates that they do tend to swing the arms more forward as they go into their final sprint near the finish line. Bunn[1] stated that a runner with heavy hips and legs in relation to his arms and shoulders must carry his arms farther from his body or increase the vigor of his arm swing to balance the force of the legs.

Since an object has inertia to any change in its state of motion (Newton's First Law), in running, as in moving any object, it takes less energy to maintain a given speed once it has been attained than to vary the speed. The greatest amount of force is required at take-off. As the level of speed which is to be attained is reached the force required is decreased.

Speed of running is increased by increasing the propulsive force and/or the length of the stride and the two are interrelated. Increased propulsive force gives more upward force which, resisting gravity, keeps the body in the air longer allowing it time to move farther, *and* more forward force which makes the body move forward faster in the time allowed and thus farther before it contacts the ground. The longer stride lowers the center of gravity and to avoid superfluous vertical motion which would detract from the forward motion, the supporting knee is flexed more. This additional flexion puts the muscles of the leg into a position for more powerful extension and thus makes possible a more powerful drive and a longer stride. Lengthening the stride to the point where a resistive phase is introduced (the foot strikes the ground ahead of the center of gravity) reduces the speed.

Movements in any direction other than the desired direction of movement detract from the efficiency of the movement. Therefore, the knees should be carried straight forward and upward and the arm swing should be inward only enough to counterbalance the rotation of the hips. Girls frequently have difficulty in running because they attempt to run with a minimum of knee lift. In order to move the foot forward without lifting the knee, the thigh must be rotated inwardly and the foot and lower leg thrown out to the side and around. They also tend to rotate the shoulders outward "hugging" the upper arms and elbows to the body and allowing the lower arm to "flap" out at the sides in response to the decided rotation of the hips. Girls may have some mechanical disadvantage in running because of the angle of the femur resulting from a broader pelvis. However, lateral sway can be kept to a minimum if the knees are bent and carried straight forward.

Emphasis on *lifting* the knee forward and relaxing the shoulders while bending the elbows so that the arms can swing in their natural position will increase both the efficiency and the aesthetic appearance of the run. When the arms are bent at the elbow in their natural position, which is with the lower arm diagonally in front of the body, it is more difficult to "hug" the arms to the body. Outward rotation tends to push the upper arm against the trunk. Practice in exercises which relax the upper arm and shoulder girdle and move the arms independently of the trunk should be helpful. Morehouse and Cooper[2] suggest holding the thumb against the tip of the second or third finger instead of making a fist in order to prevent tension in the muscles of the arm. They point out that the muscles used to press the thumb against one of these fingers are located in the forearm while clenching the fist involves muscles of the entire arm and thus may cause tensions which restrict arm action. This should be a useful device to suggest to those whose arms are tense.

Given a certain propulsive force, the smaller the vertical component, the greater the horizontal component. Therefore, the vertical component should be kept as small as will counteract gravity's downward pull, so that as great a proportion of the force as possible will be effective in driving the body forward rather than wasted in producing a bouncing run.

Because the propulsive force is stronger and is exerted in a more horizontal direction, the friction between the feet and the supporting surface is even more important in running than in walking (p. 133). Running should not be attempted unless there is sufficient friction to prevent slipping. While tennis shoes increase the friction between the feet and the tennis court or gymnasium floor, they are not effective on a wet field. If running on wet grass is likely to be required, shoes with cleats are needed (p. 257).

RUNNING IN A CIRCLE

The moving body, like any object, tends to follow a straight line (Newton's First Law). Therefore, if it is necessary to run in an arc, force must be applied toward the outside of the arc. In order to apply force outward the body leans in toward the center of the circle. The force of the leg drive is then outward as well as backward and downward and the counterpressure of the surface exerts an equal and opposite force which sends the body forward and inward. Since the force is diagonal, friction is important to preventing slipping.

CROUCHING START

The crouching start enables the runner to exert maximum horizontal force at take-off which is the time when the maximum inertia must be overcome. The center of gravity of the body is lowered and moved well forward of the feet (weight supported on hands) so that the drive of the legs is considerably more forward than upward.

Stock pointed out that "the function of the rear leg is to pull out of the starting block rather than drive against the block as the forward leg does. . . ."[3] The rear foot must move forward rapidly in order to establish the runner's balance as he drives his center of gravity forward with the extension of the forward leg. This means that the most important function of the rear leg is flexion and therefore, it is advantageous "to have a minimum of bend in the knee joint . . . and to open up or extend the hip of the rear leg."[3] This position of the rear leg places the flexors on stretch and is effective also in moving the center of gravity well forward in the starting position. In a study of four track starting positions, Stock found a "medium high hip start" to be most effective.

In any crouching start diagonal resisting surfaces must be provided for the feet so that the backward drive of the foot can be resisted directly. If a diagonal surface is not provided, the force of the driving foot will cause the foot to slip backward since the force is applied so nearly in direct opposition to the friction between the ground and the foot.

Because of the extreme forward position of the center of gravity the body is in a position of marked instability. Therefore, at takeoff short rapid steps must be taken in order to keep the runner from falling forward. During the period of acceleration the horizontal component of the propulsive force gradually diminishes as the forward inclination of the trunk is decreased and the stride lengthened.

STANDING START

There are many running situations for which the crouching start is not feasible since it requires a nearly vertical resisting surface. A forward-backward stride position with the weight on the forward foot, is taken. The knees are bent so that they are in a position to extend, and thus exert force. Since the center of gravity is relatively high and over the forward edge of the base, it is easy to move it ahead of the forward foot to a position for effective forward propulsive force. The back foot begins the overcoming of the body's inertia by moving the center of gravity forward, but the major take-off is exerted by the forward foot since, in order to get the center of gravity forward, the weight is on that foot. Since the desired motion is forward the toes of the feet should be pointing ahead. From this position they can exert force directly backward and downward. The tendency of some individuals to assume a standing position with the back foot pointing out to the side results in the force that is produced by that foot being transferred diagonally across the arch of the foot and exerted against the side of the knee. The reason most frequently advanced in favor of pushing with the inside of the back foot (toe pointing out to the side) is that it gives a larger surface with which to apply force. The size of the area is not related to the amount of force which can be produced (see p. 57). Thus friction is not increased since friction is dependent upon the total downward force and the material of which the two surfaces are made, and independent of surface area.

STOPPING

In stopping the problem is one of absorbing force gradually so that balance is regained without strain of any joint. Since the movement is forward the knee of the forward leg must give to absorb the forward momentum gradually. This giving of the forward knee drops the center of gravity and shifts it backward keeping it well within the forward limit of the base. This can be demonstrated by standing in a forward-backward stride position with the weight well forward and then bending the forward knee. The dropping of the center of gravity and the shifting of the weight backward is immediately apparent. If the forward knee is straight the momentum of the trunk carries the upper body forward over the foot. The giving of the knee is also important in that it puts the leg into position to extend and, since the center of gravity is behind the forward foot at this time, to push the center of gravity backward over the center of the base reestablishing the stability of the body. It is extremely important that the foot of the leg that is to absorb the force in stopping be placed on the floor with the toes straight ahead. If they are turned in either direction the forward momentum of the body is thrown against the side of the ankle and the side of the knee and the lateral ligament may be strained.

Forward momentum can also be stopped by jumping and landing in a stride position on both feet. A forward-backward stride gives a wide base in the direction of the momentum of the body. If a side stride jump stop is used the jump must turn the body sideways to the direction of movement to widen the base in the needed direction. Hips, knees, and ankles must give to absorb the force of landing and keep the center of gravity over the base. The jump can be used effectively to stop in basketball since the forward momentum frequently is not too great and this type of stop allows for a pivot on either foot.

SUMMARY

Running differs from walking in that there is no period of double support and there is a period of no support. Since the foot strikes the ground under, or almost under, the center of gravity, the resistive phase is eliminated or greatly reduced. The first contact is made with the ball of the foot making it possible to absorb the additional force of the run without jar by giving with the ankle, knee, and hip. Additional bending of the knee puts the muscles of the knee into position for more powerful extension. The angle of the body is more forward, reducing the air pressure and increasing the forward component of the propulsive force. The faster the run the more forward the angle of the body.

To make it easier to swing the legs forward quickly the knees are bent to shorten the levers as they swing through. The elbows are also bent to facilitate rapid swinging of the arms. The arm swing serves the same purposes as it does in walking.

Speed in running is increased by increasing the propulsive force and/or the length of the stride up to the point at which a resistive phase is introduced. Since movements in any direction other than that of desired movement detract from the efficiency of the run, the knees should be brought straight forward and upward and the arm swing should just balance the rotatory force of the trunk.

Friction is more important in running than in walking both because more force is exerted and because it is applied in a more horizontal direction.

When running in an arc it is necessary to apply force toward the outside of the arc to overcome the body's inertia to change of direction. Therefore, the body leans in toward the center of the arc.

The inertia of the body can be overcome by a crouching or a standing start. Maximum horizontal force at take-off can be exerted by the crouching start but a diagonal resistive surface for the feet is necessary. When starting from a standing position the feet should be in a forward-backward stride with the toes straight ahead so that the force can be exerted straight backward and downward. The knees are bent so that the legs are in position to exert force and the weight is on the forward foot.

In stopping the forward momentum must be absorbed gradually and the stability of the body reestablished. This can be done by giving with the forward leg absorbing the force, lowering the center of gravity, and moving it backward. A subsequent extension of the forward knee moves the center of gravity back over the center of the base. Jumping to a stride stop can also be successful if the stride is in the direction of the momentum and the knees, hips, and ankles give on landing.

REFERENCES

1. Bunn, John W.: *Scientific Principles of Coaching*. New York, Prentice-Hall, Inc., 1955, p. 113.
2. Morehouse, Laurence E. and Cooper, John M.: *Kinesiology*. St. Louis, C. V. Mosby Company, 1950, p. 245.
3. Stock, Malcolm: Influence of Various Track Starting Positions on Speed. *Research Quarterly*, 33:608–609.

13

Hopping, Jumping, Leaping, and Landing

In hopping, jumping, and leaping the body is projected through the air and therefore, the laws which govern any projectile apply to it. This means that regardless of the particular activity that projects the body, the path of its center of gravity through the air is determined by the magnitude of the force which is exerted at take-off and the angle of its application. Once the body has lost contact with the projecting surface no movement of various body segments can alter the path followed by *the center of gravity* (Chapter 9). Gravity, of course begins to act immediately to draw the body toward the earth.

In addition to the necessity for overcoming the body's inertia, the pull of gravity (the body weight) must be overcome in order to lift the body off the ground. Therefore, the force required to project the body into space is greater than that required to move the body forward along the ground. This force is dependent upon the weight of the body.

When the propulsive force is exerted by one foot and the body lands on the same foot the action is defined as a *hop*. If the landing is made on the other foot, it is defined as a *leap*. In a *jump* the propulsive force may be exerted either by one foot or both feet. The distinguishing characteristic of a true jump is that in landing both feet contact the ground simultaneously.

The leaping and hopping type of projection is probably used more in daily life than a true jump. However, jumps of various types are important in many sport and dance activities. Since the principles that apply to all of the body projecting activities are the same, they are discussed as they apply to a jump for height and a jump to cover distance.

In all of these activities the problem is not only to produce sufficient force to overcome the inertia of the body and gravity's pull, but also to control the angle at which this force is applied so that the desired purpose is fulfilled.

The force that projects the body into space must be exerted by the muscles of the body. It is produced by quick contraction of the extensors of the legs aided by a forceful arm swing. The faster the leg extension the more force produced against the floor and the greater the counterpressure which projects the body. In preparation for the production of this force the hips, knees, and ankles must bend to put the extensors of the leg in position to exert force. Up to a point, depending upon the strength of the legs, the deeper the crouch the more force obtainable. A deeper crouch puts the extensor muscles on stretch and gives a greater distance over which acceleration is possible. However, since the body must be lifted through the distance that it is lowered, more work is done when a low crouch is used, and the angle of muscle pull is also changed. The optimal depth of crouch, therefore, depends upon the strength of the leg muscles. A deeper crouch is possible if leg muscles are strong. Each individual must experiment with various depths of crouch to determine that which is most effective for him. The crouch of the jump can be likened to the backswing of a throwing or striking action. It is the preparation for the purposeful action.

The arms also have a "backswing" action. They must swing into a preparatory position for the movement which is to aid in propelling the body. When distance is the purpose of the jump, the arms are swung backward to balance the forward lean of the body and to put them into a position which gives maximum time to work up forward momentum that will aid in carrying the upper body forward. If the purpose is to gain height, the arms are dropped with the elbows somewhat flexed, again to allow for movement to develop momentum, this time upward. The flexion of the arms makes it possible to swing them more nearly upward in the direction of desired movement and shortens the lever, making it easier to move them rapidly.

When jumping from a stand, both legs are extended suddenly as the arms swing in the direction of desired movement. A push with both feet equally and simultaneously exerts maximum force available and assures that the force is applied equally to both sides of the body so that strictly linear motion, rather than rotatory motion will result, and the body will travel straight in the desired direction. Whenever the take-off is from one foot, as in the leap or a jump preceded by a run, the center of gravity is brought over the take-off foot at the moment of force application. A preparatory run which gives the body momentum in the direction in which the action is to be executed adds force to the final projection. The force gained from this momentum is greater than that which could be produced by the second foot in a jump from a stand. In order to take-off from two feet momentum must be stopped or virtually stopped.

There are many activities, for example a diving hurdle and the lay-up shot in basketball (Fig. 5, p. 18), in which it is desirable to convert forward momentum into upward momentum. Lifting one knee forcefully not only produces upward momentum but it also moves the center of gravity back over the supporting leg so that the force produced by its extension is in an upward direction. This can be demonstrated by standing with the weight well forward and forcefully lifting one knee. The shift of the weight backward over the supporting foot is evident.

The momentum of the arm swing is transferred to the upper body and if timed with the leg extension adds force to the jump. When jumping for distance the arms are swung forcefully forward which is the direction of movement. When height is the objective, the arms are swung upward. It has been suggested that added height can be achieved by swinging one or both arms downward just before the highest point of the jump is reached. It is reasoned that since a given force at take-off will raise the center of gravity of the body to a certain height, anything which lowers the center of gravity in the body will raise the height to which the head or reaching hand will move. Since the center of gravity is lower in the body when the arms are down, swinging the arms downward should cause the body to rise higher. However, experimentation by Weiss[1] did not indicate that the boys of seventh and eighth grade age could significantly increase the height of their jumps by lowering one arm just before the peak of the jump was reached. This result might be anticipated because of the difficulty of the coordination. To lower one or both arms *just before the peak of the jump* is reached takes very precise timing. Therefore, this technique is valuable only for highly skilled performers.

Since the effectiveness of any force produced by the body depends upon the interaction between the body and the supporting surface, friction between the feet and the resisting surface must be sufficient to prevent slipping if all of the force produced by the body is to be transferred back to it. Friction is particularly important when jumping for distance since the force has a backward as well as downward component.

Since a projectile continues to move in the direction in which the force was applied to it, modified by the force of gravity, the angle of take-off is extremely important to the purpose of the jump. The angle at which the force is applied to the body is determined by the line from the point of application of force (the feet) through the center of gravity of the body. In jumping for height the desired direction of movement is straight upward and therefore, the center of gravity should be directly above the feet at take-off. The forward lean of the trunk which accompanies the bending of the legs should, therefore, be kept to a minimum. If the feet are separated slightly forward and backward, the base is enlarged in the direction in which balance is precarious as the body crouches and it is easier to keep the center of gravity centered over the base. As a result the force is more likely to be exerted straight upward. This spreading of the feet should be slight so that the force is not exerted on an angle (back by the forward foot and forward by the back foot) and is important only for the individual who has difficulty in keeping the center of gravity above his base with his feet even. If an individual jumps somewhat forward when he wishes to jump upward, this slight spreading of the feet forward-backward will help him.

Experimentation with crouching with the feet together and then with one slightly in advance quickly demonstrates the added stability of the second position. The knees must bend straight forward over the toes so that the force exerted on extension can pass straight through the joint and not at an angle. Also, the toes should be straight ahead. The final force is applied by the toes and if they are turned outward the force is applied at an angle inward. If equal, the inward force of the left foot will counteract that of the right foot and while the direction of the body will not be changed, energy is wasted and strain is put upon all of the joints, particularly the arches of the feet, the ankles, and knees. To minimize the strain on ankles and knees, this knee and toe position is extremely important in any of the body projecting activities.

When distance is the purpose of projection a 45-degree angle (air pressure neglected) is the most efficient (Chapter 9). This means that in jumping for distance the center of gravity must be well ahead of the feet at take-off. Therefore, instability in the forward direction is desirable and to keep the base small in this direction, as well as to equalize the force applied by the two feet, the feet are kept in line. They should be the width of the hips apart for stability in the lateral plane and so that the force is exerted straight backward and downward without any inward or outward component. When the feet are placed farther apart than the width of the hips the force is exerted inward against the ankles, knees, and hips as well as forward and injury can result. Since the inward component of the force exerted by each leg is in direct opposition to that of the other leg, less distance results from a given force produced because so much of it is wasted. This can be demonstrated easily by standing with the feet in a wide stride (exaggerated) and attempting to jump forward. The difficulty of moving forward to any degree is apparent immediately.

As noted previously, the toes should point straight ahead and the knees should bend straight forward over the toes. The entire body must lean forward from the feet in order for the center of gravity to be moved forward. Frequently students have the feeling that they are leaning forward when they are bending forward from the hips. Actually they move the hips out and back to balance the upper trunk and the center of gravity, which determines the angle of take-off, remains back. To move the center of gravity forward the pelvis should be maintained in its normal well balanced position as the legs flex and the trunk angles slightly forward. The lean of the body forward is balanced by the backward position of the arms. The weight is over the forward edge of the base. When the arms start their forward swing the center of gravity moves beyond the base and gravity assists in carrying it still farther forward before the legs have completed their extension. The arm swing is important not only in force production, but also in the control of the angle of the body at take-off since it moves the center of gravity forward of the pushing feet.

The forceful extension of the legs in the jump for height, leaves them in a position directly below the center of gravity of the body so that equilibrium on landing is no problem and, being extended, they are in position to flex at all of the joints on contact with the floor in order to reduce the downward momentum gradually and thus absorb the force of landing without a jar to the body.

In the jump for distance, however, the legs are behind the

body at take-off and must be brought forward to catch the weight as the body falls to the ground. The center of gravity is relatively close to the ground and the legs must be shortened by flexion of all joints in order to clear the ground as they swing forward under the body. This shortening also brings the weight of the legs close to the axis of movement (the hips) and thus it is easier to move them forward rapidly. Many girls have difficulty in jumping for distance because they do not flex the joints of the legs to any degree following take-off and as a result the feet hit the ground almost immediately, stopping the forward momentum of the body. Distance can be gained by extending the flexed legs, which have been moved forward under the trunk, as far forward as possible in landing. The extension of the legs is also necessary to put them in position to give as the body lands and thus gradually absorb the force. However, it leaves the center of gravity behind the feet. The bending of the legs as the feet touch the ground not only absorbs the shock of landing, but also shortens the body lever and thus increases the rotatory velocity of the trunk around the feet so that the forward momentum of the body can carry the center of gravity over the feet.

A backward swing of the arms while the body is in the air aids in swinging the legs forward and puts the arms in position to swing forward and thus add momentum to carry the upper trunk forward over the feet as they contact the ground. This is a difficult coordination to perform in the short time available and it is questionable whether any but the most highly skilled will be successful in its use. If poorly timed the arms might be swinging backward as the jumper lands and this would keep the center of gravity back rather than aid in bringing it forward. In this case it would be better to keep the arms forward following the arm swing at take-off.

When landing from a jump, balance can be maintained or regained more easily if the base is widened to some extent (not beyond hip width). The feet should be adjusted before they contact the floor. It should be recognized that landing with the feet together as is required in the execution of many apparatus and tumbling stunts adds to the difficulty of the performance and thus is a part of the skill which must be developed. Many activities are not performed in the easiest manner because the purpose is to test skill.

In any jumping activity shoes with soft soles which will absorb some of the force of landing should be worn. If jumping is to be practiced repeatedly the use of mats or some other soft surface is advisable. In jumps that produce a great deal of force such as the running broad jump and high jump, a jumping pit must be used so that the surface can assist the body in absorbing the force more gradually. Before practicing the more forceful jump, drill in correct landing is essential.

For the same reasons that one cannot walk backward as efficiently as forward (Chapter 11), it is difficult to jump backward. However, whether jumping backward, sideways, forward or upward the same principles apply. Because of the difficulties involved the amount of force that can safely be exerted or the angle of application may have to be adjusted and distance sacrificed to safety.

The various high jumps, broad jumps, the hop, step and jump, leaps over hurdles, dives, trampoline stunts, and tumbling stunts are a few of the activities which involve projecting the body into space. Although their purposes vary, the mechanical principles are the same. Hurdling is a combination of running and leaping. The take-off in diving whether it is from a springboard in a pool or gymnasium, or from a mat is mechanically the same. The amount of force produced and the angle of application vary according to purpose but the basic principles are identical. For example, the take-off for the racing dive is the same as for the broad jump except that the purpose does not require upward force to keep the body in the air against the pull of gravity and therefore, the force can be applied at a flatter angle making a greater proportion of it effective in producing forward motion. The center of gravity can be more forward and lower than in the jump. As in the jump a vigorous forward swing of the arms helps to overcome inertia and start the center of gravity moving forward and gravity is useful in carrying the center of gravity downward to a position which allows for the most effective application of forward force. The vertical wall of the pool makes it possible to exert force directly backward by curling the toes over the edge. In this, the racing dive resembles the crouching start for the run. The take-off for the running front dive is essentially the same as the jump used in the basketball lay-up shot or any other activity in which forward momentum is converted to upward momentum.

SUMMARY

Regardless of the specific purpose of an activity, the same basic principles apply to all activities which project the body into space.

The path of the center of gravity through the air is determined by the magnitude of the projecting force and the angle of its application. The projecting force is produced by quick extension of the legs aided by a forceful arm swing in the direction of desired movement. The legs must flex in preparation for the forceful extension. The stronger the leg muscles the deeper the crouch that can be used. The angle of application is determined by the position of the center of gravity in relation to the feet at the moment of take-off. The force is applied in the direction of the line from the feet through the center of gravity. Placing one foot slightly ahead of the other increases stability and keeps the center of gravity over the center of the base. Therefore, this position is effective in jumping for height. Since in jumping forward the center of gravity must be ahead of the feet, instability is desirable and the feet are placed in line, hip width apart. The weight is moved to the forward margin of the base so that the arm swing forward moves it beyond the edge of the base where gravity can assist in moving it farther forward by the time the final force of the legs is applied. This places the center of gravity well ahead (in the direction of movement desired) of the point at which the force is applied. At any time that the feet apply a considerable amount of force it is extremely important that the toes be straight ahead and that the knees flex straight forward above the toes so that the force is exerted in a straight line through the joints and strain of ankles and knees is minimized.

In a standing jump more force is available when the take-off is from two feet equally. However, the momentum developed by a preliminary run adds considerable force to a jump. Forward momentum can be converted to upward momentum by the forceful lifting of one knee which, besides adding upward momentum, moves the center of gravity back over the take-off foot.

In any activity in which the body moves through the air considerable force must be absorbed on landing. To avoid injury, all joints of the legs must give as contact with the ground is made so that the momentum can be reduced gradually. Supplying a nonresistive surface is essential for the more forceful jumps.

REFERENCES

1. Weiss, Raymond A.: The Effects on the Vertical Jump of Downward Displacement of the Center of Gravity of the Body. Paper reported at the Research Section Meeting, National Convention of the American Association of Health, Physical Education and Recreation, March, 1956.

14

Falling

The only difference between landing from a jump and falling is that in a fall the equilibrium of the body is out of control. If, in landing from a jump, the equilibrium becomes out of control a fall results. The physical principles which are entailed are identical to those involved in any force absorption task whether it is landing from a jump or catching a softball.

The problems center around the regaining of equilibrium and avoiding of injury by the reduction of the shock of impact through increasing the distance and time over which the momentum is reduced, increasing the area of the body receiving the force, and receiving the force on the softer, more padded areas of the body.

When falling downward with little or no forward momentum the feet should be kept under the body if at all possible so that they will contact the ground or floor first. Since balance on landing is a problem, if it is possible the feet should be adjusted to form a wide base (no more than the width of the hips sideways) before the landing is made. If wider than the hips the force of landing is exerted at an angle and causes pressure against the inside of the knees and ankles. By landing with the ankles extended the weight can be taken first on the balls of the feet and then in rapid succession the ankles, knees, and hips can bend so that the downward motion can be slowed gradually. If a great deal of momentum must be absorbed, as when falling from a considerable height, the placement of the hands on the ground gives an added area of contact and the giving of the wrists and elbows further increases the time and distance over which the force is absorbed. It may be necessary to tuck the body and go into a roll in order to spend the force even more gradually.

When forward momentum is involved as it is when one trips, becomes overbalanced while running, or falls from some moving object, injury can be avoided or minimized by relaxing to allow joints to give and muscles to be soft while curling into a ball and rolling so that the momentum is retarded gradually. Whether a forward roll, a shoulder roll, or a hip roll the area taking the force is greatly enlarged and the time for reduction of momentum is increased. If the body does fall forward onto the hands and arms, the wrists and elbows must give as they take the weight. Every effort should be made to avoid landing on the head, elbow or knee since these areas are solid and no give is possible. The head being so vital a part of the body must be protected even at the cost of injury to an arm. It has been suggested that, by giving with the wrists and arms and arching the back so that the body rocks forward, the force is distributed over a large area and to some extent the force is taken gradually as the body rocks. This method of absorbing the force does keep the head up off the ground but it must be remembered that the head is at the end of a long system of levers and the force is magnified as it throws the head backward. The momentum is stopped much more rapidly than when one rolls and if it is very great a "whip lash" injury of the neck muscles may result from this method of stopping the momentum. This may also result in injury of the lower back. Therefore, if it is at all possible, curling into a ball and rolling is much safer than arching the back and rocking. Frequently when one is falling in such a way that the knee would be the first part of the body to hit, a slight twist of the body will throw the weight onto the well padded buttocks. Or when falling onto the elbow a twist will throw the weight onto the back of the shoulders which, if rounded, allows the body to roll.

Stepping off a moving vehicle frequently results in a fall since the body has acquired the momentum of the vehicle and continues to move when the feet are stopped by their contact with the ground. Since this is an extremely dangerous practice, it should be avoided. However, if it should happen, a fall may be avoided by running with small rapid steps in the direction in which the vehicle is moving since that is the direction of the momentum of the body. The speed of the steps is reduced as the body gradually loses its momentum.

When falling backward the body should be relaxed. The weight is taken by the hands and arms which give, allowing the weight to come down onto the buttocks and if the body is tucked and allowed to roll backward the momentum can be absorbed gradually.

When sliding into base as much body surface as possible should be used so that the force is distributed over a large area. The center of gravity is lowered gradually during the last steps so that the downward force is minimized.

In general, when falling the body should be relaxed and flexed so that it will roll rather than stop suddenly. When arms or legs contact the ground all of the joints give, each resisting some of the force so that the momentum is slowed gradually.

FALLING INTO WATER

Falling into water differs from falling on a firmer surface such as the ground, floor, and mats because the water gives with the force of the body allowing the body to pass through the water. The give of the water lessens the shock of impact. The larger the area of the water contacted, the greater the water resistance. Therefore, to reduce the shock of impact water should be approached with *as small a body area* as possible. A small area is directly resisted by a small area of water and the water is pushed downward and outward. The reaction force of water is inward and upward. Thus the force of the water is not directly upward and, as a result, it is less effective in resisting the movement of the body through the water. When a large area contacts the water, as when the diver "hits flat," a large area of water exerts force directly upward resisting the body's downward movement and greater force is exerted against the body. This might be likened to pressing the flat of a knife against a piece of cheese as opposed to pressing the cutting edge against it. The former being wide is resisted but the latter being narrow passes easily through the cheese. The body should be kept rigid as it enters the water as opposed to giving as it hits a less resistive surface. If in a dive the elbows are allowed to bend as the hands (which are leading the head) contact the resistance of the water, the hands and arms will not push the water particles downward and outward and the head is resisted by an area of water equal to the area of the head. The arms, when held rigid, in effect, "cut a hole" for the body to move into. In general when *falling into water*, every effort should be made to present as small an area of the body as possible to the surface of the water and to keep the body rigid. These principles are directly opposite to those which are applicable to falling on a resistive surface because in the latter instance all of the give must be within the body itself, while in the case of water the force is reduced by the gradual giving of the water.

15

Sitting

Much time is spent in sitting. In general, one sits while performing various work tasks or while resting. However, it would seem that there is a third use of sitting which is neither for concentrated work nor for rest—sitting while conversing, reading for short periods of time when one anticipates the necessity for getting up rapidly and frequently, and so forth. The so-called "straight" chair is used for work, the "easy" or "lounge" chair for rest, and the "occasional" chair which is between these two in the support offered the body, for conversing. The more the chair supports the body the more the muscles can rest but the less free the body is to perform various tasks which may be demanded of it.

Since all sitting enlarges the base of support and places the center of gravity of the body close to the base much of the strain of standing in which the relatively high center of gravity must be kept over a small base, is eliminated. The system of levers that must be held erect is much shorter, being only the trunk, head, and neck, and therefore, is easier to control. However, the same basic principles of keeping the various body segments in line which apply to standing, also apply to sitting regardless of the particular purpose for sitting or the type of chair used.

There are three major problems involved in sitting: getting into the chair, sitting in the chair, and getting out of it. When sitting down the chief consideration is that of providing a base under the backward moving center of gravity so that the body weight can be kept under control; when sitting in the chair it is that of economy of energy and avoidance of strain over perhaps a long period of time; and when arising from the chair, that of shifting the weight forward over the base. In all of these the aesthetic consideration cannot be overlooked.

SITTING DOWN AND ARISING

Straight Chair. Since a straight chair has an open space between its legs and is not as low or as deep, it does not present some of the problems that are encountered in the lounge chair. The chair being open under the seat makes it possible for the individual sitting to place one foot back under the seat. Placing one foot back under the seat as far as possible supplies a base which is under the center of gravity of the body as it moves backward and thus places the leg in a position to control the lowering of the body weight into the chair (Fig. 49). If the feet are kept *in front of* the chair either the body must bent forward considerably to balance the backward shifting hips, or the body drops into the chair with a jar since the force of gravity is unresisted. Obviously, neither is mechanically efficient nor aesthetically pleasing.

Sitting down in a straight chair easily and gracefully involves standing with the back to the chair, placing one foot as far back under the seat as it can reach easily, and then

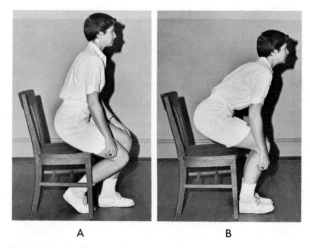

A   B

Figure 49. A, *Good—base under center of gravity.* B, *Poor—center of gravity balanced by forward lean.*

allowing the hips and knees to bend so that the body weight is lowered to the seat of the chair by a controlled giving in to gravity through a lengthening contraction of the extensor muscles. As the body is lowered the trunk is allowed to incline forward slightly. The hips are then slid back in the seat if they did not contact the chair at the rear of the seat.

Arising from the chair is accomplished by reversing the above procedure. Again, one foot is placed back under the seat so that it is in a position to apply force upward through the center of gravity of the body. If the seat is relatively deep the body will have to be shifted forward in the chair so that the center of gravity is over the back foot before an attempt to rise is made. The trunk is inclined slightly forward from the hips since this is the direction of desired movement, and the legs are extended lifting the body upward and forward, transferring the weight to the forward foot. Because the weight is forward and the push is in a forward, as well as upward, direction it is very easy to continue in a walk. If this is not desirable the trunk should be inclined forward to a lesser degree.

Occasional Chair. Since an occasional chair normally is open under the seat the same procedures are followed. Usually this type of chair has some kind of arms. Most authors have stated that the arms of the chair should never be used in lowering oneself into the chair. However, it would seem that if the hands are placed on the arms of the chair as they naturally come in contact with them and some slight amount of resistance is afforded by them as the body weight is lowered they can effectively aid the process and at the same time increase its naturalness. Also the use of the arms in rising can increase the efficiency if coordinated with the leg extension (Fig. 50). Since the legs are a great deal stronger they are better suited to the task of lifting the body weight and should, therefore, produce the major force. Attempting to avoid use of the arms completely results in an unnatural and stilted movement.

Easy Chair. The great majority of easy chairs are solid from the seat to a point a few inches above the floor and thus it is impossible to place a foot under the seat. The only way that the weight can be maintained above the base while it is being lowered, is for the individual to stand more or less sideways to the chair with the feet in a forward-backward stride position. This position of the feet gives a wide base for balance. The foot nearest the chair must be forward so that, as the weight is lowered, the body can be twisted slightly toward the chair and the weight taken on that hip. (Experimentation will imme-

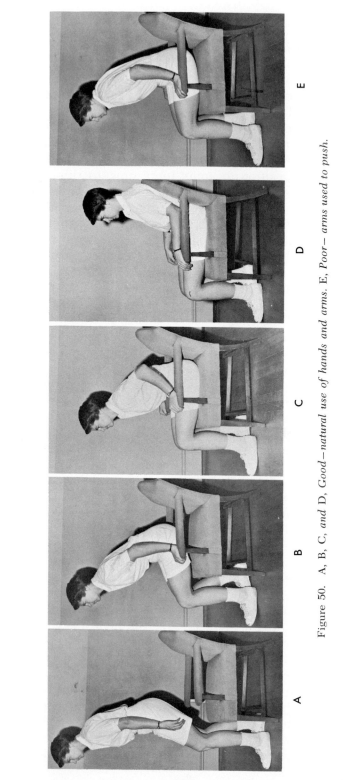

Figure 50. A, B, C, and D, *Good — natural use of hands and arms*. E, *Poor — arms used to push.*

166

diately demonstrate that it is impossible to sit in the chair if the foot nearest the chair is back.) The hips are lowered to the edge of the chair by the controlled bending of the hips and knees as when sitting in any chair and then the body is turned and slid back into the seat. Frequently the friction between the seat and the hips is considerable because of the type of material covering the chair and the clothing of the individual. Placing the hands on the arms of the chair so that some of the weight can be taken off the hips reduces the friction and makes it possible to slide into the chair more easily.

It is difficult to get out of this type of chair easily and gracefully and the deeper the chair and the greater the friction, the more difficult the task becomes. The process of sitting down is reversed. The body weight must be moved to the forward edge of the chair and again taking some of the weight on the arms aids in this process. In sliding forward the body should be turned slightly to one side so that the weight is more on one hip and the feet should be separated to enlarge the base. The center of gravity can then be brought above the base with little forward bending of the trunk. From this position the legs are extended to lift the body from the chair. Experimentation with attempting to get out of such a chair with the hips back and the body facing straight forward will demonstrate the extreme forward flexion of the trunk, usually including extension of the arms forward, that is necessary to balance the weight of the hips so that the center of gravity is brought over the feet. If the chair is very deep it is impossible to get the center of gravity above the feet in this way. Use of the hands on the arms of the chair to give some slight aid to the legs in lifting the body is efficient, but use of the arms to *lift* the body weight is not efficient since the muscles of the legs are much stronger and therefore, more suited to the task.

Floor. The problem of maintaining the balance so that the body weight can be controlled as it is lowered to the floor becomes progressively greater as one becomes taller. Since a very young child is relatively light and his center of gravity is so near the floor little momentum is developed even in a completely uncontrolled drop to the floor and therefore, the force of impact is not greater than can be absorbed by his well padded hips. The older child or adult, weighing more and having a considerable distance to drop, must control his weight to avoid the possibility of injury. There are many ways that this can be accomplished.

Those who are very flexible can be successful in squatting

and then, by extending the arms forward to balance the weight, lowering the hips to the floor. Some cross the feet and allow the knees to bend outward while gradually lowering the weight to the floor. Both of these methods take a great deal of balance since the base is extremely small. In controlling the weight with the feet in the crossed position greater pressure is exerted against the sides of the knees.

Another method is that of squatting and then placing a hand on the floor behind one hip to support some of the weight as the hips are lowered to the floor. The hand can also be placed on the floor to the side of the body and slid along the floor as the weight is lowered first onto one hip and then adjusted to rest on both. The base is enlarged by the use of the hand and the weight can be controlled easily.

Kneeling on one or both knees enlarges the base eliminating the problem of balance relatively early in the performance of the task, and from this position it is easy to slide a hand along the floor on the side of the bent knee and lower the weight to that hip. This can be modified by crossing one leg behind the other, bending the forward leg which is supporting the weight, to lower the body to the point where the hand on the side of the crossed leg can reach the floor, and thus enlarge the base and aid in the final lowering of the weight to the floor (Fig. 51). Because of the reduction in the size of the base during the first part of the process this is more difficult, but if executed smoothly this method is more graceful than that of kneeling.

Regardless of the way in which it is accomplished the center of gravity must be kept above the base if the weight is to be controlled. Enlarging the base by the use of one hand as the hips approach the point at which they, in order to reach the floor, leave their position above the feet, is the easiest method for performing this task.

To get up from the floor the problem is to move the center of gravity to a position above the feet. When sitting with the feet flat on the floor and knees bent up in front of the body it is possible to accomplish this by extending the arms forward and rocking backward and then forward to work up sufficient momentum to carry the center of gravity of the body upward and forward over the feet. While this is undoubtedly a test of skill it is far from the easiest or most graceful method of standing. Some individuals with strong legs can, from the crossed leg or "tailor position," lean well forward and stand. Most have neither the strength nor the balance to perform this stunt and again, as in using this method to sit, pressure

Figure 51. Dropping to sitting position on floor.

is exerted against the sides of the knees as the legs extend. If the weight is shifted to one hip, that hand placed on the floor and the lower leg on that side crossed behind the other leg, it is very easy to come to a kneeling position on one knee and then to a stand. This gives a wide base at the time that the hips are not above the feet and makes use of arm and shoulder girdle strength to start the upward motion, but the real task of lifting the body weight is performed by the stronger leg muscles. When executed as a continuous movement this method is both easy and graceful.

SITTING POSITIONS

Regardless of the chair or the purpose, the general principle that the position should be one in which the body segments remain in the same relationship to each other as they are when in a well balanced standing position, should be observed.

Straight Chair or Occasional Chair. When sitting in a straight chair or an occasional chair the hips should be well back in the chair so that the entire back can be supported. If the knees are bent at right angles and the feet flat on the floor some of the weight of the thighs is supported by the feet and excessive pressure on the blood vessels and nerves which run at the back of the knee is avoided (Fig. 52). When it is necessary to move the upper body forward so that the eyes are brought closer to the work, the trunk should be shifted

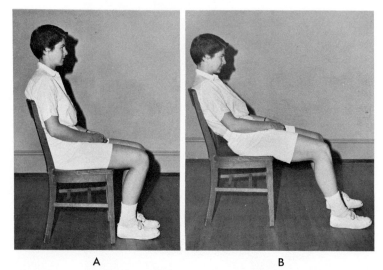

A   B

Figure 52. A, *Good—all of back supported.* B, *Poor—lower back and thighs unsupported.*

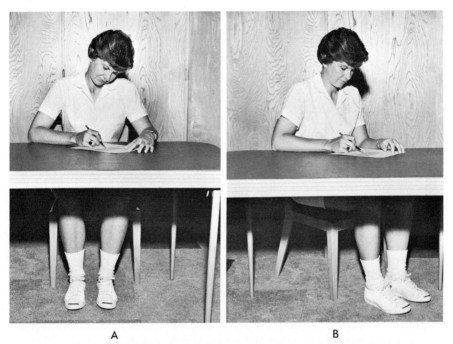

Figure 53. A, *Poor—head cocked to bring eyes equidistant from work.* B, *Good—upper body and head well aligned.*

from the hips in much the same way that the body is shifted as a unit from the ankles when the weight is moved forward in standing and walking, so that the well balanced alignment of the body segments can be maintained (Fig. 53B). When a task is undertaken for any length of time it is important that the position be such that both eyes are the same distance from the work. This means that the plane of the face must be parallel to the plane of the work and the midline of each must fall on the same line.[1] Angling the working surface allows for the maintenance of a well balanced position while retaining this relationship with the work. Sitting straight to a desk leads to "cocking" the head since the paper, because of the position of the arm as the hand is brought in front of the body, is at an angle. In order for the eyes to be equidistant from the writing, the head is tilted and slightly rotated (Fig. 53A). Therefore, it is better to sit slightly at an angle to the desk or table with the body turned away from the preferred hand (turned toward the left if right handed)[1] (Fig. 53B). This puts the eyes equidistant from the work with the head in a well balanced position (Fig. 54).

Sitting with crossed legs lifts one hip and places the pelvis on an angle causing a compensating lateral ("C") curve in the spine. This position also results in pressure on the nerves

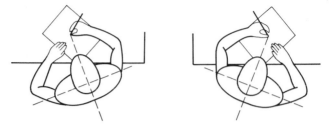

Figure 54. *Head well balanced, eyes equidistant from work. (Adapted from Harmon, D. B.: Eye Preference, Certain Body Mechanics and Visual Problems. Unpublished paper, 1963.)*

and blood vessels that run behind the crossed knee which, if continued for any length of time, causes the foot and leg to "go to sleep." However, this position will not be harmful if not maintained so long that the blood and nerve supply to the foot are cut, and if alternate legs are crossed so that the curve caused by crossing one leg is compensated by the crossing of the other. Unusual positions should not be maintained habitually but are not harmful if assumed occasionally for short periods of time for a change of position.

A complete discussion of various positions which are restful can be found in Metheny's *Body Dynamics*,[2] and, therefore, are not discussed here.

Easy Chair. Since the purpose of the easy chair is rest, the entire body must be supported so that the force of gravity simply pulls the body against the chair and the muscles are no longer called upon to support the body weight. The hips should be all the way back in the chair so that the hips, lower back, upper back and, if the most restful position is desired, the head can be supported. When the hips are forward the lower back is unsupported and gravity constantly acts to pull this part of the body downward. The back of such a chair should be soft so that it will take the contour of the body curves. Since most of these chairs are deep it is impossible to sit with the hips against the back and still bend the knees and have the feet flat on the floor. When this is the case the legs and feet must be supported by a foot stool of approximately the same height as the chair seat or slightly lower. A support of the legs which is higher than the chair seat forces the knees backward. A support under the feet only, leaves the lower leg unsupported against gravity's pull. The arms should be allowed to fall naturally from the shoulder when the lower arms are supported by the arms of the chair, the elbows being bent at approximately right angles.

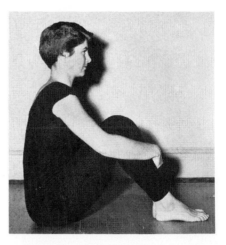

Figure 55. *Spine straight later-*
ally, arms giving some support to
back.

Floor. While, on the whole, adults do not spend a great deal of time sitting on the floor, the time so spent by children and young adults is considerable, and makes it important that they understand the advantages and problems of various positions. It is clearly evident from observation of any group that there are many different positions used in sitting on the floor. Since the posterior thigh muscles both extend the thigh and flex the leg, the position of sitting with the legs straight out in front of the body (knees straight) stretches these muscles at both the hip and knee joints and therefore, is difficult to maintain for any length of time. Various methods for relieving this strain are employed.

Placing the feet flat on the floor with the knees bent up in front of the body keeps the weight even on both hips and the spine straight laterally. Some of the strain of maintaining the upright position of the trunk can be relieved by the arms if they are placed around the knees (Fig. 55). The danger in this position is that the individual will pull the shoulders forward and round the upper back. This position poses a problem for girls unless they are wearing shorts or slacks.

Sitting "tailor fashion," that is, with the feet crossed and the knees bent and dropped out to each side, is comfortable for those who are fairly flexible, but difficult for an individual with tight muscles along the inside of the thighs (Fig. 56). In fact, this position can be useful in stretching these tight muscles. Again, unless a girl is wearing a very full skirt, slacks, or shorts, this position is impossible.

One of the most commonly assumed positions is that of sitting with the knees bent and both feet to one side of the body. This position lifts the hip on the side of the feet

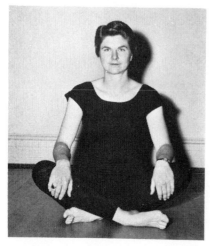

Figure 56. *Spine straight, flexibility required.*

tending to throw the upper body off balance to the opposite side (Fig. 57). To counteract this the shoulder on the side of the high hip is dropped and a "C" curve of the spine to the opposite side results. If the position is taken with the feet to the right and then to the left for an equal amount of time, the curve is compensated and no problems arise. The problem arises when the position is assumed habitually with the feet to the same side. Unfortunately, each individual normally has a preferred side, the position is more comfortable when the feet are on a certain side, and while he may shift briefly for a change of position, most of the time that he sits on the floor his feet are on the preferred side. Whether or not this contributes to the development of a permanent curve of the spine depends upon the amount of time this individual spends in the position. Physical educators would do well to explain the possible implications of such a position to leaders of young girls' groups who insist, for the sake of the pattern of the group, that during ceremonies, some of which are of considerable length, all of the girls sit with their feet to the right side.

The curve in the spine can be considerably reduced if, instead of balancing the upper body by dropping the shoulder on the side of the high hip, the opposite arm is used to support some of the weight of the trunk (Fig. 57C).

A few very flexible individuals sit with their lower legs bent under their bodies (Fig. 58). This position does allow the spine to remain in its straight position but causes pressure on the blood vessels and nerves, particularly those running behind the knees and if maintained for any length of time cuts off circulation and nerve supply to the lower legs.

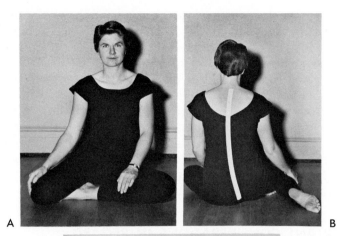

Figure 57. A and B, *Spine curved;* C, *Curve reduced.*

Figure 58. *Spine straight, pressure on knees.*

Since the back is unsupported, all of these positions are more tiring than sitting in a chair. It must be remembered that as in standing, a change of position is restful. Several of these positions may be assumed if it is necessary to sit on the floor for any length of time. The important principle is that, as in standing, walking and running, the segments of the trunk should be maintained in a well balanced position one above the other with no joints in a position of strain. When a position which violates this principle is assumed for the sake of change, a compensatory position should be taken for an equal time. However, during the greatest amount of time the principle should be followed.

IMPORTANT CONSIDERATIONS IN REGARD TO FURNITURE

Straight Chair.   Chairs should be chosen to fit the individual who will be using them. The height should be such that when the hips are at the back of the seat the feet are flat on the floor and the knees bent at right angles. The feet then support some of the weight of the thighs and reduce the pressure on the blood vessels and nerves which run behind the knee joint. If the chair is chosen at a time when the individual is wearing shoes with heels it may be too high for comfortable sitting at a future time when low heels are worn. Therefore, it is wise to slip off the shoes to test the height of the chair.

Too frequently individuals are not in a position to choose a chair of correct height but must use whatever is provided. In most school situations the chairs for a certain grade are all the same height although the length of the legs of pupils varies greatly. Placing a block of wood or a book under the feet when the chair is too high makes it possible to sit properly in the chair and still have the feet supported. Because it is so uncomfortable to have the feet unsupported the well balanced position of the body is sacrificed in order to get the feet to the floor, unless something is put under the feet. The individual slides the hips forward on the seat of the chair leaving the lower back completely unsupported.

The depth of the chair seat from its back to its front edge is just as important to comfort and the maintenance of a well balanced position as is its height. The seat should be of such a depth that the front edge crosses the thighs a few inches behind the knee. Too deep a seat necessitates the moving forward of the hips to relieve the pressure against the back of the knee or even to bend the knee. Again, this leaves the lower back unsupported and upsets the alignment of the entire upper body. Too shallow a seat results in too much of the weight of the thigh pressing against the nerves that run along the back of the thigh since not enough of the thigh is supported by the chair seat.

The back of the chair should support the back of the individual regardless of the type of chair. Since when sitting the hips protrude backward beyond the back, it is necessary for a chair back to be open or curved outward at its base in order to give support to the lower back. A straight chair back or one that slants slightly backward from the base leaves the lower back completely unsupported. A chair that is to be used for long hours of work should have an adjustable back so that the support can be fitted to the individual's back. The chair should also be adjustable in height.

Easy Chair. If the legs are supported at approximately the height of the chair seat (never higher) the height and depth of the seat are not important. The back should be soft so that it will fit the curves of the body and give complete support. When the chair back does not support all sections of the back, pillows should be used. The chair arms should be of such a height that they will support the lower arms when the elbows are approximately at right angles and the arms are hanging naturally from the shoulders. Chair arms that are too high push the shoulders up into an unnatural position and if too low they do not give maximum support to the individual's arms and thus relief to the shoulder muscles.

Desk. A desk or other working surface at which the individual sits should be at a height which is just below the bend of the individual's elbow when sitting in the chair to be used with the desk. If higher the shoulders must be hunched in order to have the lower arm on the working surface. If lower, the individual must lower the shoulders in order for the desk surface to support the lower arm. This causes a rounded back. If circumstances make it necessary to use a desk which is too low, small blocks of wood can be put under the legs to adjust it to the proper height. If the only available desk is too high, the chair should be raised either by the use of a pillow in the seat or by blocks of wood under the legs. It must be remembered that this necessitates some support which will raise the feet of the individual an equal amount so that the basic sitting position can still be maintained.

When a typewriter is to be used a lower desk or table is needed since the keyboard is some inches above the surface of the desk. The keyboard should be at such a height that the hands are slightly below the bend of the elbows when on the keys. If higher than this the lower arms and hands must be held up against the pull of gravity constantly. The use of a copy holder avoids a great deal of the dropping and turning of the head.

Kitchen Stool and Counter.   Since kitchen counters are built at a height for working while standing, when it is desirable to sit and work it is necessary to use a high stool so that the arms are in the proper relationship to the surface, that is, so that the working height is a few inches below elbow height. Since the stool is high there should be a step which supports the feet. Normally the kitchen counter has cupboards built beneath it. This makes it impossible to sit facing the counter because there is no space for the knees. Sitting sideways to the counter necessitates twisting the trunk and is very tiring. Most counters have one or more pull-out boards and use of these makes it possible to sit in a normal position and still be close to one's work.

SUMMARY

There are three major problems involved in sitting whether one is sitting to work, to converse, or simply to rest: getting into the chair, sitting in the chair, and getting out of it.

In sitting down the chief consideration is that of providing a base under the backward moving center of gravity of the body. In standing the problem becomes that of shifting the weight forward over the base so that it can be lifted by the extension of the legs. Whenever possible one foot should be placed back under the seat of the chair to enlarge the base backward in sitting down or arising. The weight can then be controlled as it is lowered since it at no time passes beyond the edge of the base, and, in standing the force of the legs can be exerted upward and forward if the trunk is shifted very slightly forward from the hips. When the chair is solid from the seat to a few inches above the floor making it impossible to place a foot under the seat, the center of gravity can be kept over the base as it is lowered by standing sideways to the chair in a forward-backward stride position. The weight can then be lowered to the edge of the seat and the body turned as it is slid backward into the chair seat. To get up the process is reversed.

When a chair has arms, the hands should be allowed to contact them naturally and can assist in taking some of the weight in lowering and lifting the body, but should *never* be called upon to produce the major force involved.

When sitting down on the floor one hand can be used to enlarge the base as the hips approach the floor, and to aid in lowering the body weight to one hip. The position can then be adjusted so that the weight is equally distributed on both hips. It is easy to come to a kneeling and then a standing position by shifting the weight to one hip, placing that hand on the floor crossing the leg on that side behind the other leg, pushing with the hand and extending the legs.

Regardless of the surface upon which one is sitting or the purpose, the general principle that the position of the upper body should be such that the segments remain in the same relationship to each other as they are when standing in a well balanced position should be observed.

The hips should be well back in any chair and the back of the body should be supported. Unless the legs and feet are supported at approximately the height of the chair seat (no higher), the feet should be flat on the floor with the knees bent at right angles. When it is necessary to bring the eyes closer to the work, the entire upper body is shifted forward from the hips.

When sitting on the floor care should be taken that no position which causes a curve of the spine is assumed habitually. In all sitting it should be remembered that a change of position is always restful and those positions which cause poor alignment of body segments are not harmful if taken *briefly* and if compensatory positions are used for an equal period of time. However, the position assumed for the majority of time should place the body segments in a well balanced alignment.

Furniture influences the position one is able to assume. Both the height and depth of chair seat are important factors at any time that the lower legs are not supported by a footstool. The chair seat should be of a height that allows the feet to be flat on the floor when the knees are bent at right angles, and its forward edge should cross the thigh a few inches behind the knee when the hips are well back in the chair. The back of the chair must support the individual's back and the arms of the chair should allow the elbow to bend at approximately a right angle when the upper arms hang naturally from the shoulders. Any working surface, desk, typewriter, or kitchen counter should be at such a height that the hands, in performing the particular task involved are a few inches lower than elbow height when the individual is sitting in a well balanced position.

REFERENCES

1. Harmon, D. B.: Eye Preference, Certain Body Mechanics and Visual Problems. Unpublished paper, 1963.
2. Metheny, Eleanor: *Body Dynamics*. New York, McGraw-Hill Book Company, Inc., 1951, pp. 178–190.

16

Pushing and Pulling

In general, pushing and pulling tasks are more common in normal everyday activities and in work actions than in sports. Individuals push heavy furniture, baby carriages, carts full of groceries, lawnmowers, and many other objects. They pull rakes, hoes, sleds. They open and close drawers, windows, and doors. They push shovels into the earth. These are but a few of the common tasks which involve a pushing or pulling movement. While not involved in the same quantity of sport activities, an understanding of this type of movement is essential in aquatic sports, since they, with the exception of diving, are entirely push-pull activities. In rowing, canoeing, and swimming the movement of the boat or the individual results from the push against the water of oars, paddles, or arms and legs. Archery is a pulling activity. The push pass or shot in basketball and the shot put in track also involve pushing movements. Essentially every movement of the human body is a pull since movement of a body part results from the shortening of muscles.

Many pushing and pulling tasks are light but several involve the application of considerable force and make economy of effort and avoidance of strain prime considerations. In heavy tasks the initial force overcomes the inertia and additional force must be applied as long as movement is desired. To accomplish successfully the particular purpose involved in pushing or pulling an object, the desired direction of movement, type of movement (linear or rotatory), distance to be moved, speed of movement, as well as the friction and other resistive forces must be considered. The friction between the feet and the supporting surface is important also. The speed of movement and distance moved, in fact whether or not movement takes place at all, are determined by the magnitude of the force applied in relation to the magnitude of the resistive forces. The direction of movement is dependent upon both the point of application of the force and the direction in which its is applied. The point of application and the resistive forces such as friction, determine whether linear or rotatory motion results.

PRINCIPLES INVOLVED

Magnitude of Force. When force rather than control of direction is the primary consideration, the strongest muscles available to the particular task should be used in order to avoid strain. This means that the legs should supply the main pushing or pulling force. Also when force is of primary consideration, the individual should contact the load and set the muscles for the task *before* the pushing and pulling force is exerted. Sudden application of considerable force before the setting of the arm and shoulder muscles has stabilized the joints, will not result in movement of the object but only in the giving of the wrists, elbows and shoulders. The firmer the arms and upper body, the more the force produced by the legs will be transferred to the object to be moved.

The amount of force that can be transferred to the object also depends upon the counterpressure of the supporting surface against the foot. It there is insufficient friction the force exerted by the individual results in pushing the foot backward rather than moving the object forward. Friction between the feet of the individual pushing the object and the supporting surface is, therefore, desirable. However, friction between the object being pushed and the supporting surface is undesirable in that it necessitates a greater force to effect and maintain motion.

Lack of firmness of the supporting surface is undesirable both because less counterpressure is applied to the feet of the individual and therefore, more force is necessary to gain a given result and because greater resistance is offered to the forward movement of the object. When the surface is not firm it gives with the weight of the object and thus forms, in effect, a series of vertical walls around the object which must be pushed down as the object moves forward.

Because of inertia to any change in movement state (Newton's First Law) it takes more force to start an object moving than to keep it moving. Sufficient force should be applied continuously to keep the load moving at a moderate rate once it has started moving. Overcoming the initial inertia is the greatest problem in any pushing or pulling task.

Direction of Force. The force should be applied as nearly as possible in the direction of the desired movement. There are some tasks that, in order to apply force directly in the line of desired movement, require the body to be placed in an inefficient position. When this is the situation more effort is wasted in attempting to perform the task in an inefficient body position than would be lost in applying the force at an angle rather than in the direct line of desired movement. However, the undesirable component of the force should be kept as small as possible. Whenever the force is applied at an angle to the line of movement, only the component of the force in the direction of movement is effective in accomplishing the desired result (Chapter 7, Force). It follows that less energy is required the nearer to the desired direction of movement the force can be applied since a greater percentage of the force is effective in moving the object in the desired direction. For example, if in pulling a cart holding several mats, a force of 50 pounds is applied at a 40-degree angle, 46 per cent of the force tends to lift the cart and only 54 per cent is effective in moving it forward. If this same force is applied at a 20-degree angle (closer to the direction of movement) 73 per cent of the force acting on the cart is effect in moving it forward (Fig. 59).

This principle is modified by the amount of friction between the object to be moved and the surface across which it must move. The greater the friction the larger the upward component of force that is desirable in order to reduce this friction. When an object is free to move only along a predetermined path, for example a window which moves up and down in its casing, force in any direction other than that of its path is not only wasted, but also adds to the difficulty of the task by increasing the friction between the window and the casing.

Point of Application of Force. The point at which the force is applied depends upon the type of motion desired. When force is applied through the center of gravity of the object, linear motion results and the object moves in the direction of the force if friction is not too great and if there is no obstacle in its path. The greater the friction the lower the force must be applied or the larger the upward component necessary.

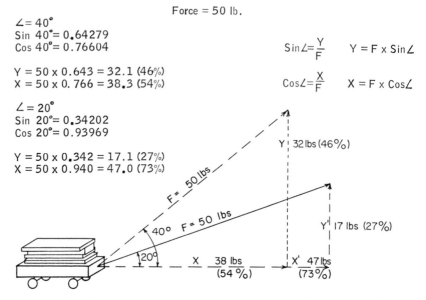

Force = 50 lb.

$\angle = 40°$
Sin $40° = 0.64279$
Cos $40° = 0.76604$

$\text{Sin}\angle = \dfrac{Y}{F}$ $Y = F \times \text{Sin}\angle$

Y = 50 x 0.643 = 32.1 (46%)
X = 50 x 0. 766 = 38.3 (54%)

$\text{Cos}\angle = \dfrac{X}{F}$ $X = F \times \text{Cos}\angle$

$\angle = 20°$
Sin $20° = 0.34202$
Cos $20° = 0.93969$

Y = 50 x 0.342 = 17.1 (27%)
X = 50 x 0.940 = 47.0 (73%)

F = 50 lbs

F = 50 lbs

40°

20°

Y 32 lbs (46%)

Y' 17 lbs (27%)

X   38 lbs
(54 %)

X' 47 lbs
(73%)

Figure 59. *Effective horizontal and vertical forces resulting from application of force of 50 pounds at forty and twenty-degree angles.*

When force is applied away from the center of gravity of the object, its direction is that of a line from the point of force application through the center of gravity of the object and the object tends to rotate. The farther from the center of gravity the force is applied, the less force needed to rotate the object.

The application of a *single* off center force, unless friction is great, both moves the object forward and rotates it toward the opposite end. If a force were applied right of center to a couch on casters, the couch would move forward and also turn toward the left. If friction were great enough the left end would not move and only rotation would result. Equal forces applied equidistant from the center of gravity act as a single force through the center of gravity (Fig. 60). Some of each force is not effective in producing forward motion since each has an inward component. However, more efficient control of direction is possible since each force has greater leverage. If force A is applied even slightly off center or, if the friction encountered by one side of the object is slightly more than that encountered by the other, the object turns and no force is immediately available to counteract this rotation. If, however, the force is applied at two points equidistant from the center (forces B and C) and the object starts to turn to the left, a little added force at B will counteract the tendency, while if it begins to

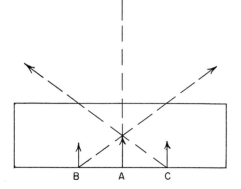

Figure 60. *Direction of force applied through the center of gravity* (A) *compared to that of forces* (B and C) *applied equidistant from the center of gravity.*

turn to the right the force at *C* can be increased slightly. Being away from the center each force is effective in producing compensatory rotatory motion and much greater control is possible. However, since each of these two forces is actually applied on a diagonal some of each will be wasted as far as forward motion is concerned. Force is sacrificed for the purpose of gaining additional control.

METHODS OF EFFICIENT PERFORMANCE

If the object is not on wheels and considerable friction is involved, consideration should be given to the possibility of reducing the friction by placing the object on a dolly (a small low platform on wheels) or by putting some object that has a lower coefficient of friction between the object and the surface on which it rests. For example, the task of pushing a heavy piece of furniture across a carpeted floor can be greatly eased by placing glass coasters under the legs of the furniture. If the legs are too large for glass coasters, small pie pans or any other material that slides easily will reduce the force required and save "wear and tear" on the carpet.

When pulling an object a longer rope reduces the upward component of force applied and increases the horizontal component. The greater the friction that must be overcome the shorter the rope should be. If friction is not a problem a longer rope is more efficient because a greater proportion of the force exerted is effective in the direction of desired movement. The rope should be attached to a point in line with, or below, the center of gravity of the object depending upon the amount of friction. The individual pulling should stand facing the direction of movement with the feet in a forward-backward stride to widen the base in the direction of anticipated move-

Figure 61.   *Using legs to pull.*

ment, and with the toes straight ahead so that the force can be exerted directly backward. An inclination of the trunk forward from the ankles puts the center of gravity ahead of the pushing foot so that the force can be exerted diagonally forward (Fig. 61). The knees must be bent so that they can exert force by extending. The degree to which they need to bend depends upon the force that must be exerted or upon the weight of the load to be moved and the friction involved. The muscles of the pelvis and trunk must be set so that the force produced by the leg extension will be transferred through the body to the arms and thus to the rope.

Individuals sometimes start a heavy load moving by standing facing the load and "sitting backward" (Fig. 62). This does use the body weight effectively as the moving force but is dangerous. It must be remembered that it takes more force to start an object moving than to keep it moving. Once the object starts to move, the individual pulling is likely to lose his balance since he is not in an efficient position to move his body rapidly. Balance backward is more precarious than forward since the base behind the ankle is so short and lacks the leverage of the toes. *If* this method is used every precaution should be taken to widen the base to the point that one foot is well back under the body weight and the individual should be prepared to move quickly and turn to face forward once the load starts to move.

In order to push an object the hands should be placed near the point opposite the object's center of gravity so that the downward component of force, which is frequently present in a

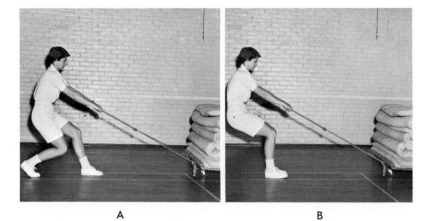

A   B

Figure 62.   *Using body weight to start momentum.* A, *Wide base for balance,*
B, *Unbalanced* (dangerous).

pushing task, is reduced to a minimum. While in pulling, the
vertical component of the force is upward and therefore may
be useful in reducing friction, in pushing the vertical component is downward and adds to the friction making the object
more difficult to move. An upward component of force is possible only when the hands can be placed lower than the center
of gravity of the object. The push should be applied through
the center of gravity in the direction of desired movement if
friction is inconsequential. However, if there is considerable
friction, the position must be adjusted so that the force can be
applied below the center of gravity to reduce the friction. The
exact point for the effective application of force can be determined by experimentation using as the criterion the object's
tendency to tip. If there is a great deal of friction an object
may tip even when force is applied through its center of gravity
because friction keeps the bottom from moving. Therefore
force must be applied below center.

Placing the hands opposite the object's center of gravity or
below necessitates lowering the body weight. This should be
done by bending the legs rather than leaning forward from the
hips. The legs are then placed in position to extend and no
strain is placed on the small muscles of the back. If the task
necessitates a very low crouch which places the body in a
difficult position to maintain or in which to move, it is more
efficient to put a rope around the object and pull than to attempt to move it by pushing.

When pushing, the individual must stand away from the
object so that he can incline his body toward it and thus put
his center of gravity ahead of his pushing foot in order that the

Figure 63. *Using legs to push heavy object. Note hands spread for control* (B).

force can be exerted more in the direction of desired movement (Fig. 63). As in all other activities the inclination of the body forward should be from the ankles and the well aligned position of the body should be maintained. The feet must be placed in a forward-backward stride position so that the pushing foot can be well back and the forward foot in a position to catch the body weight as forward movement begins. The muscles of the arms, shoulder girdle, and trunk should be set before the force is applied in order for the push of the legs to be transferred through them to the object with no absorption by the arms of the force produced by the leg extension. Since the body pushes by extending the legs, the strongest muscles available to the task are used.

When pushing upward or pulling downward the body is placed under or as near to the object as possible to enlarge the vertical component of the force as much as possible. When pushing downward or pulling upward the body weight is placed as nearly as possible over the object. Thus, in pushing a shovel straight down into the earth one stands right next to the shovel and places one foot on it so that the force can be exerted straight downward. In opening a tight or stuck window the most efficient method calls for standing close to the window, bending the legs so that the heels of the hands can be placed under the middle sash with the elbows well bent (hands close to the shoulders), and then extending the legs. The force is exerted by the strong leg muscles directly upward and the position of the arms eliminates any possibility of force being absorbed by a give of the elbows. A window which moves easily may be opened by pulling up on the handles. Since the force available in the arms is sufficient for the performance

Figure 64. *Hands spread for control—light object.*

of the task without strain, there is no need for expending the effort involved in lowering and raising the body weight. However, in this, too, the individual should stand close to the window so that the force is applied straight upward in the direction of the window's predetermined pathway. When one reaches across a table to open a window, balance is precarious and the force is diagonally up and in against the inside of the casing and therefore friction is increased. Also the small muscles of the back are brought into the task to stabilize the upper body against the pull of gravity and the weight of the window.

Frequently it is necessary to move an object which is relatively light but difficult to move in a straight path. In such a situation force is no problem and the principle of applying the force at two points equidistant from the center of gravity of the object should be followed. For example, to move in a straight line a long light object on wheels such as the portable blackboard found in many gymnasiums, one should stand close to the center of the object and grasp it as far ahead of the body as possible with one hand and as far behind as possible with the other. Being light and on wheels, the object moves easily as the individual walks and, because of the length of the lever arms, the hands are in an effective position to exercise control over the object's tendency to swing to one side or the other (Fig. 64).

Occasional arguments arise as to whether it is easier to push or to pull. Actually no broad statement can be made. The question must be settled for each particular task. Which is easier depends upon whether a downward or an upward component of force is advantageous, whether the task is a heavy one or one that calls primarily for control, and whether linear or rotatory motion is desired. A downward force is advantageous, for example, in using a vacuum cleaner, a mop, or lawnmower. It is detrimental in a heavy task in which friction is a problem. If a downward force is advantageous the object should be pushed. If it adds considerably to the forward force required to move the object by increasing the friction which is already a problem, it is easier to pull the object. As indicated earlier a pushing force with an upward component can only be applied by lowering the body so that the hands can be placed at a point below the object's center of gravity. If this causes the body to assume a low crouch in which it is difficult to move forward, it is more efficient to use a rope and pull.

The importance of the upward component depends upon the friction involved. There are many tasks in which it does not matter appreciably which method is used. In pushing a wheelbarrow the downward component of force adds to the friction of the wheel on the ground. However, a wheel which turns easily makes this a relatively unimportant consideration. In pulling the wheelbarrow the individual loses the advantage of being able to watch the load. The slight advantage gained by the upward component of force of the pull is probably not sufficient to offset the disadvantage. However, when it is necessary to move the wheelbarrow up a step, the upward component of a pulling force becomes important and therefore, the wheelbarrow should be pulled. When the force advantage is immaterial the question should be decided on the basis of the ease of body position, control, and so forth. If control is an important consideration pushing has an advantage since normally the object is closer to the individual.

Many objects that are too heavy to be pushed as a whole can be moved efficiently by rotatory motion. An individual attempting to move a heavy couch, for example, or a trunk should move first one corner and then the other. Since the longer the lever, the less the force required to rotate it, the force should be applied as far from the center of gravity as possible. Moving the couch by rotation is simply a matter of pushing one end forward and then the other. Moving a wardrobe trunk is a slightly different problem. Since it is higher and has a smaller base it can be moved most easily by placing the hands against one top corner and pushing forward slightly, enough to tip the trunk so that it rests on the diagonally opposite corner. The trunk can then be swung around with very little force. Gravity acts to assist this movement. A series of these movements, rotating the trunk first on one corner and then on the other, moves it forward. This same method can be used successfully with a heavy overstuffed chair.

SUMMARY

When the task involves any considerable amount of force the legs, which are the strongest muscles available for a pushing or pulling task, should be used to provide the main force. The body, in a well aligned position, should lean forward from the ankles to move the center of gravity ahead of the pushing foot so that the direction of force application is forward. To assure control of body balance the feet must be in a forward-backward stride position. The individual should contact the object to be moved and set the muscles for the task before exerting the pushing or pulling force.

The placement of the hands or attachment of the rope on an object determines not only whether rotatory or linear motion results, but also the direction in which the force is effective. The longer the rope that is used in pulling, the more the force is exerted in a forward direction. A shorter rope increases the upward component of force and is more efficient only when a great deal of friction must be overcome.

In pushing, the more nearly the hands are placed opposite the center of gravity of the object the more directly forward the force is applied.

When pushing or pulling upward or downward the individual should stand as close to the object to be moved as possible so that the force can be exerted in the direction in which movement is desired.

Leverage is used when control is important. Force is applied at two points equidistant from the object's center of gravity. Leverage is also important when moving an object by rotatory motion. Force is applied far from the center of gravity to move one side of the object, and then the other side is moved by the application of a second force.

Friction between the feet of the individual pushing or pulling and the supporting surface is essential for the force exerted by the legs to cause movement forward. The greater the friction between the object to be moved and the supporting surface, the greater the force required to move it. Whenever this friction is great it should be reduced, if at all possible, by placing some object with a lower coefficient of friction between the object and the supporting surface or by applying a diagonally upward force so that a considerable upward component will be present. Lack of firmness of the supporting surface increases the difficulty of the task in that there is less counter-pressure against the feet and more resistance to the forward progress of the object.

The question whether it is easier to push or to pull must be decided on the basis of the particular task involved.

17

Holding, Carrying, Stooping, and Lifting

The days are filled with a wide variety of stooping, lifting, holding, and carrying tasks that vary from very light chores to those which require a great deal of effort for their accomplishment. These activities enter into the daily routines, work patterns, and recreational pursuits of every individual. The lifting activity may be simply that of picking up a child's light toy or it may be the stronger task of lifting the child himself. In the garden one may be involved in weeding over a period of time or in transplanting a heavy bush. Sacks and heavy boxes of groceries have to be lifted and carried frequently. Heavy objects must be lifted from the floor, from tables and from, and to, high shelves. The list of such tasks is endless.

Since they involve the addition of a weight to the body, equilibrium is upset and the body weight must be adjusted. Because many of these tasks involve the maintenance of a lowered body position over a period of time or the moving of considerable weights, economy of effort and avoidance of strain are also major concerns.

Holding involves exerting against an object only that amount of upward force necessary to balance gravity's pull so that the object has no vertical motion. Carrying differs only in that the object acquires the momentum of the body as it moves. Actually, an object is held while it is carried. In lifting an additional upward force is applied in order that the object will move upward in opposition to the force of gravity.

The force required to hold and lift an object depends upon its weight. The force of gravity must be overcome if the object is to be held and moved upward. Since gravity acts in a vertically downward direction the body force must be applied upward. As much of the hands or arms as possible should be placed under the object in order to resist directly the downward pull of gravity. It is extremely difficult to hold even a light object for any length of time when it is grasped by the thumb opposing the fingers since the force exerted is inward and gravity is pulling downward.

HOLDING AND CARRYING

Whenever an object is held it becomes a part of the total body weight and the center of gravity of the body-plus-weight shifts in the direction of the weight. To maintain stability this new center of gravity must be shifted back over the center of the base by an adjustment of the body. If this adjustment is made by shifting the body as a unit from the ankles, the relative alignment of the various body segments is not disturbed. Thus the body as a whole is used to counterbalance the weight of the object held and the weight can be held with a minimum of strain on the various muscles and joints (Fig. 65). The nearer to the body's center of gravity a weight is held the smaller the rotatory force which is exerted on the body and the less the adjustment of the body which is necessary to counteract it. Therefore, a weight should be held as close to the body as possible to keep the weight arm short. The farther it is held from the body the longer the weight arm and the more force required to balance the weight (Chapter 6, Leverage). This can be demonstrated easily by holding a book on the flat palm close to the shoulder and then straightening the arm and holding the book at shoulder height but at arm's length.

Carrying a heavy object at one side of the body shifts the center of gravity to that side bringing it dangerously near, or beyond, the base of support. By raising the opposite arm sideways while keeping the body in its same basic alignment, certain weights (not too heavy) can be counterbalanced so that the line of gravity again falls through the center of the base (Fig. 65). The extended arm with its weight farther from the line of gravity becomes a greater balancing force than the arm hanging at the side since the reaction of a lever is in proportion to its length. Although the arm is lighter than the object held, the fact that its center of gravity is farther from the line of

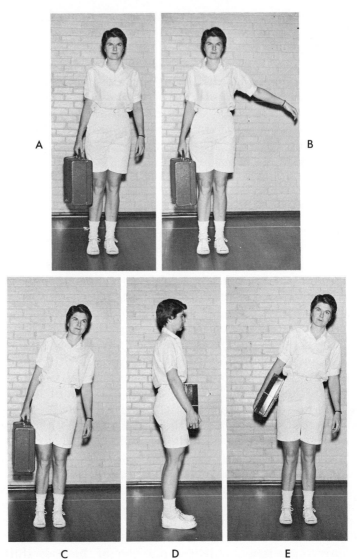

Figure 65. A, *Body shift from ankles.* B, *Weight balanced by arm.* C, *Strain on lower back.* D, *Holding close to body — little adjustment necessary.* E, *Strain on lower back.*

gravity of the body and the weight is close makes it an effective counterbalancing force.

Williams and Lissner[1] found that when a load is carried on one side of the body (for example, on the left) the force on the opposing supporting hip (head of right femur) during walking is much greater than when the load is distributed on both sides of the body. This is true even when the total load carried on the two sides is *twice as great* as that carried on one side. In other words, when a 50 pound weight is carried on each side of the body (total 100 pounds), there is less force on the head of the opposite femur at each step than there is on the right femur if 50 pounds is carried in the left hand only.

Some loads, because of their size and shape, must be carried in front of the body. When a heavy load is carried in front of the body it may be possible to support some of the weight by the thighs[2] if the knees are bent. In this case the body leans backward (as a unit) from the knees to balance the weight and keep the center of gravity of the body plus the weight over the feet.

The carrying task in which students are involved most frequently is that of carrying books. When books are held in one arm up against the chest the tendency is to "hug" them to the body. In so doing the shoulder on the carrying side is lifted, and therefore habitually carrying books in one arm is likely to lead to a high shoulder on that side. As soon as the shoulder girdle is tilted a compensatory curve develops in the upper spine. Since normally the books are relatively light they can be carried with a minimum of adjustment of body weight. They can be carried easily in one arm against the chest so long as the tension in the shoulder muscles is sufficient only to overcome gravity's pull on the books and not to pull them up against the body. The shoulder girdle should maintain its well balanced position. To counteract any possible displacement that might result it is wise to use the arms alternately rather than constantly to carry the books in one certain arm. Carrying books in both arms in front of the chest pulls the shoulders forward and rounds the upper back. The tendency is for the individual to thrust the pelvis forward to make a "shelf" for the books to rest on and this upsets the entire body alignment. When heavy loads of books must be carried, a brief case which allows the weight to be held close to the body while maintaining a well aligned position and makes it possible for the force exerted by the individual to be in direct opposition to gravity's pull (fingers *under* handle), is advisable.

When a heavy tray is carried in front of the body its center of gravity is the distance of approximately half of the width of the tray away from the body and the hands must be placed at that distance from the body to keep the tray from tipping. This means that, if the tray is large, the weight arm is long and the weight is extremely difficult to hold. If the tray is carried above one shoulder with one hand placed under the center of the tray and the other on one edge for control, the weight is brought in closer to the line of gravity of the body and is easier to carry. To balance the weight of the tray the body weight is shifted from the ankles, to the opposite side. If shifted from the waist the muscles of the back are placed in a position of strain.

Some peoples carry all objects on their heads. This method has certain advantages and disadvantages. It makes it possible to keep the weight directly above the center of gravity of the body. The center of gravity of the body-plus-weight is raised but not moved forward, backward, or to either side. It is still on the same line of gravity and therefore, no adjustment is required. However, if the object becomes even slightly off center its rotatory effect is great because it is so high. Since the very flexible neck is below the weight, strong neck muscles are essential to prevent any movement which would shift the center of gravity of the load away from the line of gravity of the body. Those who carry objects on their heads stand well because it is essential that the body be well aligned if balance is to be maintained with such a high center of gravity.

When two individuals are carrying a heavy object down an incline or stairway, the weight of the object is against the lower individual unless the one at the upper end moves closer to the center of the object and/or pulls backward to hold some of the weight back against gravity's pull.

STOOPING AND LIFTING

Lifting tasks involve pushing and pulling movements and therefore the physical principles which must be applied if they are to be performed efficiently are the same as those discussed in the previous chapter. Lifting is actually pushing or pulling in a vertical instead of horizontal direction. In lifting a low object to approximately chest height the action is that of pulling, and beyond chest height it becomes one of pushing.

To lower the body in order to contact the object to be lifted, a stooping (crouching) rather than bending motion uses the strong leg muscles instead of the weaker back muscles. The heavier the object to be lifted, the more essential the use of the leg muscles becomes. Everyone is agreed that when a lifting task involves any considerable weight or repeated lifts, strain of the lower back can be avoided only by stooping. There has been some discussion concerning the efficiency of stooping as compared to bending over for light objects. In 1955, an article in *Collier's* reported some studies made by Dr. Brouha in which the vertical force exerted against the supporting surface by both movements was measured. He found greater force was exerted when stooping than when bending and concluded that "For a single action and for lighter weights, there's no doubt now that bending is more economical for the body."[3] It would seem, however, that only one aspect of efficiency, that of vertical force expended, was investigated. Since, in stooping, the entire body weight is lowered and must be raised it seems reasonable that the vertical force would be greater. However, the *total* force exerted in the bend is *not* vertical, but has a backward component as well. This conclusion, based on vertical force only, does not consider the fact that the force required can be exerted by the strong muscles of the legs in the stoop while it must be exerted by the small and considerably weaker muscles of the lower back in the bend. Also, in stooping the force is exerted straight upward through the center of the weight to be lifted (body-plus-weight), while recovery from a bend requires a diagonally upward pull of a weight which is far from the fulcrum for the movement (the hips) and therefore, the back muscles must act under a condition of adverse leverage.

When an individual bends over to tie a shoe lace and then lifts only the upper body in order to resume a standing position the weight to be lifted can, of course, be considered to be concentrated at the center of gravity of the upper body. The length of the lever involved is the distance from the hips to this point. When he bends to pick up an object, the weight of the object is added at the hands, and the weight to be lifted is concentrated at the center of gravity of the upper trunk-plus-object (Fig. 66). The object, being at the extreme end of the lever, greatly lengthens the weight arm and thus the effect of the weight is augmented. It seems probable that the stronger

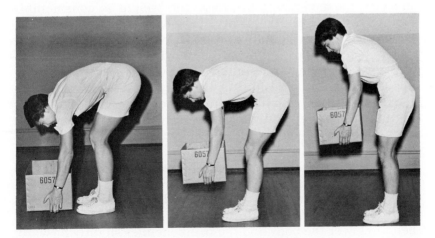

Figure 66. *Straining the back.*

muscles of the legs acting as they do under circumstances of favorable leverage are better able to cope with the additional vertical force found by Dr. Brouha to be required by the stoop, than are the small muscles of the back which are required to function under conditions of adverse leverage when pulling the body-plus-weight upward and backward from a bend. It is possible that even though less vertical force is exerted muscle strain could result.

In the case of a person who has any trouble with his knees stooping may be very difficult, or even impossible, and for him bending over to pick up a *light object* may be more efficient. For the normal person with no knee or back handicap stooping is preferred and is required when a heavy object is involved. For one with a back handicap stooping *is a must regardless of the lightness of the task*, while an individual with a knee handicap must determine the best method for each task on the basis of the demands of the task and the relative strength of his back and his knees. In general for light tasks, it is probably better for him to bend so that the knees are not involved in the lifting of the body weight. However, a heavy task should not be attempted in this way. If it is impossible or very difficult for him to stoop, some method of moving the object other than lifting must be employed or the lifting task left to someone else.

The advantages of stooping are that (1) the strongest muscles available to the task are used, (2) the weight can be kept close to the line of gravity of the body, and (3) the force is exerted in the direction of the desired movement and it is completely effective in lifting the weight upward. While less *vertical* force has been found to be required by bending, weaker muscles must perform the task, the weight is considerably farther from the line of gravity of the body, and the force must be exerted in a diagonally upward direction and thus only the vertical component is effective in moving the weight upward. Since, in stooping, the center of gravity is lowered directly above the base, the position of the body is more stable than in the bend position which keeps the center of gravity of the body high and moves considerable weight forward of the base and thus requires a compensatory backward shift of other body segments.

When lifting, the feet should be separated somewhat into a forward-backward stride position to widen the base in the direction that the body segments will be moving and thus increase the stability of the body. The knees, hips, and ankles bend to lower the body and the trunk inclines slightly forward. This places the body in an easy normal position rather than the stiff position which results when an attempt is made to keep the trunk completely upright. When the knees are bent it is impossible to arch the lower back as the trunk inclines forward, and thus there is less possibility of lower back strain. Since it takes considerable energy to lift the body weight itself, the body should be lowered only far enough to assure that the hand or hands can be placed under the object to be lifted. If the object has a handle, the fingers can be wrapped around the handle and the body weight does not have to be lowered as far.

Two methods for lifting a heavy object from the floor have been suggested. Both involve standing close to the object and lowering the body by bending the joints of the legs. However, one suggests that the object be in front of the individual and the other that it be at his side.

In the first, a wide side stride is necessary in order for the object to be between the legs so that a diagonal lift of the object up over the knees is eliminated. The base is narrow in the forward-backward plane, and balance is precarious. However, since the weight to be lifted is between the legs, it can be kept closer to the line of gravity of the body and the force is exerted straight upward (Fig. 67). This method is difficult, if not impossible, for a girl in a skirt to perform. If the skirt is very full it may be possible, although the skirt is in the way when the object is between the legs. If the object is not between the legs but is in front of the knees, it must be lifted up and over the knees and any advantage of having it in front is lost. Kendall[2] suggested bracing the elbows on the thighs whenever possible to give support to the arms at the beginning of the lift. It must be noted that this would not be possible unless there were some way to take hold of the object several inches above floor level.

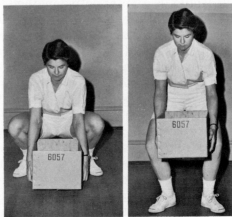

Figure 67. *Using the strong leg muscles (weight in front).*

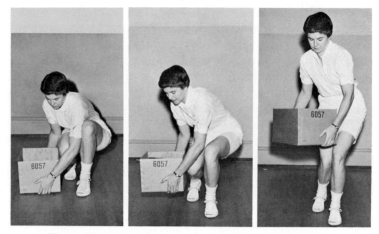

Figure 68.   *Using the strong leg muscles (weight at side).*

The second method, that with the object at the side allows for a more stable base since the feet can be separated somewhat forward-backward which is the direction in which balance is difficult. There is, however, a slightly off-center application of force at the beginning of the lift as the object is brought close to the body's center of gravity (Fig. 68). This method is much easier for girls with skirts and, because of the balance factor, it is preferred by many over the other method. It does not cause as much trunk rotation as might be anticipated because the forward-backward stride position, with the foot *away* from the weight forward, turns the pelvis toward the object and the shoulders need be rotated very little, if any, beyond the line of the pelvis. Of course, if the foot *toward* the weight is placed forward the pelvis is rotated *away* from the object, and a great deal of trunk rotation is required. Obviously, this would be an ineffective method for accomplishing the lift. Experimentation with the two foot positions makes this apparent. When an object that is to be carried at the side (such as a suitcase) is involved, there is, of course, no question. It is always more efficient to stand with the side to the suitcase, lower the body until the handle can be grasped and then straighten the legs and adjust the body weight from the ankles to counterbalance the weight (Fig. 69).

In lifting a heavy tray from a table to a position above one shoulder the tray should first be slid to the point at which a few inches extend over the edge of the table, the body should be turned sideways to the table and lowered by bending the joints of the legs. One hand grasps the edge of the tray and the other is placed under it palm up so that, as the hand at the edge

Figure 69. *Using the strong leg muscles.*

pulls the tray outward on the table, it can be placed under the tray's center. The tray needs to be pulled outward only far enough for the supporting hand to be placed under its center before it is lifted. It is lifted by the extension of the legs. The hand on the edge of the tray, having a long force arm (from hand to center of tray) is effective in controlling the tray, while the one under the center supports it against gravity's pull. To put the tray down onto a table the individual stands with his side to the table and stoops until one side of the tray rests on the table. It can then be pushed completely onto the table as he stands.

Some heavy lifting tasks can be performed effectively by the use of the body weight to overbalance the weight to be lifted (Fig. 70). A heavy overstuffed chair is both difficult to grasp and heavy to lift. However, it is easy to tilt it forward by pushing forward against the top of its back. Since the force is applied far from the chair's center of gravity it takes relatively little force to tilt it. If it is tipped far forward so that when the individual stands in a wide forward-backward stride position the thigh of the forward leg can be placed against the bottom of the chair, and the arms take a firm hold around the chair back, the chair can be lifted from the floor by a transference of body weight from the forward to the backward foot. As in any pushing or pulling task the arm, shoulder girdle, and back muscles should be set before the lifting force is exerted.

By pivoting the feet, rocking the weight well backward so that the forward foot can be lifted momentarily from the floor, the chair can be moved. Once the chair is off the floor the second thigh can be brought under the chair bottom while the

A   B   C   D

Figure 70. A, B, *Force applied at chair top makes rotation easy—legs supply force. C, D, Weight transference lifts chair.*

Figure 71. *Weight of chair balanced by body weight.*

body weight balances the weight of the chair. If a chair is so low that it is difficult to get the thigh very far under the bottom for the lift (Fig. 70 C, D), better control will be gained by placing the second thigh under the chair (Fig. 71). With the chair off the floor this second thigh can be placed well under the chair bottom. By rocking the weight toward that leg, the weight on the first thigh can be reduced so that it can be moved farther forward under the chair bottom. With both legs supporting the chair and the body weight balancing it, it is possible to walk forward slowly by very slightly rocking from side to side. In this way the weight of the chair is used to help lift each foot in turn. The weight of the body simply balances the weight of the chair and although this is a heavy object and all trunk muscles are called into action to stabilize, there is no strain on the small muscles of the back.

Before the chair is put down onto the floor one leg must be placed backward. The chair is then put down by transferring the weight to the forward foot, then tilting it backward until all four legs again rest on the floor. In this way the body weight can be used as the lifting force for any object which weighs less than the individual lifting it and which can be grasped by the arms and rested against a thigh. Besides being applicable for lifting very heavy objects, this technique is useful with large objects that are not easily grasped in the normal lifting position.

In lifting an object from a high shelf, balance is always a problem. Since the force to start the task must be applied outward in order that the object can clear the shelf, the original momentum of the object is outward and being applied against the body at a high point, it tends to tip the body backward (Fig. 72). Therefore, it is important to have a wide base in the forward-backward direction so that balance will not be lost. To avoid excessive reaching the forward foot should be close to the shelf, *the other foot well back.* The body weight is on the forward foot as the hands contact the object. The object is pulled slowly to the edge of the shelf by some weight transference. This original force must be applied carefully to avoid having the momentum of the object carry it off the shelf before the individual is ready to control its weight. It is important to remember that, because of inertia, it takes more force to start an object moving than to keep it moving (Chapter 5, Motion).

After the object has been moved to the edge of the shelf, the individual should get set for the lifting task. The object should be grasped so that force can be applied directly in

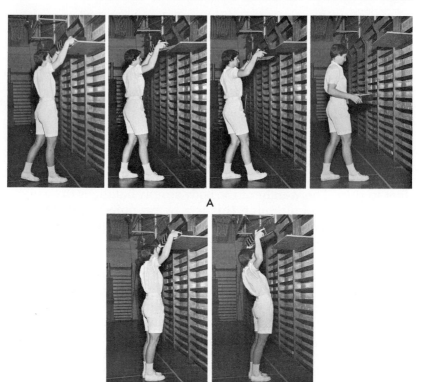

Figure 72. A, *Weight transference takes box from shelf.* B, *Strain on lower back.*

oppostion to gravity's downward pull. This means that a good part of the hands must be under the object, either centered or on both sides. If it is flat enough (like a suitbox) that it can be grasped over both ends and have the fingers well under the box and is not too heavy, it can be controlled well in this way. However, removing a suitcase from a rack in a train presents another problem. A suitcase is too thick for such a grasp but it has a handle. In such a case one hand grasps the handle for control and the other is placed in such a position that, as the suitcase is pulled slowly outward, the palm of the hand will be under the center of it. A carton with a heavy cord or rope can be handled in a similar way.

All of these objects are pulled outward off the shelf by transferring the body weight from the forward to the backward foot. This uses the strong leg muscles to do the work, the back muscles being called upon only to stabilize the trunk. It also places the body far enough from the shelf that there is space for the object to drop straight down in front of the body. As soon as the object is clear of the shelf the arm and shoulder girdle muscles resist the pull of gravity just enough to assure a controlled lowering of the object to a point where it can be carried most easily. In the case of the suitbox this might be in front of the chest while the suitcase would be lowered to a position at the side. This is a controlled "giving in" to gravity by the muscles of the arms and shoulders just as walking downstairs is a controlled giving by the muscles of the legs.

To put the suitbox up onto the shelf the opposite movement is executed. The box is lifted upward when the weight is on the back foot and the transference of body weight moves it onto the shelf. In the case of an object with a handle, such as a suitcase, the upward force required can be reduced by the use of momentum which can be created by swinging the object forward and upward. One hand is then placed under the object and the body weight is transferred from the back to the forward foot to move the object onto the shelf or rack (Fig. 73). Momentum should be used whenever possible to augment the lifting force.

Standing on a chair or stool to reduce the distance of the reach is dangerous when an object of any size and weight is involved since the base is small and allows no transference of weight backward. If the chair is close to the shelf so that the force of the body weight is straight downward to reduce the possibility of the chair slipping, there is no space between the individual's body and the shelf for an object of any size to be lowered. To make space the individual must lean backward from the waist. Since the base is small and the weight high, balance is precarious and this backward leaning may over-balance the body. In any event it puts strain on the muscles of the lower back. Not only must they support the upper body in this off balance position but the weight as well. If, on the other

| A | B | C | D |

Figure 73.   A, B, *Momentum from swing starts the lift.* C, D, *Weight transference puts suitcase on shelf.*

hand, the stool or chair is placed far enough out from the shelf to allow space for the object to drop in front of the individual, he must lean toward the shelf to contact the object. This causes a diagonally backward force against the chair and unless friction is great it is pushed out from under the individual. This practice has resulted in many falls.

If the reach from the floor causes strain, a low footstool placed under the forward foot while keeping the other foot back will relieve it to some extent. Even though it is lifted off the floor during the forward reach, one foot must be kept back in position to drop to the floor to take the body weight as it moves down and back. The force of the forward foot against the stool is straight downward so that slipping is not as great a problem but the weight can be transferred to the back foot as the object comes off the shelf. It may be advantageous to stand on a stool close to the shelf to move the object close to, or slightly out over, the edge of the shelf where it can be reached more easily from the floor. The stool should then be removed and a wide stride assumed before the object is actually removed from the shelf.

If no shelves are available for the practice of this skill in the gymnasium, they can be improvised easily by making use of stall bars. A piece of plywood cut to fit one section of the stall bars and two small pieces of wood cut out on one side to fit under a bar and thus to wedge the plywood between two bars, makes a shelf that can be put up quickly and removed at the end of the period of instruction. The height of the shelf can be adjusted according to the height of the students (Fig. 73).

Some lifting tasks, such as lifting a shovel full of dirt, involve long handled implements. In such a case the individual stands so that the load is to his side and slightly ahead, in a position where the shaft of the shovel is in front of his body. As in all lifting tasks the body is lowered by bending the hips, knees, and ankles and slightly inclining the trunk forward. One hand is placed well down the shaft in order to shorten the weight arm and the other grasps the handle of a short shovel or the shaft of a long shovel as far up as can be comfortably reached. The hand close to the weight is used as the fulcrum and the other, having the advantage of a long force arm, produces the major part of that lifting force which is exerted by the arms (first class lever). Extension of the legs plus this leverage action of the arms lifts the load. When the load is not too heavy some force is usually supplied by the lower hand also, making the shovel a combination of a first and third class lever.

If the lifting task calls for the cooperation of two or more persons, they should lower their bodies so that they can place their hands under the heaviest parts of the load in such a way that the weight can be divided equally, set their muscles for the task and, on signal, all exert force at once. In this way the load is distributed evenly and all parts of the load move upward uniformly. If one person applies force before another, the load is tilted and more weight rests on the person who is lower. When several persons are involved the load is lifted first to their knees and then, on a second signal, all stand. If any readjustment of weight is necessary it can be made before they attempt the major part of the lift. This procedure also is more likely to result in unified movement. This is the technique used in First Aid when a person is lifted by four or five individuals.

When any amount of forward lean of the body is required by a lifting task the lower back "should not be allowed to arch but should be flattened by 'tucking the hips'."[4] Kendall[5] stated that a person with tightness in the muscles of the lower back has difficulty in tucking the hips and therefore is more susceptible to strain from lifting than is the person with normal flexibility.

When, in any lifting task, the individual finds that the load does not move *as the legs begin to straighten* but that the hips push out behind leaving the upper body low, he *must stop any attempt to lift* the object and seek help. Further effort will simply strain the back. If he continues until he feels some strain in the back it is too late, the harm will have been done. AT ANY TIME THAT THE HIPS CANNOT BE KEPT UNDER THE BODY AS THE LEGS EXTEND, THE LOAD IS TOO HEAVY. If this were understood there would be fewer back strains from attempting tasks beyond the strength potential of the individual.

When possible, pushing a heavy object or rotating it around its corners is preferable to lifting and carrying it. However, friction may make pushing inadvisable or even impossible unless something with a lower coefficient of friction can be placed between the object and the surface across which it is to be moved. Sometimes the object is too low to be pushed or rotated efficiently; sometimes steps are involved. The method used to move any object depends upon all of the factors which pertain to a particular situation.

SUMMARY

Holding, carrying, and lifting all involve a pushing or pulling effort in a vertical instead of horizontal direction. Therefore, the principles of efficient performance are the same as for a pushing or pulling task.

Although various tasks may be executed somewhat differently because of the size, weight, and shape of the object to be moved and the objective of the movement, any heavy lifting or carrying problem must be approached with five basic questions. (1) What position must be assumed so that the parts of the body (hands, arms, thighs, etc.) which are to exert force directly against the object are *under* the object in a position to oppose directly the force of gravity? (2) How can body balance be maintained without the loss of the basic body alignment? (3) Does the preliminary position make it possible to exert the lifting or supporting force vertically upward rather than on a diagonal? (4) Will the major lifting or supporting force be exerted by the strong leg muscles? (5) Can momentum be used to augment the lifting force?

To avoid back strain in lifting, any attempt to lift must be stopped immediately when the hips cannot be kept under the upper body as the legs extend. The load is too heavy for the strength of the individual and he should seek help.

The most efficient method for moving any given object— lifting, pushing, pulling, or rotating—can be determined only after consideration of all of the factors which pertain to the particular situation.

REFERENCES

1. Williams, Marian and Lissner, Herbert R.: *Biomechanics of Human Motion.* Philadelphia, W. B. Saunders Company, 1962, p. 111.
2. Kendall, Henry Otis, Kendall, Florence P. and Boynton, Dorothy A.: *Posture and Pain.* Baltimore, Williams and Wilkins Company, 1952, p. 190.
3. Davidson, Bill: Stoop or Bend. *Collier's, 135*:11:30, May 27, 1955.
4. Kendall, Henry Otis, Kendall, Florence P. and Boynton, Dorothy A.: *Posture and Pain.* Baltimore, Williams and Wilkins Company, 1952, p. 191.
5. *Ibid.*

18

Throwing and Catching

THROWING

Throwing and striking differ from other methods for moving objects in that a maximum velocity is reached by the time the force is imparted to the object and the object continues to move without further impetus from the body. Throwing is primarily a sport activity. In a variety of sports balls of all sizes and weights are rolled or thrown by one hand or two. Nor is the object thrown always a round ball. The javelin, discus, and bean bag are also thrown. While given the name of "ball" the football is not round. However, regardless of size, shape or weight, whether rolled or thrown, the essential mechanics remain the same. Momentum is transferred from the body to the object thrown. The object is held in the hand or hands, or as in the case of lacrosse, in another object which is in turn held in the hand. Momentum of the hand is developed and the object is released.

Since an object acquires the motion of any object to which it is attached (Chapter 5, Motion) the object held in the hand acquires the speed and direction of the hand and when released continues to move at this velocity and in the same direction until acted upon by other forces, such as air resistance, gravity, or friction. In throwing, then, one must consider the methods for developing speed and controlling direction of the hand. Control of direction involves adjusting the angle of release in both the vertical and horizontal planes. This is the point at which rolling differs from throwing. The mechanics of rolling are the same as those for the underhand throw with the exception that, since the ball is rolled along the floor, the vertical angle of release is not involved and friction becomes an important consideration.

Factors Influencing Speed. The faster the hand is moving at the moment of release, the faster a given thrown or rolled object will travel. The longer the backswing of the hand, the more time there is to work up momentum. The backswing can be increased by turning the side opposite to the throwing arm toward the direction of the throw, by rotating the body away from the direction of the throw, and by placing the feet in a stride position with the foot opposite to the throwing arm forward. The wider base thus afforded increases balance by enlarging the base in the direction of the movement and increases the length of the backswing by making possible a backward transference of weight and by allowing maximum rotation, since the hips are rotated toward the throwing side. Experimentation with standing with the same foot as throwing arm forward while attempting to rotate the body as far as possible and then moving this foot backward, demonstrates very quickly the added rotation possible as soon as the foot moves back. When the foot on the side of the throwing arm is forward it is impossible to rotate the hips in the direction of the backswing.

The more contributing body parts that are brought into the action, if they are timed in sequence, the more speed obtainable. For maximum speed each body part must come into the action at the time that the part below has reached its maximum speed. Body rotation and the shifting of the body weight forward with the throw, both put more body parts into the throw and increase the length of the backswing, and therefore add doubly to the speed of the hand. An experiment with two women physical education majors in which the various joints were immobilized while throwing a tennis ball indicated that, for these subjects, approximately 50 per cent of the velocity of the overhand throw resulted from the body rotation and step. Since it was impossible to immobilize the fingers as this prevented grasping the ball, the finger action was involved in every item measured. In both subjects the total shoulder, elbow, wrist, and finger action accounted for approximately one-half of the force produced (53 per cent and 51 per cent) and the body rotation, step, and fingers, the other half. It is little wonder that girls who attempt to throw with their arms alone and overlook the importance of their trunks are relatively unsuccessful in throwing overhand.

Any movement of the body in the direction of the throw adds force to the throw. The transference of weight, a run, or hop all give the body momentum which is transferred to the throwing arm and thus to the object to be thrown. Transference of weight is used in any throw in which speed is a factor. If, in transferring the weight, the individual steps forward onto a straight leg, the forward momentum is restrained just as it is in walking from the time the forward leg takes any of the weight until the center of gravity of the body is over the forward foot. This results in a reduction of the momentum of the body and consequently of the speed of the throw. When the forward knee is allowed to bend as the weight is transferred there is no resistance to the forward momentum. In addition, the center of the arc of the throw (the shoulder) is lowered, flattening the arc and this is important in the control of direction.

When rolling a ball it is necessary to lower the body so that the hand can reach to, or close to, the floor. Since leaning over places the body in a precarious state of equilibrium, the center of gravity being high and the weight of the trunk forward, and puts strain on the small muscles of the back, the body should be lowered by bending the legs. Therefore, if rolling is taught before throwing, a pattern of bending the forward leg can be established and then carried over into the throwing pattern. A run preceding the roll adds even greater speed just as it does to the throw. This is the principle applied in the approach in bowling. The momentum of the body gained through the approach is added to the momentum of the arm swing.

A throw executed on a moving base (run, slide) requires perfect balance and therefore, in order to control the weight over the base, relatively small steps are taken. In order to transfer the weight from the foot on the side of the throwing arm to the opposite foot at the instant required for maximum sequential action, a hop on the back foot (right foot for a right-handed thrower) may be needed. This hop also makes it possible .to rotate quickly to the throwing side for maximum backswing.

The faster the muscles which contribute to the throw are contracted, the faster the hand will be moving at the moment of release. It is possible to go through the motions of a forceful throw in slow motion and, although the backswing is long, the trunk rotated, and the weight transferred, still the hand will not be moving with any speed at the middle of the arc of the movement.

The more nearly the release coincides with the instant

of maximum momentum of the hand, the faster the throw. Human muscles are incapable of stopping momentum suddenly without jerk or strain, and so the momentum of the hand must be reduced gradually. The hand is moving fastest at the center of the arc of the throw. If the hand is stopped or jerked back at, or immediately following release, the arc of the throw is shortened and the speed of the hand must be slowed before the object leaves the hand. A jerking back to stop the momentum actually produces force that counteracts the forward force of the throw. A follow-through places the point of release at the center of the arc, and the maximum momentum developed by the particular movement can be transferred to the object thrown. Strain of the arm and shoulder is also avoided.

If all the force produced by the body is to be transferred to the object there must be a firm surface for the feet and sufficient friction to prevent slipping. Whenever the purpose of the throw demands sufficient force to require a wide base for balance and the use of weight transference, a considerable proportion of the force exerted by the body against the supporting surface is backward. Therefore, the friction between the feet and the surface is extremely important in causing the reaction force of the surface against the feet and through the body, and thus in producing a firm base for trunk, shoulder, arm, and hand action.

The more the internal resistance is reduced before the throw, the more speed possible. Warming up the muscles by throwing easily before attempting an all-out effort may add to the efficiency of the throw and reduce the possibilities of muscular strain.

Whether or not maximum force is desirable depends upon the purpose of the particular throw. Frequently the certainty of the catch of a relatively short throw is more important than speed. Less force must be used when throwing to an individual who is running toward the thrower since this not only decreases the distance of the throw but also adds the receiver's momentum to the force of the impact, and thus increases the possibilities of a fumble of the catch. Whenever the purpose does not demand maximum distance or maximum speed the pattern of movement is adjusted so that the ball is thrown with less speed. Not every throw demands as long a backswing as possible. It is not even always necessary to have the feet in a forward stride, or the opposite foot forward. These are important only in that they contribute to force and thus to the speed of the hand and of the thrown object. The important consideration is the relationship of these, and other factors discussed earlier, to the speed that the body can produce and the magnitude of the force desired. The most suitable speed for the purpose must be determined and adjustment of movement pattern made accordingly.

If the situation calls for a toss to a player standing nearby in which the certainty of the catch is important, the small amount of force that is needed may be produced more efficiently by using the arm alone rather than by going through the whole "throw pattern." Since little force is involved balance is not a problem and, therefore, foot position is unimportant. Too frequently the pattern of maximum force is taught as *the* "throwing pattern" and this foot position, etc., is insisted upon for every throw. If the contribution of each part of the movement to speed and angle of release were understood, the student would be in a position to make judgments according to purposes and more efficient movement would result in situations which call for less than maximum force. Form is too often judged by the execution of the "maximum force pattern" rather than the movement which can accomplish the purpose with the least expenditure of effort and strain.

Factors Influencing Direction. An object continues to move in the direction in which it was moving at release until acted upon by some other force. If the hand is traveling in an arc, the thrown object moves in a line which is tangent to that arc at the point of release. This means that there is only one point on the arc at which it can be released if it is to move in a given direction. The more nearly the arc approaches a straight line, the less divergent the tangents at various points on the arc (Fig. 74). Therefore, the flatter the arc through which the hand travels, the greater the possibility of accuracy. One way that the path through which the hand travels can be flattened is by moving the center of the arc in the direction of the movement and in the direction of the circumference of the arc.

For example, in the underhand throw, since the movement is in the vertical plane, the arc can be flattened by moving the shoulder (the center of the arc) forward and downward (Fig. 75). Transference of weight to a bent forward leg and a follow-through in a forward direction accomplish this. In the overhand throw the arc is flattened by a sequential extension of the joints of the arm as the throwing shoulder moves forward due to the rotation of the spine and the transference of weight. This is an example of various levers working

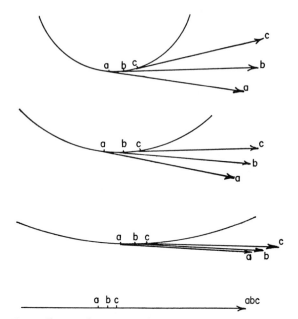

Figure 74. *Effect on divergence of various tangents as arc is flattened.*

together to produce a more linear motion of the hand. The rotation of the trunk which moves the shoulder forward and out to the side of the throwing hand is a factor in flattening the arc of the sidearm throw.

The longer the throw, the more important is control of direction since any deviation from the desired direction becomes magnified the farther the object travels. This is an important consideration in many activities, as for example in bowling in which the alley is approximately 60 feet long and a high degree of accuracy is essential to success.

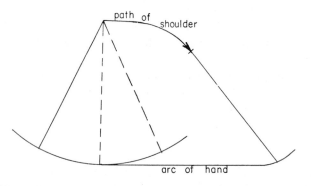

Figure 75. *Schematic representation of the flattening of the arc of the underhand throw accompanying a forward and downward movement of the shoulder.*

Many of the factors that contribute to speed are likely to decrease control of direction. For example, it is easier to control fewer body segments but maximum speed results from the use of all segments that can contribute to the movement. It is easier to control a relatively slow motion but speed results from fast muscular contraction.

Once the object has left the hand its path is influenced by any other forces which act upon it. The more accurate the allowance for these other forces (gravity, wind, and spin), the more accurate the throw. Since an object moves in the direction in which the air is moving, it should be aimed some-what into a cross wind rather than straight in the direction of the desired movement. The stronger the wind, the more it should be aimed up-wind. Since a ball with right spin curves to the right and one with left spin to the left, a destination which is straight ahead can only be reached by a ball with right spin if aimed to the left of the desired destination. Since gravity always acts in a downward direction it alters the path only in a vertical direction and thus affects the distance that the object travels.

Factors Influencing Distance. The distance an object will travel depends upon the speed with which it is released, the angle at which it is released, and the action of outside forces.

Other things being equal, the faster the object is moving at release, the greater the distance it will travel. Since gravity begins to act on the object at release, distance also depends upon the angle at which the object is thrown. The general principle that, in the absence of air friction, the greatest dis-tance for a given speed results from a projection at a 45-degree angle has been discussed in Chapter 9, Projectiles. Angle of release as well as speed must be adjusted to the purpose of the particular throw. The speed of most thrown balls is not great enough to cause the building up of considerable air resist-ance against their forward progress and therefore, if the objective of the throw is to gain the greatest possible distance, a ball should be thrown at approximately a 45-degree angle. If the purpose is to have a ball arrive as fast as possible at a given point which is not maximum for the speed obtainable by the thrower, the angle should be flattened. How much it can be flattened depends upon the force which the individual can muster. The greater the force, the faster the ball travels, the less time gravity has to pull it toward the earth and the lower it can be thrown.

When wind is involved the angle must be adjusted. A head wind resists the forward progress of the object and therefore decreases the distance an object travels. To gain maximum distance the angle of release is flattened so that a greater proportion of the force applied is directed horizontally to combat the wind resistance. Since the force of a tailwind is added to the force of the throw, distance can be gained by increasing the angle of release so that a greater proportion of the *throwing* force is applied to combat gravity's pull and keep the object in the air longer.

Spin on a ball builds up air pressure which affects the distance that it travels. Since forward spin causes a ball to drop faster than it would normally, less distance is obtained from a given initial speed and angle of release. Back spin, causing a ball to remain in the air longer, may result in greater distance. Spin is discussed in detail in Chapter 8.

Since a heavy object has greater inertia, it takes more force to work up a given speed in throwing it, but given a certain velocity it travels farther than a light object because of its ability to overcome air resistance. As the surface which is presented in the direction of movement increases, the distance the thrown object will travel decreases (given the same projecting speed) due to the additional air resistance created. Thus, a small ball will travel farther than a large one of equal weight and both will travel farther than an irregularly shaped object. A rough surface on an object also increases air resistance and cuts distance.

Throwing Patterns.   There are three basic throwing patterns. Which will be most efficient depends upon the size, weight, and shape of the object to be thrown and the purpose of the throw. The factors which contribute to speed and accuracy are identical for all. The method in which they are applied varies.

In the *overhand* pattern the many segments of the body are brought into the movement in sequence giving a "whiplike" action at the distal end of the system of levers. Because this movement allows for the longest backswing possible and the use of more body parts in sequence, more speed can be developed with this type of throw than with the underhand. It is used for speed and distance. The elbow is flexed on the backswing to shorten the lever and make it easier to move, as well as to place it in a position for sequential extension. It also makes reversal of direction to start the forward movement easier. It is more difficult to reverse the direction of the straight arm because of the greater backward momentum developed at the end of the longer lever. Many sources have indicated that the ball is released at the point of full extension of the arm. Pictures taken during electromyographic studies[1] of a skilled young woman show clearly that the ball is released well before the arm reaches full extension. In fact, there was an angle of approximately 105 degrees at the elbow as the ball was leaving the fingers. This finding has been reported also by Gollnick and Karpovich[2] who, in a study of joint action of young men throwing a baseball, found an elbow angle of 102 degrees at the time of release. Actually, this situation should have been anticipated since, as pointed out by Gollnick and Karpovich, it takes some distance to decelerate an arm moving at this speed. Undoubtedly injuries would have resulted if students had followed instructions and actually released at the straight arm point. The human body has many protective mechanisms that man is just beginning to understand.

Girls frequently have difficulty in developing the whiplike action of the overhand throw. They tend to throw with the arm ignoring the body, and to drop the elbow close to the side of the body, from which position a pushing action results since the hand is forward of the elbow and shoulder. This position allows very little backswing, and thus little time to work up momentum before release. These individuals need to understand the contribution of backswing and of the rest of the body to the force of the throw. They need to experiment with the arm position with the elbow down close to the body and that with the elbow up and away from the body so that they can determine for themselves the difference in the speed of a hand "pushed" forward and one which is "whipped" forward by the sequential extension of all joints. Forward rotation starts in the pelvis and moves through the trunk. The shoulder comes into the action followed by the elbow and wrist. The hand, since it is the end of the whip, is the last body segment to be brought forward.

Holding the end of a four or five foot rope which is behind the body and throwing the far end out and forward demonstrates the different results obtainable from the "pushing" and "whipping" motions and is frequently a successful method for giving the feeling for the throwing motion. When the hand is pushed forward the rope is simply pulled against the individual's back but when the whiplike action is used the rope is snapped forward over the head. Going through the motions with something heavy in the hand may also help individuals develop the kinesthetic perception of a throw. A tennis racket in its press is excellent for this purpose and advantage can be taken of this situation to point out similarities between throwing and striking activities, such as the tennis serve and smash, badminton overhead clear and smash, and volleyball spike (Fig. 3, pp. 12–13). Sometimes the kinesthetic concept can be given by standing close behind the individual, holding his throwing hand, and, after assuring that his arm is relaxed, actually throwing his hand. Repetition of this movement while the student concentrates upon his feeling of it is often helpful.

The overhand throw can be used only with an object which is small enough and of such shape that it can be gripped by the fingers, and light enough that it can be controlled at a considerable distance from the body. Heavy objects necessitate an underarm throw in which gravity assists the thrower at those times when the object is far from the body, or a push shot in which the object is held close to the shoulder. The shot put delivery, because of the weight of the shot, is actually a pushing action rather than a throw.

The underhand throw pattern allows for the use of more varied objects. Because the object is held closer to the body with the arm straight, a heavier object can be controlled. The only times that the object is far from the body are at the beginning of the swing and at the top of the backswing. The momentum gained by the pull of gravity during the drop at the early part of the backswing aids the arm in lifting the ball on the backswing. To initiate the movement all the thrower must do is to push the heavy object forward away from his body. Gravity then aids in dropping the ball and moving it backward. Since this throw is in the vertical plane, gravity assists the thrower in producing the forward movement of the object. A much larger object can be controlled when this pattern is used because the palm of the hand can be placed under the object and it can rest against the lower arm.

Since both backswing and body rotation are more restricted than in either the overhand or sidearm throw, this throwing pattern is not effective for the production of maximum speed or distance. However, because the throwing hand follows a straight path throughout the swing, greater right-left accuracy is possible. Accuracy becomes mainly a matter of controlling the vertical angle of release.

An understanding of, and feeling for, this pattern can be acquired rather quickly by rolling a ball along a line to a partner at a distance of some four or five feet. The importance of having the backswing and follow-through follow the line is immediately obvious. By moving to a point 25 or 30 feet from the partner and again rolling the ball so that it will reach him, the factors which increase speed and distance, such as lengthening the backswing, transference of weight, and so forth, can be discovered by each student. As the need for force is introduced balance will become a problem if the center of gravity is kept high as the ball is rolled. The importance of bending the knees can be made obvious by experimentation with a forceful delivery, first while bending over with the knees relatively straight, and then while stepping forward onto a well bent knee. Thus, the factors which contribute to speed and accuracy in the horizontal plane can be determined without the student having to be concerned with control of the vertical angle. The next step, obviously, is to consider the difference between rolling and throwing and the added control which this difference necessitates if one is to throw successfully. The student can determine experimentally the path which is followed by a ball when released at various points along the arc of the swing. The importance of flattening the vertical arc becomes apparent. The methods for accomplishing this have been discussed previously in the section dealing with the control of direction.

The underhand throw is used in many activities such as softball—particularly the pitch—horseshoes, deck or ring tennis, and bowling. It is the throwing pattern which is chosen whenever a relatively short, well controlled throw is desired. The same pattern is also extensively applied in striking activities. The volleyball serve, the badminton serve (Fig. 2, pp. 10–11), and underhand clear, an underhand or pick-up tennis shot are a few examples of such application.

The *sidearm* throw pattern allows for the use of body rotation and for a longer backswing even while throwing objects which are too large to be grasped by the fingers. Large objects eliminate the whiplike action of the arm since the palm must hold the object against the lower arm and the arm acts as one lever rather than a series of levers. Since a longer backswing is possible and more muscles contribute to the throw, more force is obtainable than in the underhand throw. Because the arc of the swing is horizontal, left-right accuracy is a greater problem than in either of the other throwing patterns. When small objects are thrown the pattern is the same as the overhand throw in all of the factors that produce force. Since the hand moves through a more horizontal arc, accuracy is not as easily controlled.

This pattern is most useful in throwing large objects for distance. The forehand drives in tennis and badminton, and the batting action of baseball and softball in general employ this same movement pattern (Fig. 4, pp. 14–15).

CATCHING

In catching, rebound can be prevented and the shock of the impact can be reduced by effecting a gradual loss of the kinetic energy of the ball through using as much distance as possible to reduce its velocity, increasing the time over which the force is absorbed, increasing the area which receives the force of impact, and making use of all of the "shock absorbers" which are built into the body—the wrists, elbows, shoulders, hips, knees, and ankles.

In preparation for receiving the force of an oncoming ball the feet should be separated in a forward-backward stride position to enlarge the base of support in the direction of the force that must be resisted and thus improve stability. A crouch position lowers the center of gravity and further increases stability. The necessity for this depends upon the speed and height of the approaching ball. Every attempt should be made to place the body in line with the approaching ball so that the force can be taken close to the center of gravity of the body. When a ball is caught high above the head or far out to the side, the force is taken at the end of a long lever arm and its rotatory effect is amplified.

A padded glove both increases the area over which the force is absorbed and supplies an absorbent surface which reduces the force to some extent before it is transferred to the hand. The distance and time over which the force is reduced can be increased by pulling the hands in toward the body as they contact the ball and transferring the weight to the back foot or, if considerable force is involved, taking one or more steps backward. When the catch is to be followed by a throw the momentum of the oncoming ball can be used to effect the backswing in preparation for the throw. By giving toward the side of the throwing arm the give becomes the backswing for the throw that follows.

The position of the hands in catching is the most important single factor in avoiding injury. Since the area of the end of a finger is very small and any force taken on the end of a finger simply jams one bone back against the next, it is essential that the tips of the fingers should *never* be pointed toward an approaching ball. The position of the hands with the fingers pointing either upward or downward places the palms of the hands, which present a much larger and more absorbent area, toward the oncoming force. Because of anatomical structure the fingers must point upward when the hands are above waist height and downward when below waist height, if the palms are to face forward. Only when a ball is dropping from above should the fingers point forward. In this case pointing the fingers forward faces the palms of the hands upward toward the approaching ball.

Catching an individual who is falling presents a somewhat different problem from catching a ball. Every effort should be made to grasp him under his shoulders so that his head is kept from hitting the ground. If a hand, arm, or leg is grasped the individual simply rotates around the point of contact and the head, being far from this fulcrum, hits with considerable force. As in any catching task a wide stride in the direction of the force makes it possible to resist the force with less probability of loss of balance. The weight can be transferred as contact with the falling individual is made, thus giving time and distance for the gradual reduction of momentum.

SUMMARY

In throwing, an object held in the hand acquires the speed and direction of the hand and when released continues to move at this velocity and in the same direction until acted upon by other forces. Therefore, the faster the hand is moving when a ball is released the greater is the speed of the thrown ball. Maximum speed results from the use of all of the body segments that can contribute to the movement when timed in sequence, fast muscular contraction, the longest backswing possible, full body rotation, follow-through, and transference of weight in the direction of the throw. Friction between the feet and the supporting surface is essential if the force exerted by the body against the surface is to be transferred back through the body to the ball. A step, run, or hop preceding the throw adds speed because the momentum of the body is added to that of the throwing movement. Follow-through is essential in that it makes possible a release which coincides with the instant of maximum momentum of the hand. The extent to which these various factors are employed depends upon the amount of force called for by the purpose of a particular throw.

Flattening the arc through which the hand moves increases the possibilities for accuracy. In the underhand throw the arc is flattened by moving the shoulder forward, by stepping forward onto a bent leg, and following-through as far as possible in the forward direction. The sequential extension of the joints of the arm as the shoulder moves forward effects some flattening of the arc in the overhand throw. The rotation of the trunk which moves the shoulder forward and out to the side of the throwing hand is effective in the sidearm throw.

The distance which an object travels depends upon the speed and angle of release and the action of outside forces. When maximum distance is desired all factors which contribute to speed should be employed and the ball thrown at an angle of approximately 45 degrees. If the purpose involves having the ball reach a certain destination in the shortest possible time, the angle should be flattened as much as possible. The degree to which the angle can be flattened depends upon the force that can be produced by the thrower. Both force and angle depend upon purpose.

A head wind resists the forward movement of an object and the angle of release should be flattened to increase the forward component of force in order to combat it. A tail wind adds its force to the momentum of the ball making it advantageous, if distance is the objective, to keep the object in the air longer and, therefore, the angle of release is increased so that a greater proportion of the force is effective in resisting the pull of gravity.

There are three basic throwing patterns. The overhand pattern, because it utilizes all of the factors of maximum force to advantage, is the most effective for high speed and long distance. Because the throwing hand follows a straight path, the underhand pattern is most effective for throwing tasks involving a high degree of accuracy. However, in order to follow the straight path many factors leading to maximum speed are omitted and speed is sacrificed to accuracy. The sidearm pattern uses many of the factors which develop speed and at the same time makes it possible to throw large objects which, because they cannot be grasped by the fingers, cannot be thrown overhand. However, since the hand moves through a horizontal arc, left-right accuracy is more difficult to control. This pattern is most useful in throwing large objects for distance. All three patterns are used extensively in many striking activities.

Since balance is a problem in receiving force, the feet should be separated forward-backward (in the direction the object is moving) in catching. Every attempt should be made to place the body in line with the approaching ball to reduce the leverage of the force as it contacts the hand or hands.

A padded glove increases the area over which the force is taken and presents a more absorbent surface. Giving with the arms and body, even to taking steps in the direction of the force, increases the distance and time over which the force is absorbed and reduces the shock of impact. This give can be used to effect the backswing of a throw that is to follow the catch.

The position of the hands is important in avoiding injury. The hands should be placed in such a position that the palms, which present a relatively large area, face the direction of the approaching ball so that they, rather than the very small area of a fingertip, will contact the force. In order for the palms to face forward the tips of the fingers must be pointing upward when the hands are above waist height and downward when below waist height. If the ball is approaching from above the palms should face upward.

REFERENCES

1. Broer, Marion R., and Houtz, Sara Jane: *Patterns of Muscular Activity in Selected Sport Skills: An Electromyographic Study.* Springfield, Charles C Thomas, 1967.
2. Gollnick, Philip D., and Karpovich, Peter V.: Electrogoniometric Study of Locomotion and of Some Athletic Movements. *Research Quarterly,* 35:3(Pt. 2):369, October, 1964.

19

Striking

While there are some household tasks that involve striking, such as beating a rug, swatting a fly, and hammering, this is a much more important skill in the field of sports. Various sports encompass striking a ball with the head, shoulder, knee (soccer); with a foot (soccer, football); with the hand or hands (volleyball, handball); with a racket (badminton, tennis, squash); with a stick, club, or bat (hockey, golf, softball, and baseball); and one object striking another as happens in basketball when the ball strikes the backboard, or in bowling when the ball strikes the pins which in turn strike other pins.

In some of these activities a stationary ball is hit by a moving object, in others a moving ball hits a stationary object (the floor, backboard, or bowling pin) and in still others a moving object (ball or shuttle) is struck by a moving object (racket, bat, hand, etc.). In some the striking surface is flat, in others it is rounded. Regardless of these differences the problem for the player is to produce the required force and apply it to the object directly or through the use of an implement, at such an angle that the particular purpose will be accomplished.

A stationary object when struck will move only if the force applied to it is of sufficient magnitude to overcome its inertia (Newton's First Law of Motion). The force must be great enough to overcome not only the inertia, due to the object's weight and speed but also all restraining forces (friction, air resistance, etc.) as well.

The direction of an approaching object is changed and

the object moves in the general direction of the movement of the striking implement or rebounds from a surface only if sufficient force is applied to overcome the force of the object. A ball striking a canvas which is hanging loosely does not rebound because the surface gives absorbing the force, and thus it does not supply sufficient resistance to produce a re-action force against the ball. The floor, on the other hand, supplies a force sufficient to resist the force of the ball and the ball rebounds.

The law of conservation of momentum states that when two or more objects collide with each other, momentum is conserved. The total momentum after the impact is equal to the total momentum before the impact. In other words, when a bat meets an oncoming ball the total resulting momentum is the sum of the momentum of the bat (the weight of the bat times its speed) and the momentum of the ball (the weight of the ball times its speed). The difference between the two determines the direction of the resulting motion. It is in the direction of the greater momentum. If the momentum of the bat is greater than that of the ball the forward momentum of the bat is decreased, and the ball is given reverse momentum which is equal to the sum of the two original momentums minus the momentum which the bat still has. Dissipating forces such as energy lost in friction and heat will, of course, reduce this somewhat.

It must be remembered that the law of action and reaction (Newton's Third Law of Motion), when applied to striking, means that during impact there are two equal and opposite forces set up between the two objects. One force is exerted by the striking implement on the object struck and the other by the struck object on the striking implement. The reaction of the object against the striking surface is just as great as the force which projects the object. As noted in the preceding paragraph this force depends not only on the force produced by the striking implement but also on the force exerted by the struck object. In both cases the force involved depends on the weight of the object and the speed with which it is moving. While the badminton racket has less *inherent* force than the tennis racket because of its lighter weight, this deficiency can be overcome by the added speed with which it can be moved at the moment of impact due to the fast wrist snap which is possible with the lighter racket.

Because of this action-reaction force the striking surface must be firm if maximum projecting force is to be applied to the object. If some of the momentum of the contact goes into pushing the surface backward (striking surface gives), the projecting force will be correspondingly decreased. Direction may also be changed by this giving of the striking implement. Projection force and direction may be changed by the give of the object struck, the striking surface, or both. The reduction of projection force due to the give of the object struck is obvious when the bat meets a fleece ball. Because the fleece ball is soft and not elastic some of the force is used to flatten the ball and it does not bounce back into shape. When the strings of a tennis racket become loose some of the force is dissipated by the give of the strings as the ball hits the racket. When a forceful hit with the hand is desired, if the flat, open palm is used, some of the force is absorbed because the hand, being constructed of many small bones and muscles, cannot be kept completely firm.

There are various methods for making the hand a more solid striking surface and these are used in volleyball. The fingers can be curled into the palm and the ball hit with the curled fingers or with the heel of the hand. Some individuals make a fist and hit with the thumb side of this fist. This provides a surface which is solid but which is relatively small since the hitting area is only the side of the index finger and the lower segment of the thumb. Since the hitting surface is small a more accurate contact with the ball must be made if results are to be as anticipated. If the force is not applied through the center of gravity of the ball in the direction of desired flight, the ball will go off at an angle. The somewhat larger area of the fingers or the heel of the hand which is available as a solid striking surface when the curled fingers are turned forward, makes it easier to apply force through the center of gravity of the ball in the desired direction.

Discounting such restraining forces as friction and air resistance, the speed of a struck object, then, depends upon the degree of restitution of the object and of the striking surface, the weight and speed of the object, and the weight and speed of the striking implement.

FACTORS INFLUENCING THE MAGNITUDE OF THE FORCE APPLIED

When striking with the hand or an implement held by the hand, or hands, the body movement patterns are basically the same as those used in throwing. Figures 1 through 5, Chapter 1, illustrate this similarity. Even though other parts of the body (principally the feet) may be used in striking, the factors involved in producing speed of movement of the striking implement are the same as those involved in producing speed of movement of the hand in throwing. Since these have been discussed in Chapter 18 they are simply mentioned here.

As in throwing, the speed of the striking implement depends on the length of the backswing or the time available to work up momentum, the number of contributing muscles which are brought into play, the sequence of contraction of these muscles, and the speed with which they are contracted. To apply maximum striking force the impact must coincide with the instant of maximum momentum of the striking implement, just as in throwing the release must coincide with the instant of maximum momentum of the hand. In both, a follow-through prevents the slowing down of the hand or striking implement before release or contact as the release or impact can then be at the center of the arc of movement, which is the instant of greatest speed. In both, if maximum force is to be imparted there must be a firm surface for the feet and sufficient friction to prevent slipping.

In striking, however, a few additional factors are involved. One, the firmness of the striking surface, has been discussed previously. The firmer the striking surface the greater the force imparted to the struck object. Since momentum is proportional to the weight of the object, it is obvious that the heavier the striking implement, up to the point of loss of control, the greater the momentum possible. If a bat so heavy that it cannot be controlled is used, speed of swing will be lost and the resulting momentum will be decreased rather than increased by the weight.

Another factor influencing momentum is the length of the striking implement. The longer the striking implement, again up to the point of loss of control, the faster the distal end will travel if a given force is applied, and the more force that can be imparted. However, the longer lever is more difficult to control. Also, it may be impossible to withstand the force of impact so far from the fulcrum and accuracy of impact may also be affected.

In addition to the above factors that involve the striking implement, the degree of restitution (the ability of the struck object to retake its original shape) is also a factor. Because the object is flattened at impact and then retakes its shape, it moves away from the striking implement at a greater speed than the speed with which the striking implement was moving at impact. The reaction force caused by the object pushing against the implement as it recovers its shape is added to the force of the striking implement. When a *moving object* is to be struck, the magnitude of the force produced by the impact depends also upon the momentum of the object, in other words, its weight and speed.

In any striking situation, the more nearly the object being struck is contacted in line with its center of gravity, the greater the force transferred to the object in the desired direction. The "topped" golf ball is familiar to all. The ball being contacted above its center of gravity is hit more down into the ground than it is forward.

As in throwing, the purpose of striking does not always require the production of maximum force. At times it is advisable to conserve energy by adjusting the movement pattern. At other times it may be expedient to go through the maximum force pattern and reduce the force just before impact by contracting opposing muscles, *for the purpose of deception.* In this case energy is sacrificed to strategy. The purpose of the energy expenditure, though not to hit the particular object with as much force as possible, is just as important to the game situation. In order to deceive successfully one's opponent it is necessary to understand the mechanics that are effective in producing maximum force.

FACTORS INFLUENCING THE TYPE OF MOTION IMPARTED TO THE STRUCK OBJECT

Force applied in line with the object's center of gravity results in linear motion of the object. The object will move straight in the direction of the resultant of the forces applied to it with little or no spin. However, some spin may be caused on various objects by air resistance or friction. When a ball lying on the ground is hit through its center of gravity it rolls forward because friction resists the movement of the bottom of the ball, but its center of gravity moves forward freely. If the force is applied off center, that is, not applied through the object's center of gravity, rotatory motion always results. When a ball is hit off center or when the striking surface moves across the back of the ball, spin results. When forward force is applied to the object above its center of gravity, top spin results. When this impact is below the center of gravity, back spin is imparted.

If the striking surface moves upward across the back of

the ball forward (top) spin is imparted; if downward, back spin; if it moves from right to left (outside-in), right spin; and from left to right (inside-out), left spin. Since in most golf shots the ball is contacted below the center of gravity, it is given back spin. A slice (curve in the flight of the golf ball to the right) results from pulling the clubhead across the back of the ball from right to left causing the back of the ball to move from right to left and thus the front of the ball to rotate toward the right (right spin). In most tennis drives the racket passes somewhat upward across the back of the ball starting the top of the ball rotating forward. Since a ball with forward (top) spin drops more quickly this aids in keeping a forceful drive within the court.

FACTORS INFLUENCING THE DIRECTION OF THE STRUCK OBJECT

The direction of the struck object depends upon the angle at which it leaves the striking surface, just as the direction of a thrown ball depends upon the direction that the hand, and therefore the object, is moving at release. In both cases gravity begins to act on the object immediately and alters its path downward. In both, any spin will alter the direction as the object moves through the air. Striking differs from throwing in that usually more than one force is involved in determining the angle at which the ball leaves the striking surface. When there are two or more forces, the object moves in the direction of the resultant of these forces.

Moving Ball and Stationary Surface. When a moving ball with no spin strikes a hard stationary surface only one force is involved and, as has been stated, it tends to rebound at an angle equal to that at which it strikes. If either the ball or surface absorbs some of the force of impact, that is, the surface is soft or the ball is not elastic, this angle is modified downward. When the surface is vertical, as is the basketball backboard for example, and a ball approaches at an angle from above, the rebound force is downward and when the ball approaches from below, the rebound force is upward (see Fig. 76). The path of the ball will not be as directly upward as the diagram indicates since gravity begins pulling the ball down as soon as it leaves the board. The ball which approaches from above rebounds at a sharper downward angle than indicated since the force of gravity is added to the downward component of the rebound force.

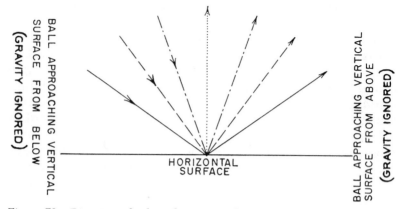

Figure 76.   *Direction of rebound—moving object striking stationary surface.*

When spin is involved a second force is introduced and the path of the ball is in the direction of the resultant of the spin force and the rebound force (Chapter 8). The speed of the spin determines the degree to which the normal rebound is altered. The faster the spin, the more the bounce is altered.

Forward spin on a ball approaching a vertical surface at a horizontal path (90 degrees) causes a higher than normal rebound, while back spin causes a rebound lower than normal (Fig. 77, *A, D*). When a ball spinning to the right *around a vertical axis* approaches a vertical surface at a horizontal path (at right angles to the surface), the rebound is more to the left than normal (Fig. 77, *C*) and when it approaches with left spin, the rebound is to the right (Fig. 77, *F*). The similarity between top spin on a ball approaching vertical and horizontal surfaces and right spin around a vertical axis on a ball approaching a vertical surface, and between back spin on a ball approaching vertical and horizontal surfaces and left spin around a vertical axis approaching a vertical surface, can be easily seen in Figure 77. If a ball approaching the vertical surface at right angles is spinning around its *horizontal axis* the rebound is not affected and the ball rebounds straight out. The same principles operate as when a ball spinning around the vertical axis approaches a horizontal surface from directly above (Chapter 8). Spin around a horizontal axis is rarely involved in striking activities.

A ball with top spin that approaches a vertical surface at an angle from below rebounds higher than normal. This means that it will rebound closer to the surface, while the ball with back spin rebounds farther from the surface (Fig. 78, *A* and *E*). The reaction is the opposite when the ball approaches a vertical

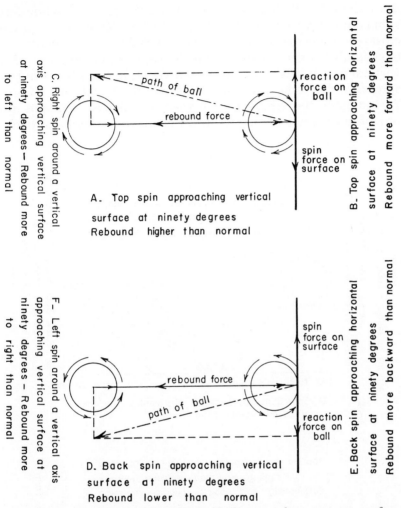

C. Right spin around a vertical axis approaching vertical surface at ninety degrees — Rebound more to left than normal

A. Top spin approaching vertical surface at ninety degrees
Rebound higher than normal

B. Top spin approaching horizontal surface at ninety degrees
Rebound more forward than normal

F. Left spin around a vertical axis approaching vertical surface at ninety degrees — Rebound more to right than normal

D. Back spin approaching vertical surface at ninety degrees
Rebound lower than normal

E. Back spin approaching horizontal surface at ninety degrees
Rebound more backward than normal

Figure 77. *Effect of spin on rebound of balls approaching stationary surfaces at ninety degrees. (Looking at side of ball in* A, B,D,E *and looking down on top of ball in* C *and* F.)

surface from above, one with top spin rebounds farther from the surface and one with back spin rebounds closer than normal (Fig. 78, *B* and *F*). Back spin on a basketball approaching the backboard from above will, therefore, keep the ball closer to the backboard and improve the chances of the ball falling through the basket.

When a ball is spinning around its *vertical axis*, right spin on a ball approaching a vertical surface from the right causes a rebound which is closer to the surface than normal and left spin causes the bounce to be farther out (Fig. 78, *C* and *G*). If the ball with right spin approaches the surface from the left, the rebound will then be farther from the surface, while left spin coupled with an approach from the left results in a bounce closer than normal to the surface. Therefore, when shooting a basketball backboard shot from the right, right spin around a vertical axis is desirable and when shooting from the left, left spin, in order to keep the ball closer to the backboard. Figure 78 indicates the similarity between a ball with top spin approaching a vertical surface from below, back spin approach-

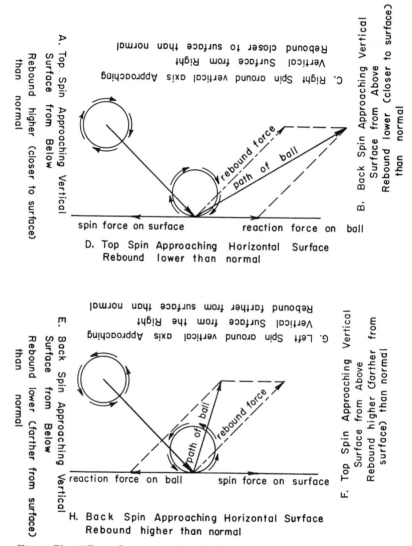

Figure 78. *Effect of spin on rebound of balls approaching stationary surfaces at forty-five degrees. (Looking at side of ball in all except C and G, looking down on top of ball.)*

ing a vertical surface from above, top spin approaching a horizontal surface, and right spin around a vertical axis approaching a vertical surface from the right. It also shows that a ball with back spin approaching a vertical surface from below, top spin approaching a vertical surface from above, back spin approaching a horizontal surface, and left spin around a vertical axis approaching a vertical surface from the right, follows a similar path.

If the right or left spin should be around the *horizontal axis*, the reaction would be similar to that of a ball with right or left spin around a vertical axis hitting a *horizontal surface* in that the direction of the back of the ball would determine the effect of the spin on the rebound of the ball. The back of a ball spinning left around a horizontal axis and approaching the vertical surface from the left would be moving downward. It would exert force downward against the surface and the reaction force against the ball would be upward causing the bounce to be somewhat higher than normal. Since the back of the left spinning ball approaching from the right would be moving upward the reaction force would be downward and the bounce would be somewhat lower than normal. Right spin around the horizontal axis of a ball approaching from the left also would result in a lower than normal bounce since the back of the ball would be moving upward. Right spin around this axis of a ball approaching from the right would move the back of the ball downward and the bounce would be higher. As stated previously, the type of right and left spin normally used in striking activities is that about a vertical axis.

Table 1 summarizes the various effects caused by different spins when a ball strikes a stationary surface.

This table points up the fact that the effect of right spin around a vertical axis on a vertical surface is the opposite to that on a horizontal surface. This is because, as explained in Chapter 8, the spin force of the ball against the horizontal surface is caused by the *back* of the ball which, since it is moving to the left, exerts force to the left against the floor and the reaction force of the floor against the ball is to the right. However, the spin force of the ball against the vertical surface is caused by the *front* of the ball since that is the part hitting the surface. Since it is moving to the right the spin exerts a force to the right against the surface and the reaction force against the ball is to the left. This action of right and left spin around a vertical axis against a vertical surface is the same as that of top and back spin against a horizontal surface.

Moving Striking Implement and Stationary Ball. The direction of the force applied to a ball by a moving implement is deter-

TABLE 1. EFFECTS CAUSED BY VARIOUS SPINS WHEN BALL STRIKES STATIONARY SURFACE

Type of Spin	Effect on Bounce	
	Horizontal Surface	Vertical Surface
Forward (Top) Spin Always around a horizontal axis	longer, lower angle* and faster (closer to floor) (forward)	higher approach from above – farther from surface approach from below – closer to surface
Back Spin Always around a horizontal axis	shorter, greater angle and slower (farther from floor) (backward)	lower approach from above – closer to surface approach from below – farther from surface
Right Spin (clockwise) Around a vertical axis	approach from directly above – no effect approach at angle – to right	to left approach from right – closer to surface approach from left – farther from surface
Around a horizontal axis (used infre- quently)	to right	approach from 90° angle – no effect approach from right – higher approach from left – lower
Left Spin (counterclockwise)		
Around a vertical axis	approach from directly above – no effect approach at angle – to left	to right approach from right – farther from surface approach from left – closer to surface
Around a horizontal axis (used infre- quently)	to left	approach from 90° angle – no effect approach from right – lower approach from left – higher

*See Discussion of fast tennis ball with top spin; pp. 90–91.

mined by the line from the point of contact to the center of gravity of the ball (center of the ball). An off-center hit not only gives the ball spin but also changes the direction of the force from that of the moving implement. However, for clarity in presenting combinations of various forces (i.e., force produced by the implement momentum and rebound force), it will be assumed that the contact is in line with the center of the ball in the direction that the implement is moving.

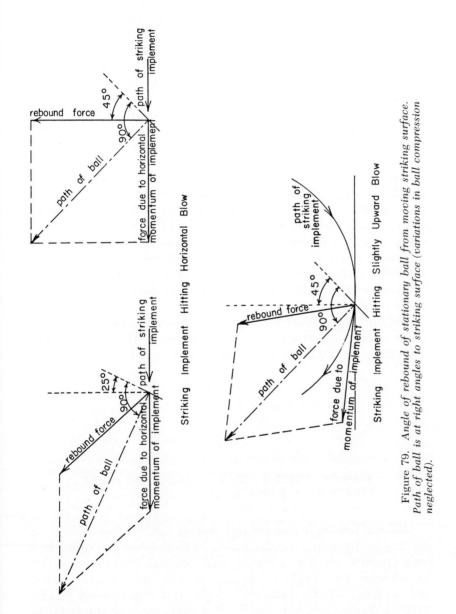

Figure 79. *Angle of rebound of stationary ball from moving striking surface. Path of ball is at right angles to striking surface (variations in ball compression neglected).*

When a moving implement such as a golf club, hockey stick, or bat (when using a batting tee) strikes a stationary ball through its center, the flight of the ball is the resultant of the force supplied by the moving implement in the direction that it is moving and the rebound force. The angle of the rebound force varies with the angle of the striking surface. However, since both the rebound force and the forward force which is due to the direction of movement of the implement are caused by the momentum of the striking implement, these forces are equal in magnitude. The path of the flight of the ball is, therefore, halfway between these two forces, or at right angles to the face of the striking surface. Figure 79 illustrates this fact. Variations in ball compression will alter this somewhat.

Just as a thrown ball is given linear force in the direction which is tangent to the arc through which the hand is moving at the point of release, a ball struck by an implement moving in an arc is given linear force in the direction which is tangent to the arc at the point of contact. The direction of flight of a stationary object, then, depends upon the direction in which the striking implement is moving, the angle of its surface, and the relationship of the point of contact to the center of gravity of the object.

When the striking implement is rounded, as is a bat, the actual striking surface is a line tangent to the curve of the implement at the point of contact with the ball (Fig. 80).

STRIKING SURFACE OF A ROUNDED IMPLEMENT
Figure 80.   *Striking surface of a rounded implement.*

Moving Striking Implement and Moving Ball, No Spin.   When a moving surface such as the hand, foot, a racket, bat or hockey stick strikes an approaching ball several factors must be considered: the angle of approach and momentum (speed and weight) of the ball, the angle and momentum of the striking implement, the direction of movement of the striking implement, and the point of contact in relation to the ball's center. The firmness of the striking surface and the degree of restitution of the ball are also factors. The following discussion assumes a firm striking surface, a ball with normal elasticity, and a hit through the center of gravity.

The direction of rebound force is at an angle equal to the angle at which the ball approaches the striking surface. If a ball approaches the striking surface horizontally and the striking surface is vertical and moving in a horizontal direction, the ball rebounds in a horizontal direction. All forces acting on the ball are in the same direction (Fig. 81, *A*). If the ball approaches from above, as it does when it is hit on the down bounce, the racket must be open to have a horizontal movement of the striking implement result in a horizontal path. The degree to which it must be opened depends upon the angle at which the ball approaches the striking surface (Fig. 81, *B* and *C*). The greater the angle of approach from horizontal, the more the striking surface must be opened if a horizontal hit is desired. A vertical racket and a horizontal path result in a downward path of the ball (Fig. 81, *D*). The degree to which the path is downward depends upon the relative momentum of the ball and the striking implement. The harder the hit, the less downward is the path of the ball.

If an upward path of the ball is desired when a ball approaches from above, the striking surface can be opened more and a horizontal blow used (Fig. 82, *A*) or, with the striking surface opened less an upward blow may be used (Fig. 82, *B*). If the striking surface is opened so that the ball approaches at a right angle and the path of the racket is in line with the approach of the ball, all forces unite to send the ball back in the direction from which it came (Fig. 82, *C*).

When a ball approaches from below, that is, it is taken on the up bounce, the striking surface must be closed somewhat if a horizontal blow is to result in a horizontal path of the ball. If the striking surface is vertical and the path of the striking implement horizontal, an upward path of the ball results (Fig. 83). Again, the degree to which the path is upward depends on the relative magnitude of the momentum of the ball and striking surface.

In striking, the right and left angle of approach must be considered as well as whether the ball is approaching from above or below. Obviously, a ball approaching from straight in front can be returned straight by keeping the striking surface facing straight ahead and the implement moving straight ahead (Fig. 84, *A*). It can be sent to the right either by turning the face of the striking implement toward the right (Fig. 84, *B*) or by moving the implement toward the right. This, in effect, is what happens when a ball is hit

(Text continued on page 240.)

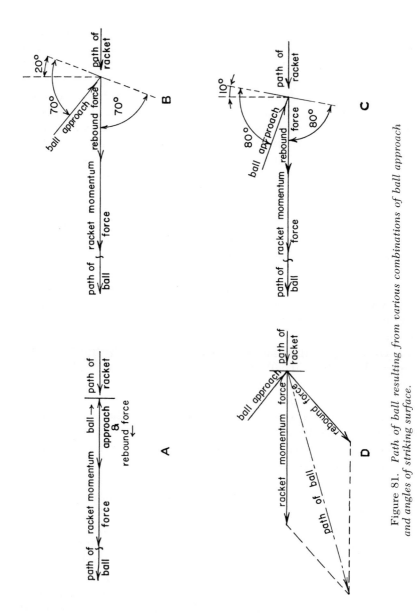

Figure 81. *Path of ball resulting from various combinations of ball approach and angles of striking surface.*

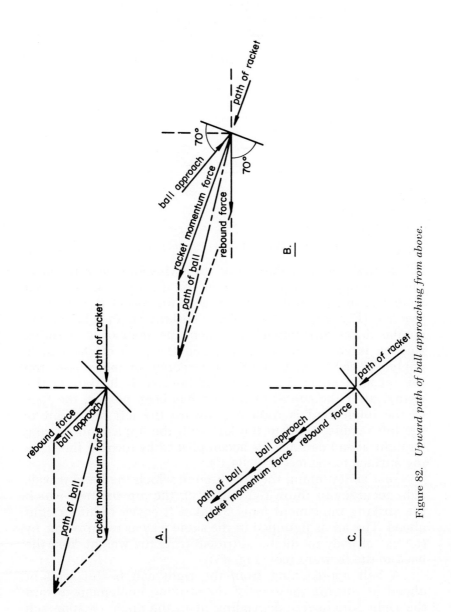

Figure 82. *Upward path of ball approaching from above.*

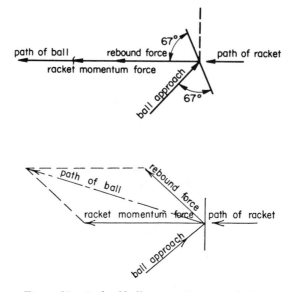

Figure 83.　*Path of ball approaching from below.*

before the center of the arc of the swing has been reached. Since the implement moves in an arc, it is moving somewhat from left to right until the center of the arc of the swing is reached (Fig. 84, *D*). Also, if the striking surface is perpendicular to the direction of movement the angle of the striking surface is constantly changing and the path of the ball is angled to the right by both the direction of movement and the rebound angle (Fig. 84, *E*). If the ball is hit late in the swing, after the center of the arc has been passed, the face of the implement is traveling toward the left and a hit to the left results. A hit to the left with the implement moving straight ahead can also be accomplished by turning the striking surface to the left (Fig. 84,*C*).

Just as flattening the arc through which the hand travels aids accuracy in throwing, flattening the arc through which the striking implement moves makes it easier to hit straight ahead. The arc is flattened in the same way as in throwing, by the use of body rotation and transferring the weight from the back to the forward foot (Fig. 85).

A ball approaching from the right can be hit straight ahead by turning the face of the striking implement toward the right (the degree depending upon the angle of approach of the ball and the relative speed of the ball and racket) and hitting at the center of the arc of the swing which would result in force being applied straight ahead (Fig. 86, *A*). If the striking surface is kept straight ahead and the force applied

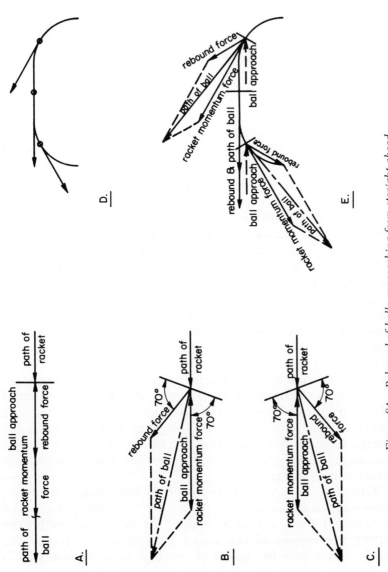

Figure 84. *Rebound of balls approaching from straight ahead.*

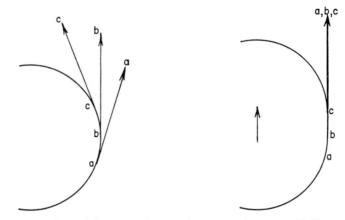

Figure 85.   *Effect of flattening the arc of swing on direction of balls contacted at various points.*

straight ahead, the ball will go to the left (Fig. 86, *B*). If a return to the right is desired, the striking surface can be turned more to the right (Fig. 86, *C*), or the implement can be moved through a path diagonally from left to right (Fig. 86, *D*). In the same way, a ball approaching from the left can be hit straight ahead by turning the face of the striking implement toward the left and applying force straight ahead; to the right by keeping the striking surface straight ahead and hitting straight ahead; and to the left by turning the striking surface more to the left or moving the implement in a path diagonally from right to left. In other words, if a hit straight ahead is desired when a ball is approaching at an angle, the face of the striking implement is turned (to some degree dependent on the angle of approach of the ball and the relative speed of ball and racket) toward the direction from which the ball is approaching. The greater the angle of approach from the straight forward direction and the faster the ball is moving in relation to the speed of the racket, the more the striking surface must be turned.

Whether the angle of approach is from above or below or the right or the left, when the racket momentum force and the rebound force are both applied at the same angle, the relative magnitude of the two forces does not change the direction, but only the speed of the ball as it rebounds from the striking implement. However, whenever these two forces are applied in different directions, the direction, as well as the speed, of the ball is altered by any change in the momentum of either the ball or the striking implement. The greater the momentum of the striking implement in relation to the ball the less effect the rebound angle has on the path of the

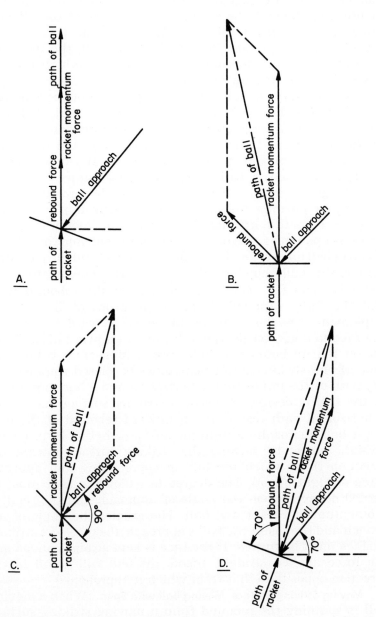

Figure 86. *Path of balls approaching from right resulting from various directions of movement and angles of striking surface.*

ball (the more the path of the ball is determined by the direction of movement of the striking implement), and the less the momentum of the striking implement in relation to the momentum of the ball, the greater the influence of the rebound force on the path of the ball. Therefore, the less forceful the hit and the greater the speed of the ball, the more important it becomes to consider the angle at which the ball approaches the striking surface.

In summary, a ball which is approaching horizontally (a ball hit at the top of the bounce) can be projected horizontally if the striking implement face is vertical and the path of the implement horizontal. It will be projected upward if the face is open and the path horizontal, and downward if the face is closed. A ball hit on the down bounce (a ball approaching the surface from above) can be projected horizontally by opening the face of the striking implement and keeping the path horizontal. The degree to which it is opened depends upon the angle of approach of the ball and the relative speed of ball and racket. If the face is vertical and the path horizontal, the ball rebounds downward. The downward angle depends upon the relative magnitude of the rebound force and the force supplied by the momentum of the striking implement. The ball can be projected upward by opening the face to a greater degree or hitting an upward blow. When hit on the up bounce (a ball approaching from below) the face of the striking implement must be closed somewhat if the path of the implement is horizontal and a horizontal path of the ball is desired. A vertical striking surface moving in a horizontal path results in an upward rebound of the ball.

A ball approaching from the left or right can be projected straight ahead by turning the striking surface toward the direction from which the ball is approaching and applying force straight ahead. The degree to which the face must be turned depends upon the angle of approach and the relative momentum of racket and ball. The greater the angle of approach and the faster the ball's approach, the more the striking surface must be turned. If the face is kept straight ahead and the force applied straight ahead, the ball will go off in the direction opposite to that from which it approached.

Moving Striking Surface, Moving Ball with Spin.   When a moving ball is spinning the rebound from a moving striking surface is changed just as it is from a vertical stationary striking surface. Top spin causes the ball to rebound higher than normal and back spin causes a lower rebound. Right spin around a vertical axis causes it to rebound from the striking

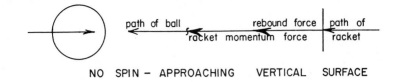

NO   SPIN – APPROACHING   VERTICAL   SURFACE

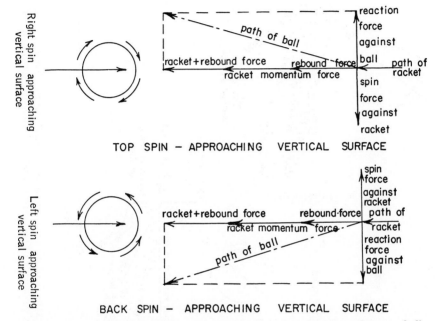

TOP SPIN – APPROACHING   VERTICAL   SURFACE

BACK SPIN – APPROACHING   VERTICAL   SURFACE

Figure 87. *Effect of spin on path of ball struck by moving implement—ball approaching at right angles to striking surface. (Looking at side of ball for top and back spin and looking down on top of ball for left and right spin.)*

surface more to the left than it would if no spin were involved and a ball spinning to the left rebounds more to the right than normal. Figures 87 and 88 illustrate this.

FACTORS INFLUENCING DISTANCE

The factors that determine the distance a struck object will travel through the air are the same as those that influence the distance of a thrown object: force of the impact, angle at which this force is applied to the object, and the outside forces of gravity and air resistance.

Just as in throwing, the more force, the greater the distance of the struck object, all other things being equal. While in throwing the force is determined solely by the movement of

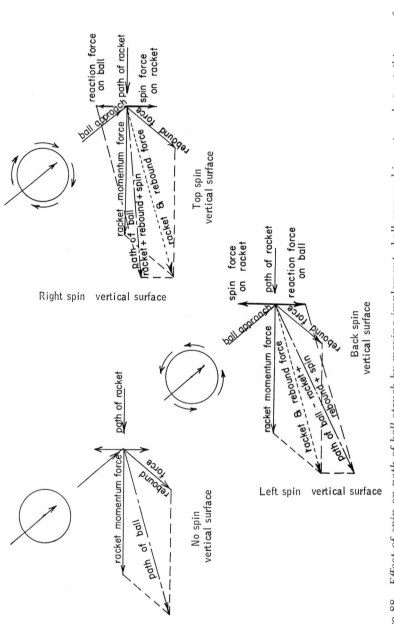

Figure 88. *Effect of spin on path of ball struck by moving implement—ball approaching at angle to striking surface from above or from angle to the right. (Looking at side of ball for top and back spin and looking down on top of ball for left and right spin.)*

the individual making the throw, in striking a moving object, it is determined by both the force produced by the individual and imparted to the object either directly or through an implement, and the force of the oncoming object. This has been discussed under factors involved in magnitude of force.

In general, the rule that, disregarding air resistance, a 45-degree angle of application of force gives the greatest distance applies also to striking. While air resistance is not a great factor in many activities involving throwing a ball, it becomes a decided factor in some of the striking activities in which the object is moving at a great speed, because air resistance increases so rapidly as speed increases. As speed doubles, air resistance quadruples. The greater the air resistance, the more horizontal force necessary to overcome it. Therefore, the angle of application of force must be lowered to enlarge the horizontal component of the force applied. A distance club in golf does not project at a 45-degree angle but at a much lower one because the golf ball traveling at a high speed meets great air resistance.

A head wind decreases distance since this increases air resistance, and again the angle of application of force should be flattened so that a greater proportion of the force applied is directed horizontally to combat the wind resistance. A tail wind increases distance since the force of the wind is added to the force of the strike. If the angle of the strike is increased so that more force is applied vertically to combat gravity's pull, the ball remains in the air longer, giving more time for the wind to act on the ball and more distance can be gained. The ball should be projected lower against a head wind and higher in a tail wind to gain maximum distance.

Since forward spin causes a ball to drop faster than normally, and back spin causes the ball to remain in the air longer, a given amount of force produces less distance for a forward spinning ball and more distance for a backward spinning ball, all other things being equal. However, any spin does cause more air resistance which slows the speed of the ball.

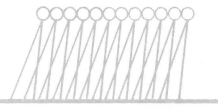

Part Four

*Application of the
Basic Mechanical Principles
to Sports and Dance*

Introduction to Part Four

It is impossible in one volume to include a complete mechanical analysis of the vast number of activities offered in most physical education programs and participated in by the American public. In fact, a complete mechanical analysis of even a few activities is not possible in a single text. In this section some possible applications to a group of activities are discussed. Some activities are treated in greater detail than are others. Since they all use various basic skills which are discussed in Part Three, repetition is avoided by reference to previous material. Golf has been analyzed in somewhat more detail and can serve as an example for further application of principles in other areas.

The applications of mechanical principles in the analysis of various activities included in this section are presented for the purpose of suggesting ideas as a point of departure for further thinking along these lines by the student and teacher of movement. The following material is presented, then, not as a complete analysis of any activity, but rather as an indication of the increased understanding that results from such an approach to the study of movement.

20

Golf

Golf is a striking activity that seems to fall into the side-arm pattern of movement. Since the ball is on the ground the swing is essentially vertical rather than horizontal as in so many other sports (e.g., tennis, softball, etc.). Because of this, it seems that golf should be classified as an underhand movement pattern. However, if the position of address is taken and the club swung back to full backswing and then, maintaining the same relationship of arms to body, the trunk position is adjusted to that of batting, it will be seen that the club is in much the same position as the bat would be at full backswing. Electromyographic records of batting and golf indicate that there is more similarity in the muscle function of these two activities than between golf and any of the underhand activities studied (underhand throw, badminton serve, volleyball serve, bowling).[1] In both golf and batting two hands must be used to control the long heavy lever. While the golf club is not as heavy as the bat, it is longer and is weighted at the extreme end of the lever.

The problem in golf, as in any striking activity, is to produce the desired amount of force and apply it by means of the clubhead through the center of the ball in the direction of desired movement of the ball. It is possible to produce considerable force because of the length of the lever used. Since golf clubs are considerably longer than most other striking implements the speed of movement of the clubhead which results from a certain amount of force supplied by the muscles, is much greater than that of shorter implements used in other sports. This extra length, however, makes control of the club-head much more difficult. Without the help of gravity, which is gained in a vertical swing, this length of lever could probably not be controlled in a striking movement. Added to this is the fact that the striking surface is small, making accuracy of contact a major concern.

However, this is one sport in which the manufacturer of the equipment has adjusted the vertical angle of the striking surface. Therefore it is possible for the player, through choice of implement, to vary the angle of the shot without appreciably changing his swing. Since the ball is stationary the player also has the advantage of having all the time he needs to make a decision concerning the desired angle and to get into position for the shot. Reaction time is not a problem. In tennis, as in most striking activities, the adjustment of the vertical angle of the striking surface must be made by the player during the swing following a split second decision. In golf the vertical angle of projection can be controlled by the implement chosen and the swing need not be changed. So long as each club strikes the ball squarely with its face in its natural position (as when the club is soled), each will project the ball at a different angle. Advanced players, having greater control of the club, do adjust the swing as well as choose different clubs, and thus have available many more possibilities for ball flights.

Besides supplying the golfer with adjusted angles of striking surfaces, the manufacturer has also varied the length of the clubs. Thus, he has made it possible to reduce the length of the swing by choice of club. Therefore, it is relatively easy for the golfer to vary the force imparted to the ball without changing his body movement to any extent since, given the same rotatory force produced by the body, the linear velocity of the shorter club is less than that of the longer club. Since the golf ball is stationary the force applied to it must be developed entirely by the player; no force is available from momentum of the ball as is the case in tennis. The force applied is dependent upon the speed of movement of the clubhead at impact and the accuracy of the contact, that is, whether the force is applied through the center of gravity of the ball. In order to contact the ball through its center of gravity the body and club must, at impact, be in the same position relative to the ball as when the ball was addressed (assuming that the ball is addressed with the club soled behind the ball perpendicular to the desired line of flight). If the distance from shoulder to clubhead is shortened by bending the arms or raising the upper body, the ball is hit above center or may be missed entirely.

The student of golf has been told to "keep your eye on the ball," "keep your chin pointed at the ball," "keep the left heel down on the ground," "keep the left arm straight," "keep the right elbow close to the side," etc. He has been given so many directives that an attempt to give attention to all of them has frequently resulted in tension with interferes with the smooth sequence of the movement so necessary to both force and accuracy. Actually, none of the above directives is, *of itself*, important. They are only devices which various individuals have found helpful in assuring that, at impact, the body and club position in relation to the ball will be the same as at address so that the clubhead will hit through the center of the ball. For example, it is not important that the left arm be straight at the top of the backswing, it is only important that it be straight at impact. If the student is relaxed in his swing, centrifugal force and gravity will pull the arms straight at the center of the arc of the swing. Too frequently concentration on a straight left arm throughout the swing leads to so much tension in that arm that the student actually pulls it in as he swings through and tops or misses the ball. In other words, the correction *sometimes* is the actual cause of the fault that it was intended to correct. It must be recognized that the suggestion to "keep the left arm straight" may be helpful with some students in assuring a straight arm at contact, but that it is simply a device, not a necessary part of the form of the golf swing which everyone must follow.

Keeping the eye on the ball is a device for keeping the head steady which in turn aids in maintaining the same distance from shoulder to ball until after the ball has been contacted. Actually, once the swing has become "grooved" the ball *can* be hit as well with the eyes closed. Many variations in the suggested placement of the thumb on the club appear in the books dealing with golf. Stanley has pointed out that:

There is no such thing as a 'right' place for thumbs on the shaft. Some players grip with thumbs along the top of the shaft, others down the side, or round it. An ex-Open champion takes his right thumb off the shaft completely. Another professional is a first-class shotmaker in spite of having his left thumb amputated as the result of an accident.[2]

Stanley does suggest that placing the right thumb straight down the top of the shaft can be used as a device for correcting the fault of overswinging. This places the thumb under the shaft at the top of the backswing and it acts as a check on overswinging. A person having difficulty bringing the clubhead through perpendicular to the line of desired flight of the ball because of overswinging, might be advised to put the right thumb down the top of the shaft. This does not mean that this is necessary for all golfers. The problem in teaching golf is that a great many devices for correcting faults have been suggested (devices which are successful with some, not with others) and some teachers, instead of using these devices one or two at a time as a need becomes evident, have lumped them together and made from them a stereotyped "form" which has been demanded of all students. These instructors have taught devices instead of teaching the basic factors involved in accomplishing the purpose of a powerful, smooth flowing movement pattern.

Perhaps it is because so many people have written about golf and all have had their own devices for correcting their individual errors that this sport has become so enmeshed in detail—detail which often hinders rather than aids learning because of the tension which it produces.

Except for the length of the lever and the smallness of the area of contact, golf should be a relatively easy sport to learn because of the fact that, as stated earlier, the ball is stationary and there are essentially only two strokes to be learned—the driving stroke and the putting stroke.[3] The same mechanical factors are involved in both and it becomes a matter of applying them according to the different purposes involved.

FACTORS INFLUENCING SPEED

The longer the club and the golfer's arms, the greater the velocity of which the clubhead is capable since the clubhead travels through a longer arc in a given time and therefore, moves faster. The length of the arc is also determined by the length of backswing. Since the longer this arc, the more time available to work up momentum, when maximum force is desired the backswing should be as long *as possible without loss of control*. If the backswing is so long that the clubhead drops below the horizontal, it must be raised *against* the force of gravity as the downswing begins. The clubhead is likely to lag behind the hands and unless the golfer has strong wrists which, despite this lag, can bring the clubhead into line at impact, the face of the clubhead will be angled to the right when contact with the ball is made. The long backswing also brings into play more muscles which can contribute to the swing and therefore more force is possible. The only muscular force available when a short backswing is used is that of the arms and shoulder girdle. As the backswing is lengthened by trunk rotation the strong trunk muscles are added to the movement. In golf, as in all sidearm throwing and striking activities, a long backswing necessitates a position of the body sideways to the intended line of flight of the ball. This body position also places the ball at the center of the arc of the swing which is the point at which the clubhead is moving the fastest.

Follow-through is important to speed at impact just as it is in any throwing or striking activity (Chapters 18 and 19). The speed with which the muscles involved in the movement contract is also a considerable factor in the speed of movement of the clubhead. The faster the muscular contraction, again up to the point of loss of control, the greater the velocity of the clubhead at contact. It is certainly possible to swing so fast that control is lost. Here again the hands may be brought through well ahead of the clubhead because the air resistance against the clubhead, increasing rapidly as speed increases and being applied so far from the fulcrum, makes it difficult to snap the wrists through and bring the striking surface in line with the hands at impact. This does not mean however, that the beginner should practice the golf swing at a slow tempo. It has been shown experimentally that skill in activities involving both accuracy and speed is developed more readily when the activity is practiced from the beginning at the speed (or approximate speed) at which it will be performed.

Stance plays an important part in the speed of the clubhead in that it makes it possible to use the entire body in the swing through weight transference from the back to the forward foot. It is also important from the standpoint of equilibrium. Since the force is moving from right to left (right-handed golfer) it is important to widen the stance in that direction. If equilibrium were to be maintained on a narrow base the length of the swing would have to be cut considerably. If the feet are placed farther apart than the width of the hips, rotation on the backswing and follow-through are restricted and thus loss of length of swing, and consequent loss of force, result. Beyond the width of the hips the farther apart the feet are placed the greater the curtailment of the swing.

Transference of weight, besides contributing to force by putting the body weight into the stroke, moves the center of the arc (the shoulder) slightly forward and thus flattens the vertical arc of the swing, giving more time in the swing during which the clubhead can hit through the center of the ball in the direction of desired movement. Only if the ball is contacted through the center of gravity is all the force available imparted to the ball. If the ball is hit above its center, some of the force pushes the ball into the ground rather than sending it forward. When the ball lies on a hard surface and a wood is used, the contact is normally above center. The driving tee is important in that it lifts the ball making it possible to hit through, or slightly under, its center of gravity. If the ball lies on grass, the clubhead can get down into the grass for a clear contact.

The degree to which the force produced by the body is effective in moving the ball depends upon the firmness of the grip and the wrists at impact. Firmness of wrists and grip prevents any recoil of the clubhead at the time of contact which would dissipate some of the force, and insures the transference of all of the available force to the ball.

Various grips have been suggested, the overlapping, inter-locking, and the "baseball" grip. Bunn analyzed the striking movement of the hands as a pushing back of the top hand as the bottom hand pushes forward, the fulcrum being halfway between the hands. This action can be more effectively exe-cuted with the hands spread as in the "baseball" grip because the force arm is lengthened. He stated that this "split-second action of the wrists at the moment of contact gives the needed extra force which produces distance."[3] Other authors[4, 5, 6] have indicated that the greatest force which can be developed with a given amount of body power, is centrifugal in nature. This is best accomplished when the hands act as a unit rather than applying a leverage action. The overlapping grip, because the hands are in contact, makes this easier. It is possible that while one individual may be able to control the leverage action of the hands suggested by Bunn and take advantage of any extra force thus produced, another might find that the "base-ball" grip leads to loss of control and that he is able to gener-ate more *controlled* force through the use of centrifugal force uninterrupted by the leverage action.

The degree to which the force produced by the body is transferred to the ball also depends upon the counterpressure of the ground against the feet. Any slipping of the feet means a loss of force against the ball since some of the force goes into moving the foot or feet. For this reason cleats on golfers' shoes aid in imparting force to the ball. Since the cleats indent or actually pierce the ground, they offer a surface which can push directly against a vertical surface of the ground rather than an area which pushes across a horizontal surface in which case the counterpressure is entirely dependent on friction. If the feet are directly under the hips as they are when the stance is widened only to the width of the hips, the pressure of the feet is more directly downward and slipping is less likely to occur. When the feet are placed apart farther than the width of the hips a more diagonal force is applied and the outward component of this force makes slipping more likely unless cleats are worn.

The speed imparted to the golf ball, as to any other ball, is also dependent upon the coefficient of restitution of the ball and the clubhead. If the ball has lost some of its ability to retake its original shape after being flattened by contact with the clubhead, some of the force is dissipated in the change of shape and does not contribute to speed.

FACTORS INFLUENCING DIRECTION

The direction of the flight of a golf ball is influenced by the direction in which the clubhead is moving at impact, the angle of the face of the clubhead (law of rebound), the relationship of the clubhead to the ball's center of gravity, the firmness of the grip and the wrists at impact, any outside force acting on it (the wind), and spin.

When the clubhead hits through the center of gravity of the ball the force caused by the momentum of the clubhead is applied to the ball in the direction that the clubhead is moving at impact. If moving in an arc, this force is applied in the direction of the tangent to the arc at the point of contact. Since the ball is stationary the rebound force and this force in the direction of the movement of the clubhead (or the tangent to the arc) are equal, both being caused by the momentum of the clubhead, and therefore the ball departs approximately at right angles to the face of the clubhead (Fig. 79, p. 235). Variations in ball compression will alter this somewhat.

It follows that the more nearly the face of the club is at right angles to the desired path of the ball at impact the nearer to the desired path the ball will travel. This means that if a ball is to go straight ahead the clubhead must be moving straight forward and must face straight ahead at impact. To assure this the stroke is begun by placing the clubhead in this position and taking a stance with the toes along a line parallel to the desired flight of the ball (square stance). Having a straight forward path of the clubhead with the face perpendicular at impact is more easily accomplished if the clubhead follows a path along the line of the desired direction of the shot both before and after impact. The square stance aids in keeping the swing along this path. If the left foot (right-handed golfer) is forward (closed stance) the path of the swing

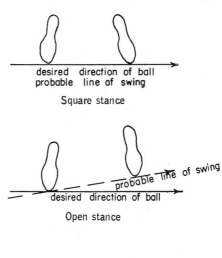

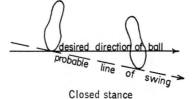

Figure 89. *Probable effect on direction of swing of various stances.*

tends to move toward the right instead of straight ahead since the follow-through straight ahead is restricted. If the right foot is forward (open stance) the opposite is true. The back-swing being restricted the path of the swing tends to be more toward the left (Fig. 89).

Just as in rolling a ball or executing an underhand throw, the arm is swung back along the line of the intended flight of the ball, the golf club is brought straight back from the ball as far as possible before being lifted up and around the body. This flattens the arc of the swing so that there is more time in which the clubhead can contact the ball with the face moving in the straight forward direction.

The force of impact causes the club to turn in the hands if the grip is not firm, or causes the face of the clubhead to turn if the wrists are not firm, when the ball is contacted. When this happens the direction which the ball will take is unpre-dictable. Only when the grip and wrists are firm does the face of the clubhead remain perpendicular to the path of the club-head as the ball is contacted.

Since the golf ball moves through the air at a high velocity, air pressure builds up rapidly. Therefore, spin modifies the flight of a golf ball considerably.

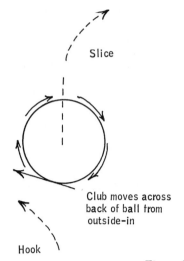

Slice

Club moves across
back of ball from
outside-in

Hook

Figure 90. *Direction of curves in flights*
of balls hit "outside-in" and "inside-out."

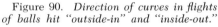

Club moves across
back of ball from
inside-out

If the clubhead moves across the back of the ball from the outside-in (from right to left), with its face square to the line of flight, the ball is given right spin and its flight curves to the right (a slice) (Fig. 90). If the face is closed (angled to the left), the ball is pulled to the left. Because of the restriction of backswing this outside-in movement is facilitated by an open stance, though it is possible even with a square stance if the clubhead is thrown away from the body on the downswing. This can be corrected by placing a piece of paper or a handkerchief between the right upper arm and the trunk and attempting to hold it there until the ball is contacted. A slice can also be caused by a lag of the clubhead behind the wrists at impact due to overswinging, snapping the wrists through too late, or to a lack of sufficient wrist strength to control such a long lever. Many women are never successful in using a number one wood for this reason. If the sequence of movement does not flow from the center of the body out to the extremities but rather starts with the arms and the body rotation is retarded, the clubhead tends to hit across the back of the ball from outside-in causing a slice.

If the clubhead moves across the back of the ball from the inside-out (left to right), with its face square to the line of flight, the ball is given left spin and its flight curves to the left (a hook). If the face is open (angled to the right), the ball is pushed to the right. This inside-out movement is facilitated by a closed stance since the follow-through is restricted, but it may result from hugging the right arm too close to the body on the downswing and then throwing it outward at impact. If the sequence of movement is interrupted or if the arms lag behind the body rotation, the clubhead will also be pulled across the ball from the inside-out.

At times it is desirable to produce left or right spin on the ball. On a dog-leg hole a stroke may be saved by producing sufficient spin on the ball to cause its flight to follow the curve of the fairway. However, normally right or left spin causes loss of strokes because it takes the ball well away from the straight line to the hole. Placing two pieces of paper on the ground, one a few inches in front of the ball and the other a few inches behind, but both along the line of desired flight, and attempting to swing through all three, the two pieces of paper and the ball, will frequently help to straighten the arc of the swing and avoid side spin.

In determining the desired direction of a shot the wind must be considered. Since the golf ball travels well up in the air, a cross wind has considerable effect upon the direction of its flight. The ball is carried with the wind. If the wind is blowing from the left to the right the ball must be aimed left of the hole, and if blowing from right to left, to the right of the hole. In other words, it should be aimed into the wind. How much the angle of the path of the ball needs to be adjusted depends upon the force of the wind. If it is forceful it may be expedient to sacrifice some length of shot and play the ball closer to the ground where the wind tends to have less velocity.

Allowance must also be made for various contours of fairways and greens. Since a ball rolls down slope due to the pull of gravity, a shot must be aimed uphill of the green or the cup.

FACTORS INFLUENCING DISTANCE

As with any projectile the distance a ball travels depends upon the force imparted to it by the clubhead, the angle at which the force is applied, and the spin imparted to the ball.

The first, the force imparted, has been discussed.

The vertical angle of application of the force depends upon the inclination of the clubface. The greater the angle of inclination of the face of the clubhead, the smaller the forward component and the greater the upward component of the force applied by it. Since the ball is projected at right angles to the striking surface, the more vertical the clubface the more distance and the less height obtainable. Owing to the strong air resistance created by the great speed of the golf ball, the optimum angle for distance is considerably less than the theoretical 45 degrees. A larger horizontal component is needed to overcome the air resistance. A club with a more nearly vertical face should be chosen when maximum distance is desired and as less distance and more height are desired clubs with progressively more open faces should be used.

Spin affects the distance a ball travels since top spin makes a ball drop faster and back spin keeps it in the air longer against gravity's pull (Chapter 8). When a ball is contacted below its center, back spin results. It has been pointed out that even the driver, which has the most vertical face of all the clubs (with the exception of the putter), has enough loft so that the ball is contacted slightly below center and imparts some back spin to the ball. Some back spin is desirable to stabilize flight in the vertical plane and to keep the ball in the air longer. As the club loft increases the point of contact on the ball is lower (Fig. 91). Harvey,[7] in an article in *Golfing* magazine, clearly explained the way spin is imparted to the golf ball. He stated that only up to a point does the golf ball follow the rule that the lower the ball is contacted the greater the spin. Since the ball leaves the clubface quicker and flattens less as the angle of divergence between the path that the

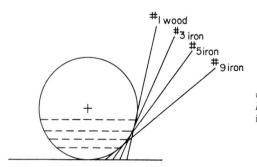

Figure 91. *Contact points of various clubs. (Harvey, T. D.: How Spin Controls Flight.* Golfing, 18:20, June, 1954.)

clubhead is traveling and the line of flight of the ball increases, with the more lofted clubs there is less flattening of the ball, less contact time and thus less back spin. He further stated that the number five iron imparts the most back spin because the angle of inclination of its face is the greatest at which there is enough flattening to permit the grooves of the club-face to hold the ball from slipping. On the clubs with greater loft the grooves on the face become narrower and shallower as far as their effect on the ball is concerned and they do not hold the ball, contact time is less, and back spin is less.[7]

Back spin can also be produced by hitting downward across the back of the ball. When the ball is hit at the center of the arc of the swing with the club in its natural position, it is hit a horizontal blow which results in some back spin because the ball is contacted below center. The amount of spin depends upon how much below the center the ball is contacted, the length of time the grooves of the club keep the ball in contact, and the amount the ball is flattened. When the golf ball is played back of the center of the stance, it is hit a downward blow, the club passes downward across the back of the ball, and back spin results. The farther back the ball is played the more downward is the hit and the more back spin is imparted to the ball. Harvey[7] also pointed out that, if the ball is played on a hard surface, a downward hit pinches the ball between the ground and the clubhead increasing back spin. However, if the surface is heavy grass, the pinching effect is not as great because of the give of the soft surface, and less back spin results. Although the surface of a sand trap gives, the sand increases the friction between the clubface and the ball preventing slipping and increasing contact time and thus more back spin than is normal for a particular club is imparted. This is not true when an explosion shot, in which the sand taken during the shot keeps the clubhead from actually contacting the ball, is used.

Spin also affects distance in that the dimples on a spinning ball carry air around the ball smoothing out the air flow at the back of the ball and thus stabilizing flight. Spin is also an important factor in the roll of the ball after it lands. The more the back spin the less the roll, since the force of the spin against the ground is opposite to the direction of movement of the ball. Therefore, for distance shots, only enough back spin to stabilize the flight and keep the ball in the air a little longer is desirable. The back spin should be minimized, as it is when clubs with a more vertical face are used, so that when the ball lands the forward force can easily overcome the back spin

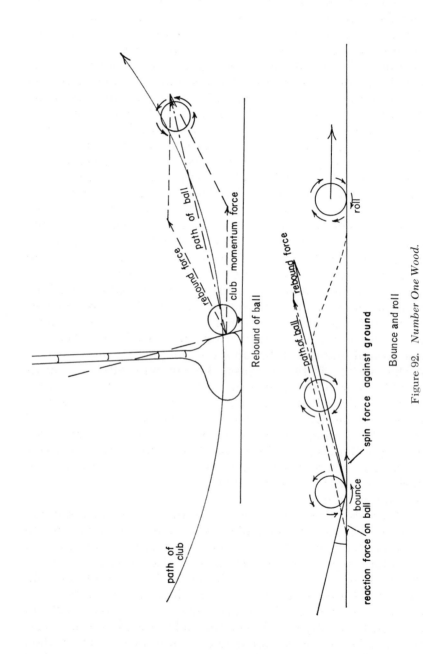

Figure 92. *Number One Wood.*

force reversing the spin and allowing the ball to roll forward. A great deal of back spin is desirable on approach shots to the green in which little or no roll is desired. Therefore, the ball is played farther back so that it will be hit a downward blow. However, it must be pointed out that the farther back the ball is played, the more open (angled to the right) is the face of the club at contact and therefore, the toe of the club must be moved forward to keep the face perpendicular to the line of flight. This moving of the toe forward reduces the vertical angle of the face of the club and as a result less loft, although more back spin, results.[8] In general, for maximum distance, a long club with a more vertical face is chosen and the ball is placed near the center of the stance so that the ball is given a horizontal blow and very little back spin (Fig. 92). A shorter club with a more open face is chosen and the ball is moved gradually back toward the right foot as less distance and less roll are desired, until in playing a minimum roll pitch shot it is placed almost opposite the right heel (Figs. 93 and 94). If a high shot with less back spin is desired, as when the golfer needs to play the ball over the branches of a tree but desires to have it roll on landing, a club with an open face is chosen and the ball is placed forward of the point that would normally be used for the particular club. In this case, unless the toe of the club is moved back, the clubhead will be closed at contact (angled to the left). Moving the toe back increases the vertical angle of the club face and thus results in more loft, although less back spin, all other things being equal.[8] In this way back spin, which would prevent roll on landing, is minimized.

The contour and condition of the ground also affect the distance of a shot in that they are important factors in the bounce and roll of the ball. When the ground is hard it absorbs little or no force of the ball as it lands, most of the force is transferred back to the ball and the ball bounces and rolls. Hard ground does not give with the weight of the ball as it rolls and therefore, offers little resistance and the ball rolls farther for a given force than it does on soft ground. In the case of soft ground a great deal of resistance is offered to the forward roll of the ball because the ground gives with the weight of the ball, in effect, forming a series of vertical walls in front of the ball which must be pushed down with each turn of the ball. Bounce and roll are also less because a great deal of the force of the ball is absorbed when the ball first strikes the ground. The longer the grass the softer the surface, the more force is absorbed on landing and the greater the resistance to the forward roll of the ball. Wet grass offers more

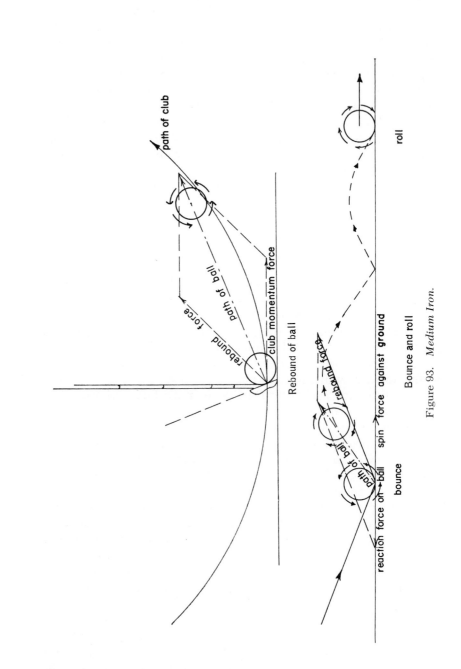

Figure 93. *Medium Iron.*

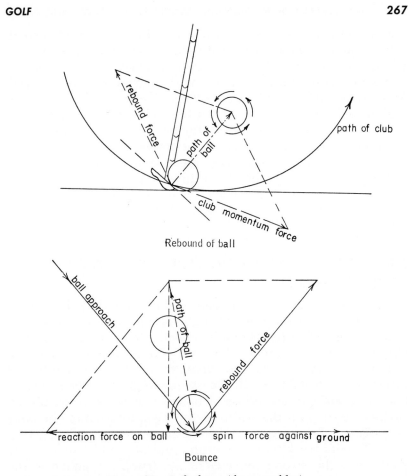

Rebound of ball

Bounce

Figure 94. *Lofted iron (downward hit).*

resistance to a rolling ball than dry grass and, all other things being equal, a ball rolls farther on dry than wet grass. In putting, therefore, the longer and wetter the grass the longer the backswing and follow-through must be to roll the ball a given distance to the cup.

Choice of club is also affected by various lies on the fairway. While it may seem that an uphill lie demands a club with a more open face to lift the ball up the hill, the opposite is actually the case. Since the golfer is standing on an uphill slope the swing of the club is in an uphill direction and therefore imparts upward force, and a club with a less angled face than would be normally chosen is needed. This is not to be confused with a flat lie at the foot of a hill in which case the golfer does not stand on the hill and so the swing is forward, not upward, and a club with an open face would be needed. When standing on a downward slope (downhill lie) the swing is downward and in order to lift the ball to send it out from the slope and straight ahead, a club with an open face is required. Sidehill lies affect the length of the club chosen. When the ball which must be hit across a hill lies below the golfer the distance from shoulder to ball is farther than usual and a club with a longer shaft needs to be used. When the ball lies above the golfer the opposite is true, the distance from shoulder to ball is reduced and either the grip on the club must be shortened or a shorter club must be chosen. If the ball is played farther away, the swing is changed. It must be less vertical and more horizontal.

SUMMARY OF SOME OF THE MORE IMPORTANT TEACHING POINTS

Driving. Soling the clubhead behind the ball with the face perpendicular to the desired flight of the ball as the grip is taken helps to insure the clubhead being in the proper relationship to the ball at impact. The feet should be placed approximately the width of the hips apart to make it possible to add force to the stroke through the use of weight transference and body rotation without a loss of balance. If the feet are placed farther apart than the width of the hips, rotation of the body is restricted. Rotating the body lengthens the backswing giving more time to work up momentum, and also adds force to the shot since the strong muscles of the trunk are added to the movement. Many students execute a "false pivot" by keeping the weight on the left foot and bending the knees straight ahead rather than in toward the opposite leg. This gives the student a feeling that he is pivoting but does not put the trunk muscles into the swing and transfers the weight in the direction *opposite* to that of the swing and thus takes force away from the hit.

Carrying the clubhead straight back low to the ground as far as possible flattens the arc of the swing and thus aids accuracy of contact. An attempt to throw the club as far as possible down the fairway before allowing it to come up and around is one device for further flattening the arc and giving added time for an accurate contact. Since accuracy at impact is dependent upon the position of the clubhead, and since at address, this position is adjusted so that force can be applied through the center of gravity in line with the desired flight of the ball, the height of the shoulders and their distance from the clubhead must be the same at impact as at address. Bending at the hips or knees during the swing shortens the distance from the shoulders to the ball, while straightening the angle at the hips or pushing up with the left foot increases it.

Tension causes a pulling of the club toward the body and shortens the distance from shoulder to clubhead. This distance is shortened whenever the arm is bent at the moment of impact. There are many devices that can be suggested to students who pull up away from the ball during the swing. Looking at the ball is perhaps the most common. A suggestion to the student to twist his body to the right about an imaginary rod running down through his body with a plate fastened against the head so that it prevents the head's sliding up and down on the rod, and then to "untwist" to the left, can be helpful to some students. Another student may be helped to develop a feeling for maintaining this distance by having a partner place a club on his head as he addresses the ball and hold this club in the same position as he swings. If the club is held steady it applies pressure to resist any upward movement of the head and if the head moves downward the club is no longer felt against the head. The student is thus made aware of changes in body position that affect the distance from shoulders to ball. Sometimes swinging while facing one's shadow and noting the position of the head during the swing aids in developing a feeling for maintaining a constant height of shoulder girdle during the swing.

Swinging the club rather than attempting to hit the ball can be one of the greatest contributing factors to a clean impact. Better results are obtainable with a below optimum speed and a square contact than with a very forceful swing and an off-center impact. In general, the club best adapted to the purpose of the particular shot should be chosen and then swung naturally, allowing the angle of its face to take care of the angle of projection. If a shot with less force is needed both the backswing and follow-through should be reduced equally so that the ball is still contacted near the center of the arc of the swing.

Putting. While force is the major concern of the driving stroke and accuracy is important only within a relatively large area, accuracy is of primary concern in putting and, while the control of force is important, the magnitude required is relatively small.

The putter having a vertical surface contacts the ball just about at its center. Since the force is applied forward through the center of gravity, the ball stays on the ground and, because

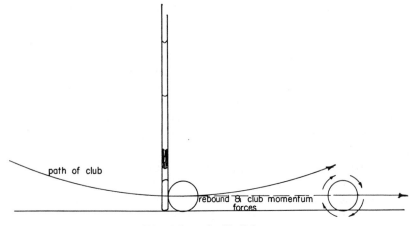

Figure 95. *Rebound of ball from putter.*

of the friction between the ground and the ball, it starts rolling immediately (Fig. 95).

There are almost as many putting styles as there are golfers. This is understandable since there are so few principles that must be followed in order to have success in putting and there are so many ways that these can be accomplished. Whether the golfer stands with a wide or a narrow stance is unimportant since, in most instances, the force needed is not great enough to require transference of weight. The only thing that is important is that the golfer feel well balanced.

Since accuracy is a major problem in putting it is important that the stroke be smooth, with equal backswing and follow-through. Only in this way is it possible to judge the amount of force that will be imparted to the ball. The amount of force can be regulated by changing the length of the swing. It is impossible to judge the force that will be imparted to the ball by a jerky stroke — one with a sudden stop. In this case the follow-through must be cut by muscular force opposing the forward movement, and accurate judgment of the degree of contraction that will reduce a given forward momentum a specific amount is improbable. On the other hand, practice will soon show the length of stroke necessary for a putt of a certain distance if a smooth stroke is used. The stroke can be duplicated almost exactly.

Accuracy is aided by utilizing all of the aids that insure the clubface moving in a straight line along the line of putt or this line extended. Moving the clubhead straight back and straight forward along the line of putt with the face perpendicular at all times insures contact at the desired angle in the right direction. This is exactly the same as moving the hand straight back and forward along the line of the intended flight of the ball in the underhand throw or of the desired path of the bowling ball. A sudden stopping of the forward momentum causes jerking of the muscles which, besides making it impossible to judge force imparted, is likely to turn the face of the club from its perpendicular relationship to the line of putt and the ball goes off at an angle. A low backswing and follow-through along the line of putt insure this smooth stroke and flatten the arc giving more distance over which the ball can be contacted and sent in the desired direction.

Pointing the left elbow toward the hole aids some individuals in keeping the clubhead moving in the forward path rather than being pulled around to the left. It is a useful device for one who has difficulty because of a tendency to swing the clubhead in an arc to the left. Any method for immobilizing parts of the body not needed for the stroke aids in accuracy because some of the possibilities of error are thus removed. Some individuals immobilize the elbows and putt with a pendular swing from the shoulders. Others rest the right arm on the right thigh and putt with the wrists. Style is not important so long as it facilitates, rather than hinders, a smooth stroke that follows the line of putt.

The putt can be no better than the judgment of the line of putt. If the line of putt is incorrectly drawn in the mind the putt, no matter how accurate, will not go to the hole. In lining up the putt it is important to stand, or even squat since this puts one into a position closer to the line, behind the ball so that it is possible to sight over the ball to the hole. When standing above the ball in position to putt, the eyes are not in line with the hole and the ball, but see the hole at an angle. Just as in spot bowling, putting across a spot on the line of putt relatively close to the ball (chosen while sighting over the ball), can aid in accuracy because the ball and spot are within the vision at the same time and distance and angle are not factors in attempting judgment.

Since the ball is on the ground, judgment of contour and surface of the green is much more important to putting success than such judgment is to driving success. Contour and surface affect both the direction of the putt and the amount of force to be imparted to the ball. More force is needed for a given distance if the putt is uphill, and the greater the angle of the green the more the force must be amplified. Therefore, the backswing and follow-through need to be longer. Conversely, the backswing and follow-through normally used to putt the ball a given distance need to be cut if the line of putt is downhill, since gravity is added to the force of the putt to move the ball downward.

When putting across a slope the putt must be aimed uphill of the cup to allow for the rolling downward which is caused by gravity. The greater the angle of the green and the farther the putt has to travel the higher above the cup the putt must be aimed. In the first case as the green angles more, gravity's pull becomes more direct and more forceful. In the second, the farther the ball has to roll the longer the time gravity has to work on it. Less force is used for a putt across a hard, dry, closely cut green. When the green is wet or the grass is long the backswing and follow-through must be lengthened to produce more force to overcome the resistance encountered by the ball as it rolls.

REFERENCES

1. Broer, Marion R., and Houtz, Sara Jane: *Patterns of Muscular Activity in Selected Sport Skills: An Electromyographic Study.* Springfield, Charles C Thomas, 1967.
2. Stanley, Louis T.: *How to be a Better Woman Golfer.* New York, Thomas Y. Crowell Company, 1952, p. 20.
3. Bunn, John W.: *Scientific Principles of Coaching.* New York, Prentice-Hall Book Company, Inc., 1955, p. 230.
4. Morrison, Alex J.: *Better Golf Without Practice.* New York, Simon and Schuster, 1940, p. 32.
5. Jones, Ernest, and Brown, Innis: *Swinging Into Golf.* New York, Robert M. McBride and Company, 1946, pp. 22–25.
6. Hicks, Betty: *Fundamentals of Golf.* Chicago, J. A. Dubow Mfg. Co., 1948, pp. 5–6.
7. Harvey, T. D.: How Spin Controls Flight. *Golfing, 18*:20–23, June, 1954.
8. Hicks, Betty: personal communication, 1965.

21

Badminton and Tennis

Badminton and tennis are two of the most popular striking activities. The application of the laws governing equilibrium, the production and application of force, and rebound, to throwing and striking activities is discussed in detail in Chapters 8, 18, and 19. A specific application to golf has been treated in Chapter 20. Therefore, this chapter deals only with some of the problems specific to tennis and badminton. Because the movement patterns are similar they can be discussed together. The few variances in movement which exist are necessitated by the differences in the equipment used in the two sports.

The tennis racket and ball are considerably heavier than the badminton racket and shuttle. The lighter racket lacks the potential force inherent in the heavier tennis racket. Compensation for the lighter badminton racket is secured by increasing its speed. This is done by the use of wrist snap at the moment of impact. The lighter weight makes it possible for the smaller wrist muscles to be used effectively and therefore the racket can be manipulated at a greater speed. Flexibility of the wrist allows the racket to swing in a greater arc, the backswing is lengthened, and there is more time to work up momentum. Wrist snap at impact moves the racket through a long distance very rapidly. The momentum of the shuttle is so much less than that of the tennis ball because it is so much lighter, that the force of the shuttle against the racket is less. Both the lighter racket and the lighter object to be contacted make greater use of the wrist muscles possible without loss of control.

Many tennis players, particularly girls and women, lack the wrist strength necessary to control the heavier tennis racket unless the wrist is kept locked throughout the stroke. The heavier ball exerts considerable force against the racket and unless the wrist is set to withstand this force at impact, the racket gives and not only is less force transferred to the ball but also the direction of application is changed since the give of the racket changes the angle of its face. Therefore beginners in tennis are usually more successful if they maintain a set wrist throughout the stroke. Squeezing the racket at impact aids in resisting the force of the ball against the racket because it tightens the wrist muscles. The student who has the wrist strength to use the wrist successfully in tennis will be able to apply more force, but with insufficient wrist strength an attempt to use wrist snap leads to loss of both force and control.

Because of the lighter equipment in badminton, this is not a problem. Therefore, one essential difference between the two sports is the degree to which the wrist is used in the production of force and this difference stems from the relative weights of the equipment.

Another major difference between badminton and tennis is in the flights of the shuttle and the ball. Because of the light weight and the shape of the shuttle, air resistance has a greater effect upon it, and it does not follow the parabolic path of the tennis ball. When a shuttle is hit with a great deal of force, air resistance to its flight through the air builds up to the point at which it overcomes the horizontal momentum of the shuttle long before the force of gravity has brought it to the ground. It follows a more or less normal path for a few yards and then slows down and drops almost vertically (Chapter 9, Projectiles).

Because of the greater effect of air resistance, the shuttle falls more slowly than the tennis ball, and thus difficulty in timing the hit is encountered by a player who expects it to fall at the rate of most balls. Time spent by a beginner in hitting a shuttle straight upward and watching it drop may be well invested since it can help him to readjust his concept of the speed with which different objects fall and thus reduce, or eliminate, the frustration that otherwise frequently accompanies early attempts at service. Most beginners swing too fast because the shuttle drops slightly slower than other objects with which they have dealt.

It sometimes is helpful to suggest that a student hold the shuttle by its feathers out, over the spot where it is to be hit, and hold the racket back ready for the forward swing. If he then says to himself, "Drop, swing" and responds in that order, his swing will be delayed long enough to give the shuttle time to fall.

His difficulty may be due also to a lack of concept of the length of his reach when holding the racket. Being used to the distance of his reach with his hand alone, he fails to judge how far toward the floor the shuttle must actually fall. Discussion and observation of the distance that the reach is extended by the racket is helpful in building the new concept which is necessary in both tennis and badminton. As has been discussed earlier (Chapter 2, p. 27) lack of this spatial concept can cause considerable loss of force in any stroke since it leads to a pulling in of the arm and a subsequent shortening of the striking lever.

In both badminton and tennis the racket is an extension of the arm lever. If one were to strike with the hand, the flat palm would be used. To maintain the normal striking movement the racket is held so that, when striking on the forehand side, it is facing in the direction that the palm would be facing if the hand were flat. If the hand is held out in striking position, the racket turned so that it faces the same direction as the palm of the hand and the shaft placed against the palm, when the fingers close around the shaft the racket simply extends the hand. This is the position described by most authors as "shaking hands with the racket." Since the wrist extensors are not as strong as the flexors, for the backhand strokes in tennis the hand moves somewhat in a counterclockwise direction (right-handed player) on the grip to place the thumb behind the shaft for added control. Those with weak wrist muscles are better able to resist the force of the ball against the racket when the thumb is placed along the shaft in position to resist directly the force of impact. This causes a rigidity in the wrist and while it helps to prevent give at impact it also eliminates fast wrist action. Therefore the thumb up the shaft should not be used in badminton. Because of the lighter weight of the equipment it is not necessary to sacrifice the force which comes from the wrist action.

The position of readiness is the same for both sports. The player stands with his feet apart in a side stride, his knees are slightly bent and his weight is forward on the balls of the feet. This somewhat unstable position makes it possible to start the body moving quickly. The wide stride also gives a more advantageous angle of push. It is possible to push the body in any direction by extending one of the bent knees. Time is not lost in having to bend the knee in preparation for its extension.

In moving around the court, small steps are taken so that the weight is balanced over the feet at all times and the direction of movement can be shifted rapidly. Large steps leave the body weight back during a part of each step and introduce a larger resistive phase (Chapter 11, Walking). Tennis shoes increase the friction between the feet and the court surface and, therefore, all of the force applied by the body against the ground is returned to the body. None is lost in slipping.

Except for the wrist action the strokes used in the two games are the same. Both sports employ the underhand, the overhand, and the sidearm patterns of movement discussed in Chapters 18 and 19, Throwing and Striking.

The service in badminton is underhand by rule and the pattern is the same as for the underhand throw (Fig. 2, pp. 10–11). It is sometimes performed with the same, rather than the opposite, foot forward. Since the distance to be traversed by the shuttle is short, all of the force necessary for a short service can be supplied by the wrist and arm muscles. Weight transference is not needed and balance is not a problem when little force is required. This stance (same foot forward) restricts backswing but increases the distance that the racket can follow through and, therefore, may increase accuracy of placement. A long service may require the use of the full pattern.

The service in tennis is, on the other hand, a very forceful stroke. It follows the same pattern as the overhand throw (Fig. 3, pp. 12–13). This same pattern is also used for the smash in tennis and badminton and the overhead clear in badminton. Gravity is useful in aiding the backswing of the racket. The arm and racket are fully extended at contact in order to take full advantage of the longest lever possible and thus produce maximum linear speed. Hitting the ball at as high a point as possible also allows more leeway for gravity's action since it will take longer for the ball to be pulled down to net height.

Various devices for suspending the tennis ball at the full reach of the player are useful in aiding the development of a kinesthetic perception of this movement pattern without the additional problems involved in the tossing of the ball for service. Since the body weight has been transferred to the forward foot at the time of contact, the center of the arc of the swing is above this foot and therefore, this is the point at which the racket is traveling its fastest and can be facing directly forward so that it can strike a horizontal blow. This means that the ball must be tossed straight upward above the forward foot. Perhaps it would be advisable to give the beginner the concept that this motion is more of a "push" than a "toss." The beginner frequently allows his hand to follow the normal arc and thus tosses the ball back over his head instead of straight upward. Whatever the words used to explain the toss, the importance of a straight upward application of force and follow-through must be understood.

Many textbooks indicate that in teaching the tennis service the student should be taught to hit *down* on the ball. If a ball is hit at a point eight feet above the ground and at a downward angle of only eight degrees it cannot clear the net. *Even without the action of gravity* this angle places the ball only two and one-half feet above the ground at the point 39 feet from the server (distance to net). Since the net is three feet high, this point is one-half foot below the top of the net (Fig. 96). Actually, gravity's action causes the ball to hit considerably lower than this.

An angle which is only five degrees downward places the ball four and one-half feet above the ground at the point above the net without considering the force of gravity. (Fig 97.) This means that gravity can pull the ball downward less than one and one-half feet if it is to clear the net. Since gravity pulls an object downward one and one-half feet in 0.306 second, this ball would have to be above the net 0.3 second after service. Therefore, the ball has to travel 39 feet, the distance to the net, in 0.3 second or have an *average* velocity of 130 feet per second.

$$S = \frac{1}{2} gt^2 \qquad\qquad V = \frac{S}{t}$$
$$1.5 = 16\, t^2$$
$$t^2 = 0.0937 \qquad\qquad V = \frac{39}{0.3} = 130 \text{ ft./sec.}$$
$$t = 0.306$$

This is an improbable velocity for a beginner and it is doubtful whether he would be able to keep the downward angle as small as five degrees if he were attempting to hit downward on a ball. Most beginners serve a high percentage of their balls into the net for this reason.

If, however, the ball is hit a horizontal blow from this same height (8 ft.) it can clear the net with a much lower velocity. If a ball were to clear the net by 0.2 foot, gravity could pull it down 4.8 feet ($8' - 3.2' = 4.8'$) by the time it got to the point above the net. Since a ball drops 4.8 feet in 0.55

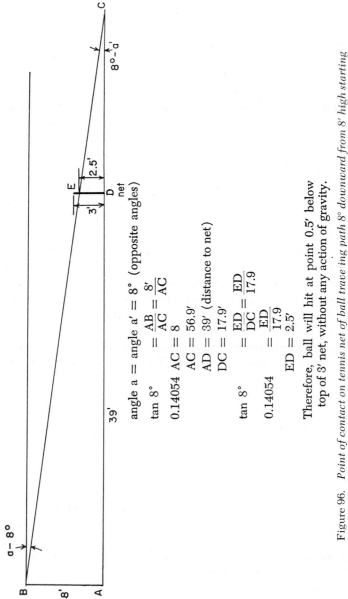

angle a = angle a' = 8° (opposite angles)

$$\tan 8° = \frac{AB}{AC} = \frac{8'}{AC}$$

0.14054 AC = 8

AC = 56.9'

AD = 39' (distance to net)

DC = 17.9'

$$\tan 8° = \frac{ED}{DC} = \frac{ED}{17.9}$$

$$0.14054 = \frac{ED}{17.9}$$

ED = 2.5'

Therefore, ball will hit at point 0.5' below top of 3' net, without any action of gravity.

Figure 96.   *Point of contact on tennis net of ball travelling path 8° downward from 8' high starting point (force of gravity neglected).*

$$\tan 5° = \frac{8}{AC}$$

$$0.08749 = \frac{8}{AC}$$

$$0.08749 AC = 8$$

$$AC = 91.4'$$

$$DC = 91.4' - 39'$$

$$DC = 52.4'$$

$$\tan 5° = \frac{ED}{52.4}$$

$$0.08749 = \frac{ED}{52.4}$$

$$ED = 4.58'$$

Figure 97

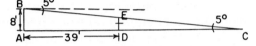

second and since it would need to travel 39 feet in this time, it would require a velocity of 71 feet per second for a horizontal hit to clear the net. A ball traveling at this speed and angle will land well within the service court. This is a more realistic goal. Beginners unable to produce this velocity will need to hit slightly upward. However, since it is difficult to keep the angle small when attempting to open the racket face on service, it is probably not wise to suggest an upward angle. Instead of telling beginners to hit down on the ball which is actually impossible for them to do successfully, a horizontal blow or straight outward hit should be suggested and the reasons for the suggestion explained. The higher the ball can be contacted and the faster the racket is traveling at impact, the flatter or more downward (up to a point) the angle that can be used and still have the ball clear the net.

In making any type of shot, the vertical angle of the flight of a ball or shuttle which is necessary to clear the net depends upon the distance between the player and the net, the height of contact, and the force of the hit. A sharp downward angle is possible only when the object is hit high and close to the net. A smash from center court results in the struck object falling on the striker's side of the net. An object contacted at net height must be given some upward force to counteract the pull of gravity. The farther from the net the hit is made and the slower the hit, the more time gravity has to act and the more upward the angle must be. If the object has fallen below the top of the net, the flight must be upward, the closer to the net the more sharply upward. Particularly in badminton, which presents the problem of a higher net, a low shuttle contacted near the net can be played most successfully by a shot which angles it across the court. Since the shuttle can climb to the height of the net over a longer distance it does not have to be hit at such a sharp vertical angle in order to clear the net. If hit straight forward over the net it must travel so directly upward that it is setup for a smash return by the opponent (Fig. 98).

The angle of the flight of a ball or shuttle following impact depends upon the direction of movement of the racket, the angle of the face of the racket, the angle at which the ball or shuttle approaches the racket, and the relative momentum of racket and object struck (Chapters 8 and 19).

In many throwing and striking activities the arm or implement must stop to reverse direction at the end of the backswing. In tennis and badminton this can be avoided by the use of a circular backswing. The circular backswing adds considerably to the time available for the development of momentum of the racket. However, it increases the difficulty of timing the stroke and of controlling the angle of the hit. The direction of movement of the racket must be adjusted as the racket moves forward. Since the racket is carried backward flat in order to reduce air resistance, the angle of its face must be adjusted also. If the backswing is separated from the forward swing and is not used for the purpose of working up additional momentum, the racket can be carried backward in the same plane in which it is to be brought forward and the angle of the racket face can be adjusted before the stroke begins and maintained throughout the stroke.

The advantage gained in additional force possible through the use of circular backswing must be balanced against the added difficulties of timing and control. It is probably advisable to suggest to beginners that they carry the racket straight back

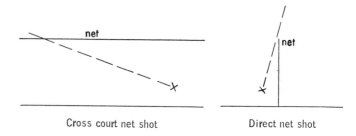

Cross court net shot   Direct net shot

Figure 98. *Vertical angles necessary to clear badminton net with cross court and direct return of low shuttle.*

with the face perpendicular, since this presents fewer problems than the circular backswing. If, however, a beginner
naturally uses a circular backswing and is successful, it should
be recognized that this stroke has a greater force potential.
Too frequently students are required to follow the particular
pattern presented by the instructor.

Talbert has likened the tennis volley to the catching of a
baseball. He stated that the volley is started with the head of
the racket where the mitt would be. "Then, taking a short
step forward with the left foot, the arm and racket as one
lever make their short, sharp movement into the oncoming
ball."[1] Since there is little, if any, backswing in a volley the
speed of the shot is largely dependent upon the speed with
which the ball approaches the racket.

Tennis and badminton differ in the use of spin in the two
games. Spin can be applied easily to a ball but usually is unsuccessful with a shuttle. Since top spin causes a ball to drop, it
is useful in keeping a rather flat drive within court limits. Side
spin both changes the direction of a ball's flight and bounce,
and makes it more difficult for the person returning it to judge
the reaction of the ball to his hit and, therefore, it contributes
to tennis strategy.

Several tennis serves, among them the American twist,
make use of spin to increase the difficulty of returning the ball.
In the American twist service the racket passes across the back
of the ball from the southwest to the northeast[2] (Fig. 99) and
thus starts the top of the ball moving forward in a diagonally
right direction. This spin might be classified halfway between
top and right spin around a horizontal axis. Because of this
diagonal spin the reactions of the ball occur in a somewhat
unusual combination. Since most balls that are spinning right
or left are moving around a *vertical axis* they both curve and
bounce in the same direction (Chapters 8 and 19). In the case
of this diagonally top-right spin, the air moving with the ball
as it spins, and the air resisting the forward motion of the ball,
come into conflict at the top of the right side of the ball increasing the pressure at this point and causing the ball to *curve*

Figure 99. *Direction of spin in American twist serve.*

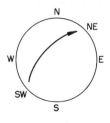

left through the air. As the ball approaches the ground it is moving diagonally to the left and could be expected to bounce left. However, it is spinning forward and right and therefore the bottom of the ball, moving diagonally back and left pushes back and left against the ground which pushes forward and right against the ball. Thus the ball *bounces right* of its anticipated position. Because the bounce force from momentum has a *left component* and the spin force against the ball has a *right component* and these are in opposition, the ball tends to bounce more upward than normal. (Note: Left and right are in relation to the server.)

The reaction of spinning balls has been treated fully in Chapters 8 and 19. To avoid repetition the reader is referred to Chapters 8, 18, and 19 for further material applicable to these two activities. Also relevant is the application of the principles of striking to golf (Chapter 20).

REFERENCES

1. Talbert, William F.: Tennis, Now You Can Play it Better. *Sports Illustrated*, 6:23:61, June 10, 1957.
2. Driver, Helen Irene: *Tennis for Teachers*. Philadelphia, W. B. Saunders Company, 1941, p. 43.

22

Bowling

The problem in bowling is that of applying force which will give the ball sufficient velocity in an effective direction to knock down all of the pins.

Bowling uses the underhand pattern of movement, and the general mechanics for the production of force and the control of direction are the same as for any rolling or underhand throwing activity. Since these have been discussed in detail in Chapter 18, Throwing and Catching, only a few specific considerations are included here.

APPLICATION OF FORCE

Because of the length of the alley, a bowler must be accurate to a fine degree. A deviation of one degree in the path of the ball results in changing the ball's location by more than a foot after it has traveled the 60 feet from the foul line to the head pin (Fig. 100). Therefore, while sufficient force is needed

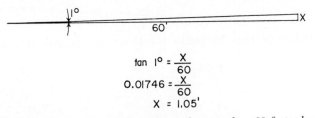

$$\tan 1^\circ = \frac{X}{60}$$
$$0.01746 = \frac{X}{60}$$
$$X = 1.05'$$

Figure 100. *Distance a ball will angle-in after traveling 60 feet when bowled at an angle of one degree.*

to roll the ball 60 feet with enough speed so that its momentum will knock over pins and throw them against other pins, the control of direction is more important to success than is the production of considerable force.

Production of Force.   As explained in Chapter 18, the underhand pattern does not produce maximum force because of restrictions on body rotation. However, it allows for maximum use of gravity in the production of force. This advantageous use of gravity is important with the heavy ball. Since the effectiveness of a given force producing rotatory motion (the moment of force) is dependent upon its perpendicular distance from the fulcrum (p. 65), the ball must be pushed away from the body to increase the force potential. The greater the distance from ball to shoulder the greater the moment of force. When the ball is pushed away from the body the arm and ball form a pendulum on which gravity acts as it does on any pendulum. Since the force of gravity acts straight downward, the velocity with which the ball is traveling at the bottom of the arc of the swing is dependent upon the height of the swing.

$$V = \sqrt{2gh}$$

This formula is derived directly from two basic formulae which have been explained previously (p. 37 and p. 70).

$$V = at$$

$$S = \tfrac{1}{2}\, gt^2 \text{ or } S = \tfrac{1}{2}\, at^2 \text{ since the}$$
acceleration is entirely
due to gravity

To determine the relationship of velocity to distance these two equations can be combined. The second is first solved for "t".

$$S = \tfrac{1}{2}\, at^2$$

$$t^2 = \frac{2S}{a}$$

$$t = \sqrt{\frac{2S}{a}}$$

Substitution of this formula for time in the velocity formula gives:

$$V = at$$

$$V = a\sqrt{\frac{2S}{a}} = \sqrt{2aS}$$

Since gravity is the accelerating force and the distance over which it is effective is the height of the swing, this formula, in the case of a pendulum becomes $V = \sqrt{2gh}$. Gravity being a constant, the velocity varies with the height of the swing.

The height of the backswing depends on the height at which the ball is held and pushed away from the body, since the last half of the backswing is caused by the momentum built up by gravity's pull on the ball during the first half of the backswing. The higher the push away the greater the force which must be controlled, since gravity acts on the ball over a longer distance. Therefore more strength of trunk and shoulder muscles is required to stabilize the shoulder position when a higher push away is used.

The distance that the hand can be raised straight backward is limited by the bony structure of the shoulder joint. A forward lean of the trunk is used to increase the height of the backswing without causing the swing to deviate from its straight path.[1] This forward lean of the trunk is also useful in balancing the weight of the ball at the top of the backswing.

In bowling additional force is produced by the use of the approach. Since the momentum of the body is transferred to any object held by the body, the forward momentum which the bowler acquires through the use of the approach, if timed with the swing of the ball, is transferred to the ball and augments the momentum produced by the arm swing. Since the effective summation of forces requires that the second be added to the first, when the first has reached its peak of speed (p.72), the forward swing should coincide with the slide. Whether the bowler takes three, four, or five steps, momentum is gained. An uneven number of steps is more difficult for most individuals to time with the even arm swing. With a three step approach the bowler is likely to arrive at the foul line before the ball is ready to be released. In this case the momentum of the approach is lost before release and is not transferred to the ball. This can be likened to stopping the circular backswing of a tennis serve to wait for a late toss of the ball. The momentum gained by the backswing is lost since the racket must start from rest at a position close to the point of ball contact. The bowler might as well start in a forward-backward stride position at the foul line if he arrives at the foul line before he is ready to release the ball.

When using a five step approach the bowler may not arrive at the foul line soon enough and thus the swing must be slowed. Most individuals find it easier to time four steps with the swing of the ball so that they go into their slide as the ball swings forward. All forward momentum is thus effective at the same time. The use of three or five steps is more likely to result in an uneven approach which uses a "hoplike" movement than is the use of four steps. This produces upward force which detracts from the forward momentum of the body as well as interfering with the smooth arc of the swing. Because the first of four steps is taken on the right foot (right-handed bowler), the four step approach has an added advantage of providing a base of support under the ball at the moment that it is pushed away from the body to start its swing.[2] If a bowler is able, with three or five steps, to control the ball at the beginning of the swing and to time his swing with his steps and thus gain sufficient momentum without upsetting the smoothness of the arc of his swing there is no reason for change, since the approach is accomplishing its purpose. Since most individuals find it easier to time four steps with the swing, as well as to keep the approach smooth so that it does not interfere with the normal arc of the swing, the four step approach is recommended for beginners.

Regardless of the number of steps used, the approach should be in a straight line with the desired direction of force application. Any sideways movement detracts from the forward momentum and interferes with accuracy. It is important that the bowler toe straight ahead so that the force exerted by the push of the toes against the floor will result in straight forward momentum (Chapter 11, walking). Sometimes a student lacking the muscular strength to adjust to the weight of the ball at the right side of the body, toes out with the right foot. This is an unconscious adjustment to widen the base to the right (under the weight) and thus reduce the amount of body adjustment necessary. It results in a zigzag approach. If not already doing it, this student should be taught to let the free hand and arm swing away from the body to help balance the weight of the ball. He should be given a lighter ball and taught exercise which will strengthen his muscles, particularly the trunk muscles.

Since in rotatory motion the maximum force is at right angles to the radius, the ball should be released when the arm is perpendicular to the floor. The hand must be lowered close to the floor. Lowering the body by bending the knees and hips results in a well balanced position since the center of gravity of the body is low and remains over the center of the base (p. 45). The final forward step onto a well bent left leg and the slide flatten the forward arc and thus contribute to a smooth release. The slide also allows for a gradual slowing of the momentum of the bowler. If the ball is dropped or thrown rather than released close to the floor, the acceleration of gravity causes it to hit the floor with considerable downward force. This reduces the forward momentum, as well as the accuracy of the ball.

Control of Direction. As in any underhand throw the angle of force application is dependent upon the arc of the swing and follow-through. It has been suggested[3] that before starting the swing, the ball be moved to the right so that the right arm is close to, and parallel with, the right side. This position allows the ball to drop backward in a straight line without brushing the leg or forcing the body to twist. Any twisting of the body interferes with the straight path of the swing. If held in front of the center of the body as the swing begins, unless the body twists, the ball must be dropped diagonally outward and backward and as a result the forward swing tends to be forward and inward. Thus the path of the swing must be straightened by the bowler while the ball is moving. This calls for greater control than simply keeping the ball in a straight line from the start of the movement to the release.

A circular swing of the ball around the body is normally due to lack of strength. Because of insufficient strength to control the ball at the top of the backswing when it is far from the body, the student adjusts the swing to keep it close to his center of gravity. As a result he swings the ball in a semicircle around the body. Since the ball continues to move in the direction it was moving at the moment of release, a ball moving in an arc travels along a path which is tangent to that arc at the point of release (p. 213) (Fig. 101). This means that there is only one point at which this ball which is swung in a semicircle around the body can be released and still travel in the desired direction. If released early it will go into the right channel (gutter), and if released late it will roll to the left,

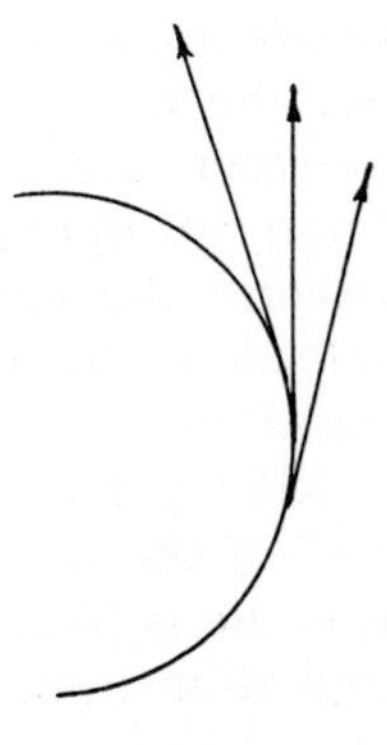

Figure 101. *Path of ball released at various points on an arc.*

probably into the left channel. Again, the student needs to be given a lighter ball until exercises and practice are effective in increasing his arm, shoulder girdle, and trunk strength.

Don Carter uses a bent elbow throughout his swing[4] to shorten the lever and thus reduce the difficulty of control at the top of the backswing. Because of this his form has been criticized. If a bowler has sufficient strength of the arm flexors to maintain a *consistent* angle at the elbow when holding the heavy bowling ball against the pull of gravity, the bent arm may be a useful device for gaining control at the top of the backswing since the lever is shortened and the weight is closer to the fulcrum. If the angle of bend in the elbow is consistent throughout the swing, it does not interfere with the arc. However, it must be remembered that because a straight arm does give a longer lever, the arc of the swing with a straight arm is longer and greater momentum results. A straight arm also reduces the muscular tension necessary in the arm as well as the distance that the body must be lowered for release. Because of the arm flexor strength this device for gaining control of backswing demands, it is doubtful that girls or women would find it usable since they would be unable to maintain a consistent position. It is a device that one individual has found useful. There is no question of form involved since the mechanics of the movement are not affected except that the length of swing is slightly shortened.

Spin depends on off center application of force at release. If side spin is not desired (bowling a straight ball) the hand must be kept in the same position throughout the swing. Since the ball is heavy it is easier to control if the hand is under it with the thumb up. The hand is then in a position to oppose gravity directly as the ball drops and it is behind the ball as it swings forward. If the "V" of the hand is up, the ball must be held by opposing inward pressures of thumb and fingers. This can be likened to carrying a box by holding the tops of the sides between the thumbs and fingers instead of with the hands under the box. Gravity tends to pull the sides of the box down between the thumb and fingers. If, with this position of the hand, an individual is able to hold the ball, keep the hand in exactly the same position throughout the entire swing, and release smoothly, there is no need to change to the thumb up position.

If a person who is in the habit of holding the ball with the "V" of the hand up attempts to change to the thumb up position, he is likely to revert to habit during the end of the swing and thus impart left spin to the ball. Any twist of the wrist during the swing causes a side spin of the ball. Rather than to attempt to change the hand position of a student who is holding the ball with the "V" up, it is advisable to teach him to bowl a hook ball from the beginning. The important considerations in the hand position for bowling a *straight* ball (one with no spin) are that the position be one that the individual can control, that it remain the same from the start of the swing through release and follow-through, and that the thumb and fingers be withdrawn so that no off center force is applied. In his grip Carter[5] uses an unusual device for reducing off center force at the moment of release. He suggests eliminating the little finger from play by curling it back under itself against the ball. This might be a useful device to suggest to an individual who is applying off center force with the little finger at release and causing right spin of the ball.

Top spin increases the speed of the ball since the spin force pushes backward against the floor causing a reaction force which pushes the ball forward and thus combines with the forward force given the ball at release. It has no effect on the direction of the ball. When releasing the ball with the palm upward, top spin can be produced by first removing the thumb and then the two fingers simultaneously. Back spin decreases the speed since the spin force pushes forward against the floor. The forward force given the back spin ball at release causes it to slide along the floor until friction overcomes the back spin and the ball can roll forward. Thus the speed of the ball is reduced. A ball with left spin curves to the left and one with right spin curves to the right. The faster it is spinning left or right the more the ball is deflected from a straight path. The greater the speed of the ball, the farther down the alley the ball will be before its path is altered by any spin imparted to it at release. The greater the spin imparted to the ball, the sooner it takes effect.

A hook ball results from the application of an off center force which starts the ball spinning to the left as it is released. This spin can be caused by swinging the ball with the "V" of the hand rather than the thumb upward. In this position the thumb comes out of the ball before the fingers and since the fingers are on the right side of the ball an off center force is applied causing the ball to spin left. "If the hand is cocked upward at the point of release, a hook will be assured as the force exerted by the fingers on the right side of the ball will be made greater."[6] This lifting action of the fingers causes the ball to roll forward, and since it is applied to the right of the center of gravity of the ball, it increases the right to left spin. This lifting action can be caused by wrist action which lifts the hand at release. Because the forward momentum is great in comparison with the speed of the spin, the ball travels in a straight path for some distance down the alley before curving to the left. For this reason the hook ball approaches the one-three pocket at a greater angle than does the straight ball and therefore, is more likely to contact directly a greater number of pins (Fig. 102).

Many bowlers and bowling instructors argue about the relative merits of "pin" and "spot" bowling. As in so many similar discussions concerning form it is assumed that one is

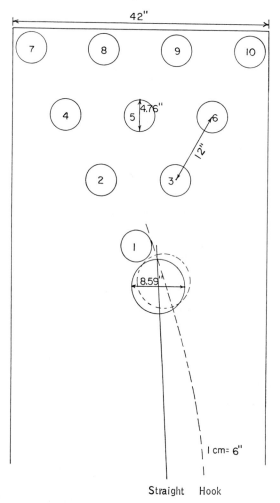

Figure 102. *Approximate angles at which straight (bowled at one degree angle) and hooked balls enter one-three pocket.*

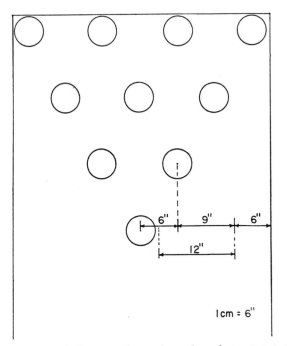

Figure 103. *Distance ball can angle-in when released at point six inches from edge of alley.*

correct and the other incorrect. Mechanical analysis of the situations indicates that this is not true. The accuracy of the roll is dependent upon the arc of the swing and the release of the ball. It is only as the swing and point of release are affected by the judgment of the bowler as he sights his target that the type of aim is important.

Since the center of the head pin is 21 inches from the side of the alley, a straight ball placed on the alley six to eight inches from the right edge can angle in only seven to nine inches if it is to enter the one-three pocket (Fig. 103). A one degree angle results in a straight ball, after traveling 60 feet, being one foot to the left of the point directly opposite the point of release (p. 283). Thus to enter the one-three pocket, a straight ball must be bowled at an angle of less than one degree.

Normally, several alleys are side by side and the total alley space is large in width as well as in length. This tends to foreshorten the length of the alley as viewed by the bowler and, when looking at pins 60 feet away, it is extremely difficult to judge the desired path of the ball. Many individuals find it

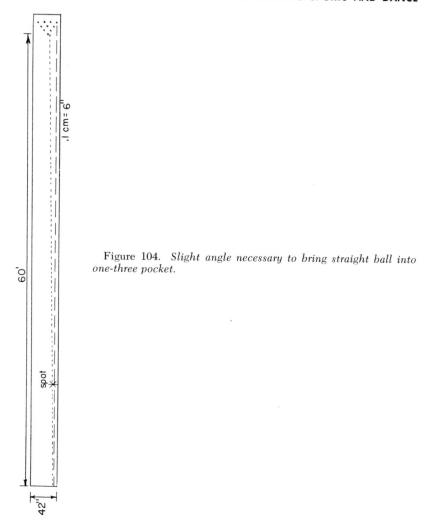

Figure 104. *Slight angle necessary to bring straight ball into one-three pocket.*

easier to use a spot considerably closer to the point of release since a truer judgment can be made of the direction to the target when it is moved closer. When aiming for the spot (see Fig. 104) it is clear that the swing must be practically straight forward. However, when looking at the head pin there is a tendency to judge that the swing must be angled to bring the ball into the pocket. As a result the swing may be angled too much resulting in the ball's hitting to the left of the head pin, sometimes missing the pins altogether. Some individuals argue that spot bowling is more difficult because such a small spot must be crossed by the ball that any slight error will result in a wide deviation by the time the ball has traveled the additional distance to the pins. The point which this argument overlooks is that, *regardless of the type of aim used, a straight ball must roll over the same spot if it is to enter the one-three pocket.* If it does not, it will not enter the pocket whether the bowler was aiming for the spot or the pins.

It seems reasonable that it is easier to roll a ball across a spot when looking at it than when looking at pins some 60 feet away. There may, however, be a psychological problem connected with spot bowling. Since the bowler is interested in hitting the pins there is a great temptation to look up at the pins at the last moment. This change in point of aim is likely to be disastrous. A bowler who finds that he is unable to discipline himself to concentrate on the spot until he has completed his follow-through may be more successful with pin bowling. If the bowler is successful in judging the angle of swing when looking at the pins there is no reason for changing to "spot bowling." The use of the closer target is simply a device for eliminating the necessity for a judgment made extremely difficult by distance. It is frequently a very useful device for beginners. However, it must be remembered that it is essential that the point of release be consistent. Any change in point of release changes the angle of the line to the spot and thus the angle of the ball down the alley. This same device is used by many golfers to assure accuracy in putting (p. 271). Since eye focus is important to balance (p. 46), the eyes should be focused on the point of aim from the time the bowler takes his stance until after the ball has been released whether spot or pin bowling is used. The eye focus also assists in maintaining a straight line of movement.[7]

Second Ball. When the pins left standing after the first ball has been rolled are in the center of the alley (strike area), the same starting position and point of aim are used as when bowling the first ball. However, when the pins left are on either side of the alley a cross-alley ball will have a greater chance for success. The ball approaching the number 10 pin on an angle to the right can vary more than one rolled straight for the pin and still have its center of gravity over the alley (Fig. 105). When rolling cross-alley balls the starting point and the point of aim must be adjusted depending on the pins left standing. Kidwell and Smith[8] discussed this problem in detail and their diagram has been simplified by Culver (Fig. 106).[9]

REBOUND

The ball is deflected somewhat by contact with a pin but since it is moving and is so much heavier, the force exerted

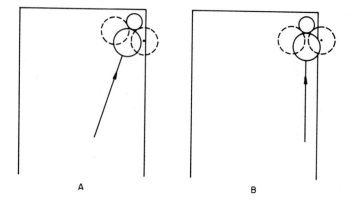

Figure 105.   *Balls varying same degree. A, Center of gravity still above alley.*
B, Center of gravity over channel (gutter).

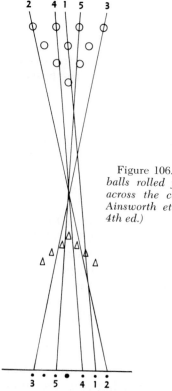

Figure 106.   *The pathways of diagonal straight*
balls rolled from the various starting positions
across the corresponding points of aim. (From
Ainsworth et al.: Individual Sports for Women,
4th ed.)

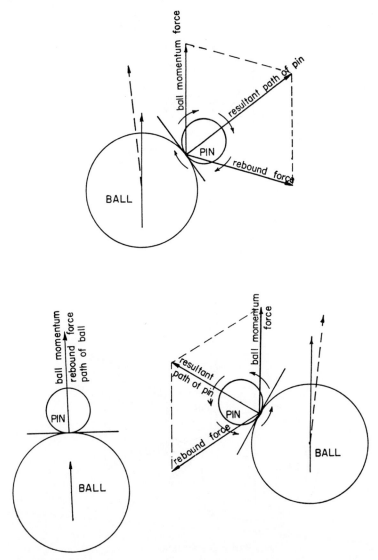

Figure 107. *Direction of pin rebound from bowling ball with no side spin.*

by the ball against the pin is much greater than the force exerted by the pin against the ball (p. 50). The heavier the ball and the faster it is traveling the less its path is altered by contact with the pins. For this reason it is best to bowl with as heavy a ball as *can be easily controlled*. The amount of ball deflection also depends upon the angle at which it strikes the pins. Since it is impossible for a ball to contact all of the pins, a strike is dependent upon some pins being struck by other pins.

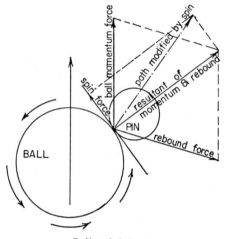

Ball with left spin

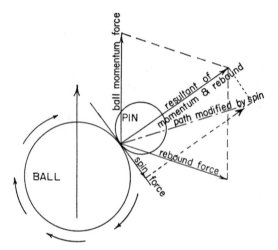

Ball with right spin

Figure 108. *Change in path of pin rebound caused by spin of ball.*

The angle at which the pins are thrown by the ball is extremely important.

The center of gravity of a pin is higher than the point at which the ball contacts it. Therefore, the bottom of the pin is more or less knocked out from under it and the pin begins an end-over-end rotation. The angle of rebound from a ball with no right or left spin is perpendicular to the tangent on the circumference of the ball at the point of contact (Fig. 107). A pin hit on the left is given right spin since the ball passes across its left side. A pin hit on the right is given left spin. A ball spinning to the left as it approaches a pin causes the path of the pin to be to the left of its normal rebound path for the particular angle of contact, while one spinning to the right rebounds the pin to the right of normal (Fig. 108).

SUMMARY

McKee[10] summed up the conclusions that the teacher could draw from an application of mechanical principles to bowling as:
1. The desirable speed of the steps is related to the length of the arm. The time taken by the swing is constant for every bowler of a given arm length regardless of length of backswing.
2. Greater velocity can be obtained by increasing the length of the backswing. Since the swing will take place in a given time, the longer swing results in greater velocity (greater distance is covered in a given time). The most advantageous height depends upon the strength of the individual, since the longer swing generates more centrifugal force which must be overcome by the bowler.
3. The minimum muscular effort for successful bowling is that effort necessary to walk to the foul line, grip the ball, and push it away from the body into a position enabling gravity to act upon it effectively. The anti-gravity muscles and those that stabilize the trunk, arm, and shoulder girdle must function throughout the swing.

REFERENCES

1. McKee, Mary Ellen: The Mechanics of Bowling. *Official Bowling-Fencing-Golf Guide, June 1956-June 1958.* Washington, D.C., American Association for Health, Physical Education and Recreation, 1956, p. 15.
2. Barnet, Nan: Mechanical Principles of Bowling. Unpublished paper, University of Washington, Seattle, 1959.
3. Carter, Don: 10 Secrets of Bowling. *Sports Illustrated,* 7:21:28, November 18, 1957.
4. *Ibid.,* p. 31.
5. *Ibid.,* p. 26.
6. Culver, Elizabeth J.: Bowling, in Ainsworth, Dorothy S. (ed.): *Individual Sports for Women.* Philadelphia, W. B. Saunders Company, 1963, p. 102.
7. McKee, Mary Ellen: The Mechanics of Bowling. *Official Bowling-Fencing-Golf Guide, June 1956-June 1958.* Washington, D.C., American Association for Health, Physical Education and Recreation, 1956, p. 20.

8. Kidwell, Kathro and Smith, Paul: *Bowling Analyzed.* Dubuque, Iowa, William C. Brown Company, 1960, pp. 40–44.

9. Culver, Elizabeth J.: Bowling, in Ainsworth, Dorothy S. (ed.): *Individual Sports for Women.* Philadelphia, W. B. Saunders Company, 1963, p. 110.

10. McKee, Mary Ellen: The Mechanics of Bowling. *Official Bowling-Fencing-Golf Guide, June 1956-June 1958,* Washington, D.C., American Association for Health, Physical Education and Recreation, 1956, p. 21.

23

Basketball

The game of basketball involves the skills of throwing and catching, running, stopping, dodging, jumping and landing, and striking. The rebound principles of striking are involved in the dribble and in the use of the backboard when shooting. Since all of these skills are discussed in detail in Part Three, only a few specific applications are included in this chapter.

Basketball is a game of accuracy rather than force. Speed and control are of primary importance. Since the ball is large, greater control is possible through the use of two hands and a grip which holds the ball in the fingers rather than the palms of the hands. The force can then be applied over a large area and the ball can be more easily directed.

The various methods of throwing to another player or to the basket utilize all three basic throwing patterns: underhand, overhand, and sidearm and variations of these patterns. Since for the chest pass (or shot) the ball is held in two hands in front of the center of the body it is easy to control. However, the position does not allow for the usual type of backswing. A circular movement of the ball in front of the body gives time to work up momentum before release. The chest shot moves the ball directly between the eyes and the basket and therefore, allows for accurate aiming. However, this pass (or shot) is easily guarded since the ball moves diagonally upward and away from the body at a relatively low height.

Most girls lack the strength to shoot for goal from the free throw line with one hand. In fact many, particularly younger girls, can be successful only with the two-hand underhand shot which allows for a long backswing and uses the strong leg muscles.

The two-hand overhead throw (or shot) can be likened to the overhead volley in volleyball. Even more than normally, weight transference is important since the backswing is so limited. The movement of the hook pass (or shot) is essentially a sidearm pattern adjusted to a vertical instead of a horizontal arc. The body movement is, therefore, a side bend rather than rotation.

In getting the body off the floor for a lay-up shot the same basic movement pattern is employed as is used in the volleyball spike[1] and in the hurdle of a running front dive (Fig. 5, p. 19). In teaching the dive to a basketball player, Kilby[2] found that when she suggested that he go out on the end of the board and "do a lay-up shot" the student, who had been having a great deal of difficulty with the hurdle, was successful immediately. He was able to apply a familiar movement pattern to the new situation when the similarity was pointed out to him.

In using a dribble it is important to coordinate the angle at which the ball is pushed against the floor with the distance that is to be covered. A ball pushed to the floor at a large angle allows little change in body position on the floor, while one pushed to the floor at an acute angle may bounce so far ahead as to make recovery impossible. Back spin on a ball bounced to oneself cuts down the distance that must be covered while forward spin increases it and may put the ball beyond recovery, depending on the angle used.

Since spin makes catching more difficult it should not be used in passing. However, it is very important in shooting. A lay-up shot (which does *not* use the backboard) given spin in the direction of the basket (when shot from the right side of the basket given left spin) is carried toward the basket. Also, spin can be used on a *rebound shot* to reduce the angle of rebound and thus keep the ball closer to the backboard. This is discussed in detail in Chapter 19. Whether or not it is desirable to reduce the angle of rebound depends on the spot at which the ball hits the backboard. If it hits near the basket, the spin which reduces the angle of rebound (right spin if approaching from the right) may keep the ball so close to the backboard that it rebounds between the backboard and the basket. When the ball hits near the basket it is also important that the force of rebound be very light.

With little regard for the mechanics of the situation some authors have made suggestions as to the location on the backboard of a spot, or spots, which should be used for rebound shots. The spot on the backboard that will rebound the ball into the basket varies with the point on the floor from which the shot is taken, the height of the arc, the force of the shot, and spin on the ball. A ball with no spin rebounds at an angle equal to that at which it approaches the backboard. If the shot is made from a point on the right side of the floor at a 45-degree angle from the spot on the backboard which it hits, the spot must be at a 45-degree angle from the center of the basket or at a point 15 inches to the right of the middle of the basket if no spin is involved (Fig. 109). Since gravity is constantly acting on the ball it must also be above the basket. How much above depends upon the downward (or upward) angle at which the ball strikes the backboard. If the ball strikes at an acute downward angle it rebounds close to the backboard, while if it strikes at a wide downward angle it rebounds out away from the backboard and may be beyond the basket by the time gravity has pulled it down to basket height (Fig. 110). Actually, gravity will cause the ball to drop closer to the backboard than the diagram indicates. A ball striking at an upward angle tends to rebound upward at an equal angle. Gravity immediately alters the angle but the ball curves upward before dropping.

By varying the arc of the shots, spots of *various heights* can be used with successful results when shooting from the same point on the floor. Spots at *different distances* to the right (or left) of the basket cannot be used with equal efficiency when shooting from the same point on the floor unless the condition of spin is altered. Only when the angles between the backboard and the lines to the point on the floor and the line to the basket are equal will a ball with no spin rebound over the basket. As the spot is moved out from the basket the angle between the backboard and the line from the point on the floor to the spot becomes greater, but the angle between

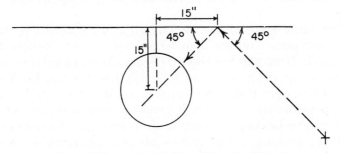

Figure 109. *Angle of rebound from backboard.*

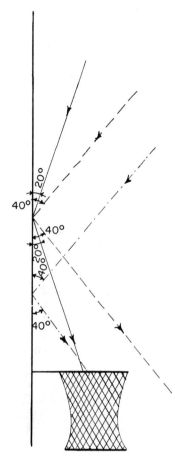

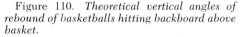

Figure 110. *Theoretical vertical angles of rebound of basketballs hitting backboard above basket.*

the backboard and a line from the spot to the center of the basket becomes smaller (Fig. 111). When shooting a ball with no right (or left) spin from a given point on the floor, only one spot can result in a rebound which causes the ball to pass over the center of the basket (Fig. 112). Therefore, the spot contacted can vary little if the ball is to drop through the basket.

The same spot on the backboard can be used effectively from those points on the floor which are at approximately the same angle from the backboard (Fig. 113) provided the arcs of the shots are such that the ball approaches the backboard at approximately the same vertical angle. Some slight variation is possible because a ball need not pass directly over the center of the basket in order to drop through. In general, as the player making a shot moves his position toward the sidelines, the rebound spot must be moved farther out from the

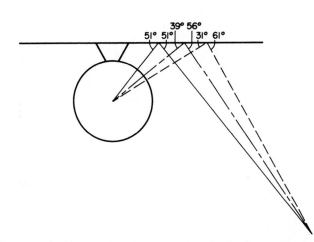

Figure 111. *Variation in angle between backboard and line to center of basket as the spot is moved outward on the backboard.*

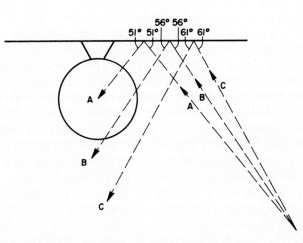

Figure 112. *Paths of balls shot from the same point on the floor, but hitting different spots on the backboard (no spin involved).*

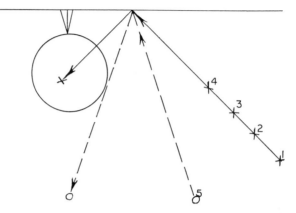

Figure 113. *Paths of basketballs shot from different points on the floor and hitting the same spot on the backboard.*

basket; as he moves in toward the center of the floor, the spot must be moved in closer to the basket; as he moves his position on the floor straight backward away from the end line, the spot must be moved in toward the basket; and as he moves closer to the end line, the spot must be moved out on the backboard. When spin is used, the point on the floor from which the shot is made or the spot on the backboard, or both, must be changed.

The force with which the ball should be shot depends upon the angle at which it approaches the backboard. If the ball hits at an acute right (or left) angle it must hit farther out from the basket and more force is needed to carry it to the basket before gravity pulls it down to basket height. In this case the lower the spot, the more the force needed since the ball will drop to basket height faster from the lower spot. When it hits close to the basket a great deal of force may carry it beyond the basket before gravity can pull it down to basket height (Fig. 114). Thus, when the ball strikes the backboard close to the basket it must hit with little force so that the rebound force will be dissipated quickly and gravity can pull the ball into the basket. Since in the lay-up shot the ball is always played close to the basket, whether or not the backboard is used, it cannot be given much force. To keep the ball velocity at a minimum the ball is released at the height of the jump, when the momentum of the body has been overcome by gravity.[3]

Since the basket faces directly upward the largest opening is available to a ball approaching directly from above. As the angle of approach becomes more acute (the arc of the shot

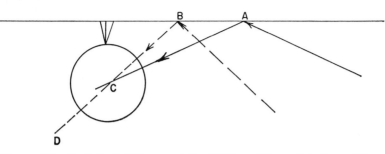

Figure 114. *Basketball hitting spot B with force BD equal to force AC may rebound beyond basket before gravity can pull it down to basket height.*

becomes flatter) the size of the goal available to the ball becomes smaller. This can be seen clearly by looking up at the bottom of the goal from various points on the floor. When standing directly below the basket the entire width of the opening is visible. As one moves backward away from the basket the visible opening becomes smaller and smaller. Thus it is obvious that a ball, shot at a flat arc, is more likely to hit the rim and rebound away from the basket than is a ball approaching at a greater angle. Therefore, it appears that a shot which does not use the backboard has a greater chance for success when arched so that the ball approaches at a large angle. This is true up to a point. Mullaney pointed out that the high arch shot has two disadvantages. In the first place, it is a longer shot and therefore any initial sighting error is magnified. Secondly, in dropping from the greater height the high arched shot gains considerable momentum because of the acceleration of gravity and if it should hit the rim of the basket, the rebound will be forceful. He suggests that, in order to reduce failure due to rebound, the ball should be shot so that its total velocity is minimum when it reaches the basket. "This minimum total velocity occurs when the horizontal and vertical velocities are equal—when the entry is 45°."[4] However, because of the decrease in the size of the basket available to the ball as the angle becomes smaller, it is better to err on the high side of the 45-degree angle than on the low side.

When playing a rebound shot, the use of a higher spot results in the ball approaching the basket at a larger angle. A spot one foot above the basket has been suggested frequently. A ball rebounding from the backboard at a point 12 inches above the basket approaches the center of the goal opening at an angle of approximately 38 degrees (Fig. 115). Actually because gravity is constantly acting to pull the ball downward,

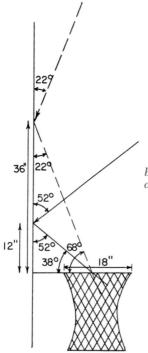

Figure 115. *Change in angle of approach of basketball to basket as rebound spot is raised (gravity not considered).*

it approaches the goal at a slightly larger angle. In general, the lower the spot, the smaller the angle of approach and the narrower the opening of the goal available to the ball. However, back spin can be used to reduce the angle of rebound and thus increase the angle of approach to the basket. A ball with back spin pushes upward against the backboard which pushes downward against the ball, and this force added to gravity makes the ball fall faster and thus rebound closer to the backboard. Obviously if a ball is to rebound over the center of the basket from a higher spot it must approach the backboard at a smaller angle or be given back spin. Again, the problem of greater vertical velocity must be considered.

A discussion of the application of mechanics to basketball involves considerable repetition since essentially the game of basketball is made up of several of the basic skills. For further information applicable to this game the reader is referred particularly to Chapters 12, 13, 18, and 19 which deal with the application of the physical laws to the skills of running, jumping, throwing, and striking.

REFERENCES

1. Broer, Marion R., and Houtz, Sara Jane: *Patterns of Muscular Activity in Selected Sport Skills: An Electromyographic Study.* Springfield, Charles C Thomas, 1967.
2. Kilby, Emelia-Louise: Western Washington College of Education, Bellingham, Washington, personal correspondence.
3. Barr, George: *Young Scientist and Sports.* New York, Whittlesey House, McGraw-Hill Book Company, Inc., 1962, p. 116.
4. Mullaney, Dave: Free Throw Technique. *Athletic Journal,* 38:3:53, November, 1957.

24

Swimming

Swimming, like walking or running, is a means of locomotion which results from the body pushing against a surface and the surface exerting an opposite force against the body. The body as a whole is given linear motion as a result of angular motion of its extremities. It differs from walking and running in that the surface against which the push is made is not as resistive as the usual walking surface and the surrounding medium offers a great deal more resistance to the movement of the body—it both offers resistance to body progress and affords the surface against which the body applies its force. Also, the body is in a horizontal, rather than vertical, position and the effect of the force of gravity is greatly minimized—in some cases eliminated.

Because water is not as resistive as the ground or floor it gives as pressure is applied against it. Therefore, all of the force exerted by the swimmer is not effective in moving him; some of it is dissipated in moving the water backward. Progress is slower and requires more effort. However, the swimmer normally uses both arms and legs to push against the water instead of the legs only as in movement on land. In walking one moves through air which, because of its relatively low density, normally offers little resistance to the progress of the body. The swimmer moves through water which is considerably more dense, making the minimizing of the resistance of the water in the direction of the desired movement one of his major concerns. At the same time this medium which resists his progress, is the substance which supplies the force to move the swimmer and therefore another basic concern is that of increasing the resistance of the water in the direction opposite to that in which movement is desired. Thus, swimming is a problem of minimizing the resistance of the water to movement in the direction the swimmer wishes to progress and increasing, to its maximum, the resistance of the water to movement in the opposite direction.

Because of the density of water, it exerts a supporting force against the body and removes the necessity for withstanding the pull of gravity which is ever present in standing, walking and running.

BUOYANCY

Archimedes' principle states that a body submerged in a liquid is buoyed up by a force equal to the weight of the displaced fluid. The upward force which acts on the swimmer is equal to the weight of that volume of water which is identical with the volume of the swimmer's body. Buoyancy, then, depends upon the relationship between weight and volume. The heavier the individual for his size the less buoyant he is. Normally the human body floats because its specific gravity (weight per unit volume) is less than that of water. The degree of buoyancy is dependent upon body build. Bone and muscle have a higher specific gravity than does adipose tissue. Bodies which are made up largely of bone and muscle are less buoyant than those containing a high percentage of fat. For this reason girls and women, on the whole, are more buoyant than men.

The chest area containing the lungs which are filled with air is very light for its size, and is the most buoyant segment of the body. Although in the air the body rotates around its center of gravity (hip region), in the water the fulcrum becomes the center of buoyancy (chest region). The center of body weight, being approximately in the region of the hips, is toward the feet from this fulcrum. The legs are likely to have a high percentage of bone and muscle and therefore their specific gravity is high. Also the leg end of the body lever is longer (distance from the chest to the toes) than the head end (distance from the chest to the top of the head). The farther the weight from the fulcrum (in this case the center of buoyancy) the greater its effect (Chapter 6, Leverage). All these factors cause the body to be overbalanced at the leg end and it tends to rotate around the chest as the fulcrum, and the legs sink (Fig. 116)[1]. The only time that the legs do

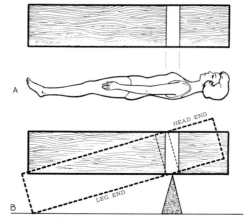

Figure 116. *Tendency of body to rotate around the chest area.*

not exert a rotatory force on the body is when their specific gravity is so low because of the presence of adipose tissue and their size large enough that they displace a volume of water that weighs as much as, or more than, they weigh. In this case the center of buoyancy of the body is no longer in the chest region but is moved downward in the body. It may be moved downward to the point that coincides with the center of gravity of the body in which case the body balances perfectly in the water and the individual floats in a horizontal position.

When this condition does not exist – and it does not exist in the majority of persons – the feet sink until the center of gravity is below the center of buoyancy (Fig. 117). The buoyancy and balance of the human body in the water can be increased by enlarging the volume of the body without increasing its weight and by raising the center of gravity so that it is brought closer to the center of buoyancy, thus decreasing the length of the weight arm.

The jellyfish float position, in which all segments of the body are as close as it is possible to get them to the center of buoyancy, and the lungs are filled with air adding to the volume of the chest area, is the most buoyant position which can be assumed by the human body. The center of gravity and center of buoyancy are at approximately the same point. It is the position used to determine whether an individual who is having trouble floating on the back possesses sufficient buoyancy to make a back float possible if certain adjustments in position are made. If, even though the lungs are filled, the individual's back is below the water in the jellyfish float it is useless for him to attempt a *motionless* float on his back.

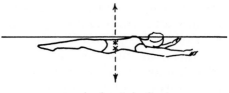

a.   horizontal   float

Figure 117. *Floating positions resulting from various locations of the center of buoyancy.*

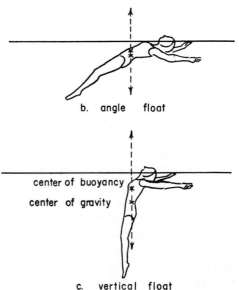

b.   angle   float

center of buoyancy

center of gravity

c.   vertical   float

In floating on the back most persons need to redistribute the body weight around the center of buoyancy. Moving the arms to a position in the water above the head both lengthens and adds weight to that part of the body lever which is above the fulcrum (center of buoyancy) and is effective in helping to balance the heavier legs. It raises the center of gravity of the body, bringing it closer to the center of buoyancy. The center of gravity can be raised further by bending the knees and drawing the feet toward the body in the frog position. This shortens the leg end of the body lever while maintaining the full resistive surface area of the legs. Arching the back and laying the head back into the water expands the chest thus aiding full breathing which adds volume and places more of the head in the water, displacing an additional volume of water. Buoyancy varies considerably with the amount of air in the lungs. A less buoyant individual may be able to float only when his lungs are filled completely. If this person wishes to float motionless it is necessary for him to take quick deep breaths, holding each until it has lifted him far enough in the water that the drop accompanying the next exhalation will not put his mouth and nose under water.

Since, in most individuals, the center of gravity is considerably lower in the body than the center of buoyancy and thus causes a rotatory force on the body, the floating position for the great majority of persons is somewhere between the vertical and horizontal. Some even float with the legs directly below the chest, in a vertical position. This means that when a motionless horizontal position is taken the legs sink. As they sink they gather momentum because of the acceleration caused by the force of gravity. This momentum may pull an individual down under the water even though his body buoyancy would normally cause him to float at an angle well above the vertical. While the buoyancy force can support the weight of the body, it is not great enough to overcome the momentum built up by the dropping of the legs. Therefore, it is important to place the body vertically in the water before assuming the motionless floating position. The legs, having no downward momentum to overcome, will be lifted to the point of balance according to the buoyancy of the particular individual. The practice of kicking the feet to the surface in assuming the floating position causes many relatively buoyant individuals to draw the conclusion that they are unable to float.

Raising the head always tends to lower the feet in the water. The body lying in the water is a first class lever revolving around its center of buoyancy and might be likened to a teeter-totter. When one end of a teeter-totter is lifted the other end drops.

Many beginners are afraid in the water because they assume that they will sink. Actually the sinker is very rare. The problem is to learn to balance the body so that the mouth and nose can be out of the water at regular intervals to allow breathing. Buoyancy rather than its lack may, however, be a considerable problem for many girls and women first learning to manipulate their bodies in the water. An individual with very buoyant legs finds it difficult to replace her feet on the bottom of the pool. Frequently this inability to get the feet down under the body into the position to which the individual is more accustomed causes as much, or more, panic than the idea that she will sink. It is, therefore, extremely important that such a person understand her problem, the reasons for it, and the mechanics for dealing with it.

Since in this case the legs displace a volume of water that weighs as much or more than the legs, the lever must be shortened to remove the mechanical advantage gained by the force of buoyancy when the lever is long. When the knees are brought in to the chest, the body lever is shortened making it easier to rotate the hips downward by the force applied by the arms. When the body is on its back with the arms out from the shoulders (approximately), a downward and forward force exerted by the arms lifts the upper body and pulls the hips down and backward. When in a prone position with the arms on the water overhead the downward and backward force of the arms lifts the upper body and pulls the hips forward. The forceful lifting of the head also aids in the dropping of the legs. Once the hips are beneath the chest, extension of the legs sends the feet down to the bottom of the pool. Extension before this time simply puts them diagonally out in the water above the bottom and the force of buoyancy lifts them again to the surface.

It is easier to maintain a horizontal position when the body is moving through the water than when it is motionless, since the resistance of the water planes the body.

WATER RESISTANCE

A body moving through the water in a diagonal position causes greater resistance than one which is horizontal because it presents a greater surface area against which the water acts. The larger the surface area, the greater the resistance to the movement of the body through the water. Therefore, the body position in swimming should be such that the smallest area possible is presented to the water in the direction of desired movement. Keeping the body planed on the surface of the water reduces resistance to forward progress since the surface presented to the water is only the distance of the thickness of the body from front to back. When the hips and legs drop a very large area resists forward progress. Figure 118 shows that the size of the resistive surface varies with the sine of the angle that the feet drop. The fact that resistance varies with the sine of the angle was reported as far back as 1888 by Saint-Venant.[2] Burying the head in the water when swimming the crawl stroke presents the entire back of the head to the water. When the face lies on the water a much smaller area resists forward progress. This head position is important also in that it maintains the basic alignment of body segments discussed earlier and facilitates breathing during the stroke without a lift of the head which, as previously explained, leads to a sinking of the feet and

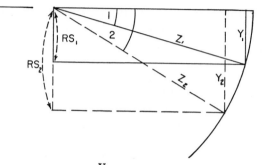

$$\text{Sin angle}_1 = \frac{Y_1}{Z_1}$$

$$\text{Sin angle}_2 = \frac{Y_2}{Z_2}$$

$$Z_1 = Z_2$$

$$\frac{\text{Sin angle}_1}{\text{Sin angle}_2} = \frac{\frac{Y_1}{Z}}{\frac{Y_2}{Z}} = \frac{Y_1}{Y_2}$$

Y_1 = Resistive Surface (RS_1) caused by angle$_1$
Y_2 = Resistive Surface (RS_2) caused by angle$_2$

$$\frac{\text{Sin angle}_1}{\text{Sin angle}_2} = \frac{RS_1}{RS_2}$$

Resistance varies with the sine of the angle of inclination.

Figure 118. *Relationship of resistive surface to sine of angle.*

thus to greatly increased resistance. Uneven force exerted on the two sides of the body results in a zigzag path through the water and increases the frontal area which resists forward progress (Fig. 119). Up and down movement in the water should also be kept to a minimum since this also increases surface area and causes waves which further resist progress. Heusner pointed out that when a swimmer causes waves some of his energy is spent in lifting the water and this energy is not available for propulsion. Wave action also varies with speed; therefore, the speed at which the least wave action results is the "speed of maximum efficiency."[3]

To further accomplish a reduction in resistance the body is streamlined as much as possible, especially during the recovery and gliding phases of the stroke. When the swimmer wishes to move forward the problem is to determine how to maneuver the extremities forward into position to exert force backward without presenting a large surface which resists the desired forward movement. If, in the elementary back stroke, the legs were simply drawn apart and then pulled together, the

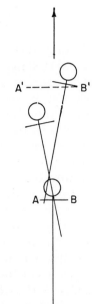

Figure 119. *Increase in frontal area caused by zigzag path through the water.*

surface area in both directions would be equal and movement through the water would depend entirely on any difference in the speed of the two actions. It may seem that when recovering the legs in the wedge kick of the elementary back stroke a large surface area is presented. However, when the legs are kept together as they are bent, the hips sink and thus the entire surface of the back resists the forward movement of the swimmer. By bending the knees outward the legs are shortened so that only the thighs resist the water and the surface area of the thighs is not as great as that of the back of the body. In all strokes the arms are kept close to the body as they move forward in order to keep the body as streamlined as possible. Having the fingertips lead also reduces the surface area resisting forward movement. This can be demonstrated easily by running the flat hand through the water with the fingertips leading and then facing the palm in the direction of the movement of the hand and pushing it through the water. The marked difference in resistance is easily perceived.

Since resistance increases approximately with the square of the velocity[4] any quick movement under water *in the direction of the desired movement* of the body should be eliminated. Karpovich[5] reported finding that the relationship of water resistance to speed is somewhat different for the prone and the back positions.*

―――――――――――

*These figures apply when skin surface area is 19–24 sq. ft.

Water resistance for prone position = speed^2 × .65
Water resistance for back position = speed^2 × .75

When the recovery phase of any stroke is under water, pressure is exerted in a direction which tends to send the body backward. Therefore, it is important that these movements be performed slowly as well as be kept as close to the body as possible to reduce surface area. Since the resistance of the air is considerably less than that of water, recovery of the arms out of the water reduces resistance to forward progress. The out-of-water recovery of the crawl arms reduces resistance to a minimum. Therefore, the efficient manipulation of a long extremity above the water rather than resistance is the problem in arm recovery of the crawl stroke. Bending the elbow greatly reduces the length of the lever and makes it easier to move it forward. Lifting a bent elbow and carrying it forward before reaching with the hands makes it possible to relax the muscles of the lower arm during a part of each stroke and thus reduces the effort necessary.

Just as the type of shoe worn influences the degree of friction between the feet and the floor, the material of the swimming suit is a factor in water friction. Karpovich[6] found that a woolen suit offered more resistance to progress than a silk suit. Also a loose suit especially when relatively tight around the legs, adds to resistance. Since the space between the suit and body fills with water, the area of the body is, in effect, enlarged.

A low pressure area which causes a suction force is created immediately behind the body moving rapidly through the water. This tends to pull the body backward.[7] This cavitation effect is greater the faster the swimmer is moving.

All movements of the body or any of its segments tend to create swirls and eddies which also cause low pressure areas around the body of the swimmer and have a retarding effect. Therefore, all movements which do not contribute to progress in the desired direction should be kept to a minimum. When water encounters curves in the swimmer's body eddies are also produced. This is another reason for streamlining the body. The basic well aligned position of body segments which is most efficient in standing is also most effective in streamlining the body in the water, except that since vertical balance is not a problem, the feet should be together. Streamlining the body during the gliding phase of any stroke results in gaining the most distance for a given amount of force applied, since it reduces resistance to a minimum.

PRODUCTION OF FORCE

The body is propelled through the water by a pushing and/ or pulling motion of the arms and thrusting and/or pincer action of the legs. Since the body moves in the opposite direction to that in which the force is applied, backward pressure sends it forward, downward pressure lifts it, upward pressure sinks it, pressure to the right moves it left, and pressure to the left moves it right. The fastest motion results from the reduction of resistance to the body in the direction that the swimmer wishes to progress and the production of the *greatest* resistance possible to the movement of the body segments in the opposite direction. The factors which are important in increasing the propulsive force of any stroke are the opposite to many of those discussed in connection with the reduction of resistance to progress. Maximum force is attained by presenting *as large a surface* as possible in the direction opposite to that of desired movement, by pushing through as great a distance as possible *in this direction*, and by moving it through the water as fast as possible.

While during recovery the arms and legs are bent to shorten the levers and reduce surface area, they are extended during the drive to present as great a surface as possible and to take advantage of the extra leverage. Fingertips lead during recovery but the palm of the hand pushes through the water during the drive.

Since the extremities move in an arc, relatively direct pressure opposite to the direction of desired movement is exerted only during the middle portion of the action. Pressure applied at the extremes of the arc may introduce undesirable forces. For example, if in the crawl stroke the hand starts pulling forcefully at the surface of the water and pulls all the way to the side of the body, the force produced during the early part of the stroke is downward and lifts the upper body; while that produced at the end of the stroke is upward and, being applied approximately at the center of gravity of the body, sinks the entire body. The result is an up-and-down motion of the body which increases resistance and wastes energy.

Figure 120 illustrates the components of the forces applied at various points on an arc. Because, in the crawl stroke, the center of the arc (the shoulder) moves forward as the hand moves backward, the arc is actually considerably more upright than this diagram indicates. In fact, as the arm approaches the body, the arc is upward and slightly *forward*

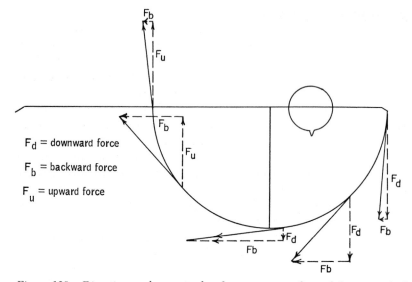

Figure 120. *Direction and magnitude of components of equal forces applied at various points on an arc.*

(Fig. 121). If, instead of pulling through the full arc, the fingers cut into the water a few inches before complete extension of the arm, when the arm is extended ready to pull, the hand is a few inches below the surface of the water and the part of the arc which causes the greatest lift is eliminated. If the elbow begins to bend and lift the arm when the hand has passed below the body, all upward force which would sink the body is eliminated. If the arm and hand were one straight lever the most effective force would be from a point 45 degrees downward in front of the shoulder to a point 45 degrees downward in back of the shoulder. However, wrist flexion makes it possible to place the palm of the hand in a position to exert

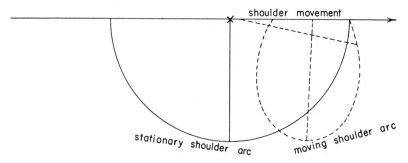

Figure 121. *Comparison of arcs resulting from movement about stationary and moving fulcrums.*

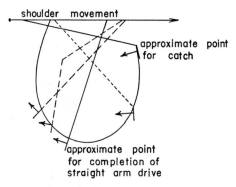

Figure 122. *Direction palm of hand can face at various points on arc of the crawl drive.*

considerable force backward before the 45-degree angle position is reached.

Figure 122 illustrates the direction that the palm can face at various points on the arc. The actual force produced would be the resultant between a force in that direction and the force tangent to the arc at the particular point. Since both are produced by the same movement they would be equal in magnitude and the effective force would be at an angle half way between the direction that the palm is facing and the direction of the tangent to the arc. Wrist action is not effective in increasing the backward force beyond the vertical but bending the elbow keeps the palm facing backward (Fig. 122). The straight arm pull, therefore, should be from a point a few inches below the surface of the water to just beyond the point vertically downward from the shoulder. Beyond this point as the elbow bends and begins to lift the hand, some additional backward force is produced since the palm of the hand is faced backward. Pulling too far with a straight arm introduces a great deal of upward force because of the uprightness of the arc and sinks the body. It also places the shoulder in a forward position, making a lift of the elbow difficult.

Reaching high overhead in the arm recovery of the elementary back stroke increases the distance over which force can be applied, but the first part of the drive is wasted in producing forces which tend to send the body to the right and left. If the forces applied by the two arms are equal the straight direction of movement of the swimmer is not affected but a great deal of energy is wasted. The last part of the arc has a pincer action, the water being forced backward as the arms approach the body, and thus does aid in moving the body forward. The arc of the arms, therefore, should be from a point at approximately 45 degrees above the shoulder to the sides of the body.

In the down beat of the crawl kick, backward force can be

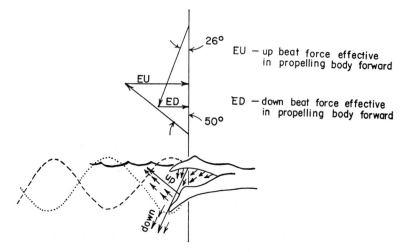

Figure 123. *Relative value of up and down phases of the crawl kick. (Modified from Cureton, Thomas K.: Mechanics and Kinesiology of Swimming, Research Quarterly, 1:40:101, December, 1930.)*

produced by the top of the hyperextended foot as the leg moves downward as a result of hip flexion. Bending the knee slightly puts the top of the foot into position to apply the force more directly backward. During the up beat the sole of the foot applies backward force as it moves from a flexed to an extended position. Since the application of backward force is so dependent upon foot position, flexible ankles are necessary for success in the crawl kick. Because of the forward component of the force which is exerted by the thigh on the down beat and the additional effective force that can be exerted by the whip of the foot on the up beat, more force is obtainable on the up beat of the kick (Fig. 123). Therefore, this is the portion of the kick that should be emphasized.

A kick which is wider than the depth of the body (approximately 15 to 18 inches) increases the resistance of the water to the forward progress of the body. As the kick becomes wider, the forward component of the force exerted by the movement of the thigh on the down beat also is increased. This is greater if the leg is completely straight at this time. Thus it is possible to move the body backward by a wide straight leg kick that emphasizes the down beat since a large forward component of force is produced. The general action of the legs in the crawl kick is very similar to walking. The central action of both is at the hip; both begin with some bend of the knee; there is a resistive component to the first part of the action; ankle action is very important. The action of the swinging phase of the walk is the same as that of the down beat of the kick while the propulsive phase is like that of the up beat.

In the drive of the wedge frog kick the first backward pressure against the water is applied by the front of the lower legs but the soles of the feet, if the ankles are flexed, are almost immediately brought into position to push directly backward. Flexing the ankles gives as large a surface area as possible with which to exert effective force. The final force of the kick results from squeezing the water backward as the legs come together. Because, during the recovery phase of this stroke, the thighs exert forward force which tends to stop forward momentum, it is extremely important that this movement be executed slowly. The forceful movements should be reserved for the drive phase of the kick. The ankles are extended during the first part of the recovery to reduce the surface area moving forward as much as possible. When the ankles are flexed the entire top of the foot is presented to the water in the direction of movement and thus the body is retarded. They then flex so that the toes can lead reducing the resistive surface as the feet reach outward, and so that they are in position to extend on the drive.

Since resistance increases with the square of the velocity, and since the progress of the swimmer is dependent upon the resistance of the water to his movements, greater progress results from faster movements of those body parts that are in position to apply force against the water in the direction opposite to that in which the swimmer wishes to progress. While movements in the direction of progress impede the desired motion of the body through the water and are made slowly to reduce resistance, movements in the opposite direction are responsible for the swimmer's progress and are made rapidly to increase resistance.

Best results from a given application of force can be gained by the advantageous use of momentum. Since it takes more force to start an object moving than to keep it moving, the timing of the gliding strokes is extremely important to efficiency. If one stroke is executed immediately after the other, the swimmer does not gain the advantage of a short period of relaxation between strokes which is possible, since the momentum of the stroke planes the body for a considerable time. If, on the other hand, the swimmer waits for his second stroke until the momentum of the first has been dissipated by the resistance of the water, he must overcome inertia on every stroke. In addition, since most individuals do not float horizontally, his feet will start to sink into a position which presents a broader surface and thus increases resistance to progress and requires that more force be exerted to move a given distance through the water. Since it takes time to go through the motions of the recovery phase of the stroke to prepare to exert the force, the second stroke should be started ahead of the time that it is desirable to apply the second force.

One might assume that in speed swimming, the speed that could be gained from a complete stroke would be the sum total of that which could be produced by the arms alone, plus that which could be produced by the legs alone. However, Karpovich reported finding that, for the crawl stroke, "the square of the maximum speed of the whole stroke is equal to the sum of the squares of the maximum speeds developed with the arms and the legs separately." [8]

$$V_w^2 = V_a^2 + V_l^2$$

This means that the total speed is considerably less than the sum of the speed of the arms plus that of the legs. If a swimmer were able to swim at 5 ft./sec. with the arms alone and 4 ft./sec. with the legs alone, the total speed which would result when swimming with both would be the *square root* of 41 ($5^2 + 4^2$) which is 6.40 – much less than the sum of 5 + 4 (9).*

MacDonald and Stearns[9] found that in the breast and butterfly strokes, there is an even greater loss when arms and legs are combined.

$$V_w^2 \text{ (breast)}\quad = 0.75\ (V_a^2 + V_l^2)$$
$$V_w^2 \text{ (butterfly)} = 0.90\ (V_a^2 + V_l^2)$$

Endless examples of the manner in which the physical principles apply to various swimming strokes and stunts could be cited. However, space does not permit such a discussion here. The important point is that, regardless of whether a beginning stroke, a racing stroke, or a synchronized swimming stunt is involved, the swimmer must determine how the body can be manipulated in the water so that: (1) as large an area as possible can be moved as directly as possible, in the direction which is opposite to that in which the swimmer wishes to progress; (2) the areas that must move in the direction of the desired progress can be kept as small as possible; (3) the movements which are in the direction of desired progress are executed slowly and those in the opposite direction relatively rapidly, the degree of speed being dependent upon the purpose of the stroke; and (4) maximum advantage can be taken of momentum and buoyancy.

---

*Hypothetical figures chosen for clarity of illustration.

REFERENCES

1. Broer, Marion R.: Teaching Individual Sports, in Ainsworth, Dorothy S. (ed.): *Individual Sports for Women.* Philadelphia, W. B. Saunders Company, 1963, p. 11.
2. de Saint-Venant, M.: Resistance Des Fluides. *Mémoirs de L'Académie des Sciences de L'Institute de France,* Tome Quarante-Quartrième (Deuxieme Série), 1888, p. 27.
3. Heusner, William W. Jr.: Mechanics and Its Relationship to Kinesiology. Paper presented in Kinesiology Section, A.A.H.P.E.R. Convention, Dallas, March 20, 1965.
4. Bowen, Wilbur Pardon and Stone, Henry A.: *Applied Anatomy and Kinesiology.* 7th ed. Philadelphia, Lea & Febiger, 1953, p. 418.
5. Karpovich, Peter V.: *Physiology of Muscular Activity.* Philadelphia, W. B. Saunders Company, 1965, p. 95.
6. Karpovich, Peter V.: Water Resistance in Swimming. *Research Quarterly,* 4:3:26, October, 1933.
7. Wells, Katharine F.: *Kinesiology.* 3rd ed. Philadelphia, W. B. Saunders Company, 1960, p. 377.
8. Karpovich, Peter V.: *Physiology of Muscular Activity.* Philadelphia, W. B. Saunders Company, 1965, p. 96.
9. MacDonald, F. W. and Stearns, W. J.: A Mathematical Analysis of the Dolphin-Butterfly and Breast Strokes. Master's Thesis in progress. Springfield College.

25

Tumbling

Although there are numerous tumbling stunts, essentially they are of two types, feats of balance and rotatory stunts.

BALANCE STUNTS

Some balance stunts involve only one individual while others involve two (couple stunts) or more (pyramids) tumblers. An understanding of the principles of equilibrium (Chapter 4) greatly facilitates the learning of any of these stunts. Some stunts are difficult because of the small base required (e.g., hand stand), others because of a high center of gravity (e.g., shoulder stand), and still others because of the adjustment necessitated by the addition of the weight of another person (e.g., planché). Many stunts could be listed in each category.

Head Stand. The head stand is taught in almost all beginning classes and is an excellent example for the application of the principles of equilibrium. The hands and head form a tripod base which is of sufficient size to allow some sway of the legs in any direction without the center of gravity of the body falling beyond its edges. If the hands are placed in line with the head, the base is wide from side-to-side but narrow in the forward-backward direction which is the direction of the greatest movement of the legs. In the tripod position the base is wide in both directions and when the center of gravity is approximately centered above this tripod, the hands are in an excellent position to apply force diagonally upward and backward should the legs begin to fall forward. If the center of gravity should sway backward and approach a point above the back edge of the base it is more difficult to readjust it toward the center, since the head and neck do not have the leverage for the production of forward force that the hands have for backward force. Therefore, it may be wise to teach beginners to keep slightly more weight on the hands than on the head. This means that the center of gravity is very slightly forward of the center of the base and sway will be forward rather than backward.

Two methods are commonly used to raise the legs to the position above the head, (1) forcefully kicking the legs upward, and (2) drawing the knees into the chest and then straightening the legs upward. The first uses a push off by the foot and a throw of the legs to provide the upward force, and momentum carries the legs backward. The problem lies in stopping the momentum when the legs reach the position above the center of the base (Fig. 124). The long leg levers have considerable rotatory momentum and this tends to carry them on beyond the base. Since this momentum is in the backward direction it is the head and neck with their relatively ineffectual leverage that are called upon to resist it. It is difficult to judge the exact amount of force necessary to produce the momentum which will carry the legs up into position but which will be dissipated by the time the legs reach the point above the center of the base. When the knees are brought in to the chest and the legs

Figure 124. *Momentum of kick-up tends to carry center of gravity beyond base.*

are then straightened upward, the weight is centered over the base with the center of gravity low and it is kept over the center of the base as the center of gravity moves upward. No momentum other than straight upward, which is the direction of desired movement, is involved (Fig. 125). Greater abdominal strength is required at the beginning of the performance but success is much more likely. Most overbalancing tendencies are in a forward direction since the legs are in front of the body, and the hands and arms of the performer are in a good position for control. Sometimes a beginner will tend to straighten the hip joints and lower back before starting to straighten the knees. This places the lower legs well back of the base and overbalances the performer backward (Fig. 126). It is important that all joints of the hips and legs be extended simultaneously so that all parts of the legs are kept over the base as they move upward.

Just as it is possible to balance a forward hip thrust in standing by a backward lean of the upper body, the person standing on his head can keep the center of gravity of the body over the base in an arched position. The diagonally forward body is balanced by diagonally backward legs. Since the various body parts are not balanced one above the other, additional effort is needed to maintain this position. Strain is caused on the lower back just as it is when standing with the hips forward and the shoulders back. Since a more exaggerated position is frequently assumed in the head stand, the strain is even greater. While the arched head stand may be desired for the sake of line in a given pyramid, the most *efficient* position is that in which the various body parts are aligned just as they are in standing (Chapter 10).

Figure 125. *Head stand from tuck—center of gravity over base.*

Figure 126. *Over balanced — hips extended before knees.*

Shoulder Stand. In any couple stunt the effect upon the center of gravity of the addition of the mass of a second person must be considered. In the shoulder stand the greatest problem is that of balancing the weight of the top while he is getting into position to stand on the shoulders of the person acting as base. A beginner is likely to allow his body to swing away from the body of the base as he moves behind him and upward. This lengthens the lever arm of his weight and thus moves the center of gravity of the two performers backward so far that it is beyond the back edge of the base of support and the performers fall backward. This can be avoided if, in mounting, the top keeps his body close to the body of the base and the person acting as base separates his feet in a forward-backward as well as side-to-side direction and keeps his own weight forward so that the center of gravity of the combined weight will remain above the base of support. When the top has mounted to the base's shoulders and his center of gravity is above that of the base, the base can then bring his feet together to complete the stunt. Since in the completed stunt the combined center of gravity is very high and the base small, little sway is possible.

Angel Balance. The preliminary form of the angel balance, in which the top's hands are supported by the base's hands, gives a much longer base of support for the top than does the final stunt in which the base supports the top only in the pelvic region. Side-to-side balance is difficult in both forms of the stunt since the base is narrow in that direction. If, in the preliminary form, the distance from the shoulders of the top to those of the base is not equal on the two sides, the top twists to the low side moving his center of gravity to that side and placing the top in an unbalanced position. If the shoulders of the top are lower than his hips, the angle of push of the top against the base is in a forward-downward direction making diagonally backward and upward resistance necessary. The resistive force must be applied at an angle instead of straight upward directly opposing gravity. If the shoulders are higher than the hips, the force of the top's weight is applied diagonally backward and downward. Since the muscles of the pelvic region and legs are much stronger than those in the arm and shoulder girdle region, this force is easier for the base to resist than is the forward-downward force.

The height of the shoulder can be determined by elbow adjustment of either the top or the base. However, when both attempt to make adjustments, over-adjustment is likely. For example, when the top sways to one side, the chances are that both will adjust simultaneously by bending the arm on the other side. While the adjustment made by either would probably be successful, the combined adjustment is too great and the top is overbalanced in the other direction (Fig. 127B). Since the base is the only one who can adjust the height of the top's hips, it would seem wise when teaching beginners this stunt, to suggest that *all* adjustments be made by the base. This means the top would keep his arms straight at all times allowing the base to judge the adjustments necessary both from side-to side and forward-backward.

When, in performing the more advanced stunt, the hands are removed, the top moves his arms backward to lower the center of gravity in his body so it will be over the supporting

A   B

Figure 127. Angel balance. A, *Balanced base making all adjustments*. B, *Both top and base adjusting arms — balance lost.*

feet of the base. The base can apply pressure with his toes to lift the upper body of the top or with his heels to lift his legs. Since the body being moved is a long lever and the force is applied near its center of gravity these adjustments take considerable effort. However, very little movement at the point of force application causes considerable adjustment at the ends of the top's body lever. Therefore, students should be cautioned to make *very small* adjustments with their feet.

Other Stunts. The individual acting as base of the *chest stand* can more easily resist the force of the mounting top if the knee and hand on the side opposite to that from which the top is mounting are placed diagonally outward rather than directly under the hip and shoulder (Fig. 128). The force of the top mounting from the left of the base is toward the base's right. Placing the right hand and knee outward widens the base in the direction of the force and makes it possible for the base to apply force diagonally upward and to the left in opposition to the force of the top, and thus more easily to avoid being overbalanced to the right.

The narrow base in the forward-backward direction which is required in the *planché* makes this stunt difficult. The forward weight of the top must be balanced exactly by the backward weight of the base at every point in the stunt.

In the *knee shoulder stand* forward pressure by the base against the top's shoulders moves them beyond the top's center

A   B

Figure 128. *Chest stand.* A, *Right side of base in position to apply force diagonally to left.* B, *Weight centered over base.*

of gravity causing him to rotate around his center of gravity and his feet to fall over backward. The base must be taught to maintain the position of the arms taken before the top lifts his legs. He must be prepared to apply additional force to offset the added force of the top against his hands as the feet of the top move upward, but he must apply only that amount of force necessary to maintain the position of his arms—not enough to move his hands forward of their starting position.

If the top places his shoulders in the hands of the base *before* throwing his feet upward, the base can adjust his arm position to support the weight of the top and set his muscles to withstand the sudden force that will be exerted against his arms as the top pushes off. Thus, he is more likely to be able to maintain his arm position. When the top drops his shoulders into the base's hands *at push off* all force (the weight plus the push off) is exerted at once against the hands. The base must immediately find the most effective arm position for supporting the top's shoulders. He cannot set his muscles to withstand the force of the leg fling and therefore, sometimes his hands are forced back and downward and the base falls, or he overcorrects and pushes his hands too far forward and pushes the base's shoulders out from under him. Beginners or girls who do not have considerable arm and shoulder strength and control would be wise to have the top place his shoulders in the base's hands before lifting the feet.

ROTATORY STUNTS

In some rotatory stunts the body simply rotates around an axis that passes through the center of gravity of the body. Somersaults and twists executed while the body is free of support are examples of this type of stunt. In others, such as the forward roll, cartwheel, etc., the body rotates around a point of support at the same time that it is rotating around the axis that passes through its center of gravity. The principles of angular motion that are discussed in Chapter 5 are particularly applicable.

Speed of movement of the body is always dependent upon the force produced and the direction of its application. In rotatory motion the radius of rotation is an additional factor. Since the rotatory velocity of a body is equal to its linear velocity divided by the radius of rotation (Chapter 5), a given force turns the body faster in the tuck than the lay-out position. Because the radius of rotation is so much longer, rotating the body in the lay out position requires a greater expenditure of energy than is required for rotation in the tuck position.

The *front flip* is performed more easily in a tuck position because it takes less energy to cause the rotation and also because the turn is accomplished faster. Time is important since the force of gravity is constantly pulling the body downward. The force needed to complete the flip must be developed while the body is still in contact with the floor. Once it is completely free of the supporting surface it is impossible to increase or decrease the force. The body can produce force which is effective for its own movement only when it can apply its force against a resistive surface which then applies an opposite force against the body causing it to move. Although he cannot increase the force of rotation once he is in the air, the performer may increase or decrease his speed of rotation by shortening or lengthening his radius of rotation.

In those stunts which involve rotation around the body's center of gravity when the body is free of support, the principles of projection must be applied. The time available to the performer for the execution of the stunt depends upon the height of projection which, in turn, depends upon the amount of force and the angle of its application (Chapter 9). Once the body is free of support, change in the position of the extremities and head can cause the body to revolve or to twist around its center of gravity but cannot change the path of the center of gravity through the air. The center of gravity follows the same path as that of any other projectile of equal mass to which the same propelling force is applied at an identical angle.

Heidloff[1] pointed out that centrifugal force (Chapter 5) is involved in all rotatory motion and in tumbling this force tends to cause the body to straighten out from the tucked position. The force produced by the flexor muscles must be equal to the centrifugal force if the body is to remain tucked.

In all rotatory stunts the body must be in an unstable position. If the center of gravity is above the base no rotatory movement will take place. Therefore, the principles of stability are applied in reverse. The loss of stability is used to advantage; that is, the body is placed in such a position that the force of gravity is effective in aiding the rotation.

Forward Roll.   The forward roll is one of the basic tumbling stunts (Fig. 129). This stunt involves rotation around a constantly shifting point of contact with the floor at the same time that the body rotates around its own center of gravity. The beginner may start the forward roll in a squat position.

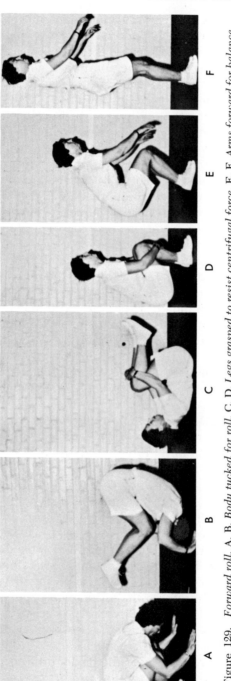

Figure 129.   Forward roll. A, B, Body tucked for roll. C, D, Legs grasped to resist centrifugal force. E, F, Arms forward for balance as come to feet. Extending body slows momentum.

Since the object of the stunt is to roll forward, he pushes with his feet and legs backward and downward against the floor to displace his center of gravity forward and somewhat upward until it passes beyond the forward edge of his base (his toes). This is more easily accomplished if the base is narrow in the forward-backward direction. Therefore, the toes should be in line. This position also makes it possible to apply force evenly to both sides of the body and reduces the possibility of an off-center application of force that would cause a roll to be at an angle rather than straight forward.

As the center of gravity passes the forward edge of the base the force of gravity is added to the force produced by the legs and the body is pulled downward. Since the body is well rounded it rolls forward. As long as it is kept rounded, friction is the only force acting to slow its momentum. Grasping the lower legs is one method of resisting the tendency of centrifugal force to extend the body. When the performer has rolled to the point where the feet are on the mat, extension of the body, which greatly lengthens the radius of rotation, slows the rotatory velocity, making it possible to stop the center of gravity above the feet and thus regain a standing position.

As the performer becomes more skilled and begins his roll from a stand or a run the rotatory force becomes greater and the speed of the roll increases. The sudden lengthening of the radius at the end of the roll may not slow the momentum sufficiently to allow the performer to maintain his balance. The momentum can be stopped gradually either by running forward a few steps or by converting the forward momentum to upward momentum by a jump, and by absorbing the downward force by giving with the ankles, knees, and hips as the feet return to the mat.

At the beginning of the roll, after the center of gravity has passed beyond the feet, the weight is taken momentarily by the hands and sufficient upward force must be exerted by the arms to hold the body high enough to allow the head to clear the mat and gradually lower the shoulders to the mat. The literature indicates a difference of opinion as to the most effective position for the hands on the mat. Some authors suggest that the hands should be placed on the mat with the fingers pointing toward each other (hands sideways). This is advocated because it reduces the resistance to forward movement caused by the fingers when facing forward. Others feel that the hands are important in applying force which is added to that applied by the legs and the force of gravity to give greater rotatory force to the body and, therefore, the hands should be placed on the mat with the fingers pointing ahead so that they are in a position to apply downward and backward force which aids in sending the body upward and forward. Since most girls have little strength in the arm and shoulder girdle muscles, it is advisable for them to place their hands in the most effective position for the application of force if they are to be able to support the body weight long enough to allow the head to clear the mat and to control the lowering of the shoulders to the mat.

Backward Roll. As in the forward roll the body must be placed in an unstable position so that gravity can act to cause rotation around the feet. In this case the center of gravity must be moved back of the base. This is done by bending the legs and hips. Gravity acts to pull the body downward and backward and if the body is well rounded the momentum causes it to roll. Bunn[2] states that some straightening of the body and drawing in of the legs as the hips become the base put the center of gravity back of the hips causing additional rolling momentum. The tucking of the body not only curves the body so that it will roll but also shortens the radius of rotation and increases the turning speed. As in the forward roll the body rotates around two axes, its own center of gravity and an ever-changing point of contact with the mat. The hips, various points of the back, and finally the hands are successive axes for the rotation around the point of contact with the supporting surface. After the center of gravity of the body has moved forward of the hands any force exerted by the arms is applied upward and in the direction of movement. Thus it is effective in both lifting the body to allow space between the mat and shoulders for the head and in adding to the rotatory momentum. Again the rotatory motion is stopped by straightening the body, thus lengthening the radius of rotation.

Backward Roll to a Head Stand. In this stunt the body straightens so that the momentum is slowed as the hips approach the position above the head. The hands must be shifted as far as possible forward of the head to widen the base in the direction of the moving force and to place them in position to apply force diagonally backward and upward to stop the forward momentum of the body.

Forward Tuck Somersault. The forward tuck somersault is essentially a forward roll completed in the air, free of support. The body rotates around its own center of gravity. Since the body must be projected forward and upward and at the same

Figure 130. *Backward roll. Extending body slows momentum.*

time rotated forward, it must be placed in an off-balance position forward. The trunk and arms start the rotating force and the extension of the bent legs projects the body into the air. The higher the angle of projection, the more time available to complete the rotation. Obviously, the greatest height of projection is possible if the body is projected straight upward. However, an angle of less than 90 degrees at take off puts the body into a position of imbalance so that gravity can assist the other forces in producing rotation.

Since the body turns faster in the tuck position due to the shorter lever, it is possible for the performer to complete the turn with less height when in a tuck position than when in a lay out position. Also, less force is necessary to rotate the body in the tuck position. The arms holding the legs close to the body overcome the tendency for the legs to straighten caused by centrifugal force and thus prevent the lengthening of the radius of rotation.[3] The forward rotation is slowed or stopped at the completion of the turn by straightening the body and thus greatly increasing the radius.

NOTE

The principles of equilibrium (Chapter 4), motion (Chapter 5), leverage (Chapter 6), force production and absorption (Chapter 7) and projectiles (Chapter 9) are all applicable to the stunts involved in tumbling. It is impossible in one short chapter to apply these principles to all of the various stunts found in the tumbling literature. The preceding discussion offers examples of some of the possible applications to a few of the stunts commonly included in a basic tumbling class. Further application is left to the teacher or student of tumbling.

REFERENCES

1. Heidloff, Raymond Conrad: A Logical Application of Physics to Selected Tumbling Stunts. Unpublished master's thesis, Springfield College, 1938, p. 31.
2. Bunn, John W.: *Scientific Principles of Coaching.* New York, Prentice-Hall Book Company, Inc., 1955, p. 201.
3. Heidloff, Raymond Conrad: A Logical Application of Physics to Selected Tumbling Stunts. Unpublished master's thesis, Springfield College, 1938, p. 69.

26

Other Activities

Space does not permit the discussion of every activity in the same degree of detail. However, some attention to other common activities may be of help to the student or teacher of movement. This chapter, therefore, treats briefly only a very few of the possible applications of mechanical principles to several activities.

ARCHERY

Archery is essentially a pulling activity as far as the force produced by the archer is concerned. The archer applies force which bends the bow. Thus the bow is given potential energy, energy due to its position, which, in turn, is applied to the arrow when the force which caused the bow's unnatural position is released.

The task of stringing the bow involves forcing it into a greater bend than is normal. This can be accomplished easily by using the two hands to produce a leverage action on the bow. The axis of the lever is the point of contact of the bow with the inside of the archer's foot. One hand grasps the bow handle so that it can apply force to pull the center of the bow outward at the same time the other hand pushes the far end downward. These two forces acting together bend the bow and make it possible to slip the string into the nock at the end of the bow.

The position of the archer with the side toward the target makes possible the longest draw of the string in a straight line. With the head turned toward the target the tonic neck reflex enhances the steadiness of the extended arm.[1] A stance with the feet farther apart than the width of the hips places the body in an effective position for applying sideways force. Since in drawing and releasing the bow, the forces against the body are exerted in a side-to-side direction such a stance is desirable. It makes it possible to hold the body steady during the draw and release since the right foot can exert diagonal force toward the left, and the left leg can exert force to the right.

The speed with which the arrow leaves the bow depends upon the weight of the bow, its natural elasticity, its construction, the length of the draw, and the sharpness of release.

Unless the bow and arrow are angled upward considerably, the tip of the arrow is below the level of the eye. Therefore, as the eye sights over the tip a downward angle is involved. At short range the angle at which the arrow is projected must be small (Chapter 9) and therefore, the tip is well below the eye. Since the line from the eye to the tip of the arrow angles downward, the point of aim is well below the spot toward which the arrow actually points. As the flight of the arrow is lengthened the angle at which it must be projected becomes greater (the arrow must be angled upward) and the tip comes up more in line with the eye. This means that as the distance increases the downward angle of the line from the eye to the arrow tip decreases and therefore, the point of aim must be raised.

Any change in the position of the archer's head changes the angle at which he sights the arrow and thus affects its direction.

Wilson[2] has suggested that the aim be taken *before* the bow is drawn. He stresses that, after the archer establishes his bow hold and finger position on the string with the arms down, he raises his head and looks directly at the gold. He *then* raises the bow and *before drawing* shifts his eyes, keeping the head and shoulders still, to the aiming point and moves the tip of the arrow to this point. *Without moving the head or bow arm* he shifts his eyes back to the gold and then draws. This method allows the aiming point to be closer to the gold than does aiming at the position of full draw because the line of sight over the arrow tip is at a more acute angle, since the tip of the arrow is farther forward of the eyes (Fig. 131). The shift of the eyes back to the gold after aiming but before drawing is important because as the archer draws, the tip of the arrow will no longer point to his aiming point but will point progressively lower, and if he looks at the arrow tip and shifts

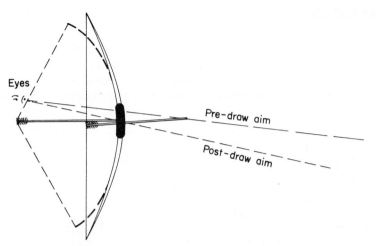

Figure 131. *Different angles of sight resulting from pre-draw and post-draw aiming.*

his position to bring the tip up to the original aiming point, the arrow will go high. Because the aiming point is on the target and the archer, after some practice, can keep his eyes on the gold and see his aiming point in his peripheral vision, this technique offers advantages that lead to more consistent aiming. Wilson suggests using the white on the bottom of the target as the pre-draw (called by him "pre-gap") aiming point at 20 or 30 yards. He does not recommend teaching this method until the student has learned the basic fundamentals of shooting at very close range (maximum 20 feet) at a 36-inch target.

The degree to which eye dominance affects the aim of the arrow is interesting to consider. If an individual has a strongly dominant eye an arrow drawn to the middle of the chin actually is sighted at a slight angle. It may be, that for the individual with a dominant right eye the anchor point under the right side of the jaw is preferable as this gives a straight line from the dominant eye to the tip of the arrow. For the archer with a dominant left eye, this point of aim would cause difficulty in aiming since he would be sighting diagonally to the right over the tip of the arrow. His arrow would, therefore, go to the left. The importance of eye dominance to archery needs further study.

The application of the mechanical principles to the sport of archery is fascinating and a number of books have been written on this subject. The reader who wishes to pursue such study is referred particularly to the book by Hickman et al.[3]

CANOEING

The principles of buoyancy, equilibrium, leverage, and application of force are all important in understanding canoeing just as they are in understanding swimming. Application of knowledge of swimming can be helpful in learning canoeing and vice versa.

A canoe is buoyed up by a force equal to the weight of the water displaced. A sponson canoe which has air chambers running from bow to stern on both sides gives the maximum stability. These sponsons add considerably to the size of the canoe and when in contact with the water displace a great volume in proportion to their weight. Therefore, this type of canoe is very buoyant particularly at the gunwales. Because of this it takes more force to push the gunwale below the surface of the water and thus this type of canoe is less likely to tip over. It has certain disadvantages, however, since the paddler must reach out farther from his body to apply force against the water. As this lengthens the resistance arm more effort is needed to overcome the resistance of the water. Canoes are made in various sizes and shapes and each is particularly effective for a specific purpose.

Both the canoe and the paddle are levers and all the principles of leverage apply. The canoe is a lever of the first class with its fulcrum at its center of gravity. The center of gravity shifts according to the load in the canoe. At any time, the canoe rotates around the center of gravity of the canoe plus any additional weight which it carries. The paddle, like the shovel, is a combination of levers. The resistance is offered by the water and thus is always applied against the blade of the paddle. The lower hand is the fulcrum for any force applied by the top hand (first class lever) and the top hand is, at the same time, the fulcrum for the force applied by the lower hand (third class lever). The farther down the lower hand can be placed comfortably on the paddle, the longer its force arm and the more effective the force produced by that hand.

When an individual enters a canoe or puts a pack or other object into a canoe, the center of gravity of the canoe plus the added weight must be considered. If the canoe is to remain in equilibrium this center of gravity of the total weight must be over the base of support. Since the base of the canoe (the keel plus a few inches on either side) is narrow from port to starboard and long from bow to stern, the canoe lacks stability from side-to-side but is extremely stable from end to end. It is important for the paddler to keep his weight and that of any added load as low as possible to reduce the rotatory tendency resulting from a high center of gravity. To keep the center of gravity over the base it is necessary to step into a canoe directly over the keel. The canoe must be close to the dock so that the force of the step can be straight downward. If the weight of the individual exerts force diagonally outward and downward as he steps into a canoe, the outward force will push the canoe (and foot) farther from the dock and the paddler will be unable to get his center of gravity over this moving base. As a result, he falls into the water between the canoe and the dock.

To reduce the rotatory force inherent in a high center of gravity, the paddler should immediately lower his body by kneeling on the bottom of the canoe, or squatting if he has to move toward an end. To make it possible for the individual to exert straight downward force when stepping out of a canoe, the canoe must be broadside close to the dock. It is important that the push to move the individual up out of the canoe be straight downward. If it is on an angle the canoe will move away from the dock and the individual will not receive enough counter force to move his center of gravity over the foot on the dock and, again, he may find himself in the water.

To keep the center of gravity as low as possible and still leave the trunk and arms in a position to function in paddling, it is best to kneel in the bottom of the canoe. Sitting on seats raises the center of gravity and makes the canoe much less stable. To keep the center of gravity over the base from port to starboard the paddler must kneel in the center (from side-to-side) of the canoe keeping his own center of gravity over the keel. Since the base is narrow, any slight shift of his center of gravity can put it beyond the edge of the base. When two paddlers are in a canoe, it is important that both keep their weight centered. It is possible, of course, to balance a canoe by both paddlers kneeling slightly off-center in opposite directions. Since one has to paddle beyond the side of the canoe there is a temptation to sit toward the paddling side to apply force more easily in the desired direction. Sitting as close to the gunwales as possible does make paddling easier because the force is applied closer to the body and the two paddlers can trim the canoe. HOWEVER, any slight shift of either paddler toward the center of the canoe puts so much weight toward the side on which the other is paddling that the center of gravity of the total (canoe plus the two paddlers), falls beyond the side edge of the base and the canoe tips over.

To keep the center of gravity over the center of the base from bow to stern and thus keep the canoe level in the water, a single paddler must kneel in the center (bow to stern) of the canoe. The center of gravity of the canoe plus the paddler can be shifted forward or aft and still be well within the base, since the base is so large in this direction. However, when a single paddler kneels in the stern the center of gravity falls toward the stern, the weight of that area of the canoe is increased in relation to its size, and the stern moves downward in the water and the bow lifts. When this happens the broader surface of the bottom of the canoe resists forward movement through the water and more bow surface is exposed to any wind. If a cross wind is blowing its effect is magnified. The center of gravity being so far toward the stern the resistance arm of the canoe lever is lengthened increasing the effectiveness of the force produced by the cross wind on the canoe's bow. When a single paddler kneels in the center of the canoe (bow to stern) so that his center of gravity is over the center of the canoe, the canoe remains level, the resistance arm is shortened, and he has equal control over both ends of the canoe. This can be likened to standing astride the fulcrum of a teeter-totter so that force can be applied against both ends, either to balance the board or to rotate it around its fulcrum.

To keep the center of gravity low and over the base while changing positions in a canoe, the body should be lowered by bending the hips and knees and a portion of the weight should be supported by the right hand on the gunwale as the remainder is taken by the left foot and vice versa. In this way the two forces on either side of the center can be balanced at all times.

Since a canoe presents relatively little surface area to resist the water when traveling forward or backward and a large surface when moving broadside, less force is required to move it forward or backward than directly to the side.

When traveling with a wind or current, both forces (wind and paddler) are acting to push the canoe ahead and the forward momentum is the resultant of the two forces. Less force is needed to maintain a given speed. When traveling into a wind or current the force of the paddler is in direct conflict with the force of the wind (or current). The direction and speed of the canoe depend upon the relative magnitude of the two forces. If the wind (or current) is stronger than the force applied by the paddler, the canoe moves backward. If the two forces are equal, it stands still. Only if the force produced by the paddler exceeds the force of wind and current does the canoe move forward. When traveling across a current or in a cross wind, force must be exerted by the paddler in opposition (on the downwind side) if a straight course is to be maintained.

Canoeing is a pushing and pulling activity. As in swimming, the canoe moves in the direction opposite to that in which the paddle applies force. Since force must be applied at the side of the canoe (off-center) it produces rotatory motion unless counteracted by another force. To produce linear motion (straight course) of the canoe equal rotatory forces must be exerted on opposite sides of the canoe, or balancing rotatory forces must be exerted in opposite directions on the same side. The first part of the J stroke applies force off-center backward which sends the canoe forward and rotates the bow to the opposite side. The final part of this stroke exerts pressure both backward and outward sending the canoe ahead and rotating the stern to the opposite side, thus bringing the bow back toward the paddling side. In this way the rotatory force of the first part of the stroke which tends to turn the bow to the opposite side is counteracted by the rotatory force of the final part of the stroke which tends to turn the bow back into the line of direction.

Pressure straight backward (bow stroke) on the right side of the canoe sends the canoe forward and, because it is applied off-center, to the left. The paddle is placed in the water as far forward as possible, still allowing the blade to be almost perpendicular to the top of the water. If the reach is too far forward the paddle must enter the water on an angle and the pull on the paddle produces force diagonally downward and backward. This tends to lift the canoe as well as move it forward. The flat surface of the blade faces the direction of movement through the water so that the large area will produce as much counterpressure as possible. By pushing with the top hand and pulling with the lower hand the blade is moved straight backward to the point where backward force diminishes and upward force becomes a factor. This gives the greatest distance for application of force in the direction opposite to that of desired movement. Beyond this point force pulls the canoe deeper into the water and resistance to forward progress is increased. This stroke follows the same principles of force production as the arm stroke of the crawl (Chapter 24). By dropping the top hand in front of the body, the blade of the paddle is lifted with the side of the blade, which offers very little resistance (very small surface) cutting the water. The blade is carrier forward with the side leading to keep air resistance to a minimum.

Pressure straight in toward the canoe draws that part of the canoe toward the paddle (draw). The same principles apply as in the bow stroke; the difference lies in the fact that the reach is out to the side instead of forward and the paddle is drawn toward the canoe instead of backward. In both strokes the canoe is pulled toward the point where the paddle entered the water. When a single paddler in the center of the canoe uses this stroke, the canoe tends to move broadside since the force is supplied in line with the center of gravity of the canoe. When two paddlers use this stroke on the same side of the canoe it again moves broadside. Since both are applying force in the same direction both ends move in the same direction. When two paddlers use this stroke on opposite sides of the canoe, the canoe rotates sharply around its center of gravity.

Pressure straight outward from the side of the canoe pushes that end of the canoe in the opposite direction. In the pushover stroke the paddle enters the water with the blade parallel to the side of the canoe so that the flat surface is in position to push outward against the water. The paddle is pushed against the water and that part of the canoe in which the paddler is kneeling moves away from the paddle.

Pressure can also be applied at an angle backward and inward, or backward and outward and again the canoe moves in the direction which is opposite to the direction of the force against the water. The diagonal draw on the right when performed by the bow paddler moves the canoe ahead and toward the right. The sweep or C stroke combines the forces of a diagonal pushover and a diagonal draw. The complete stroke executed from the center of the canoe (bow to stern) is effective in turning the canoe in a broad turn to the opposite side. The first half of the stroke moves the canoe forward and turns the bow to the opposite side (diagonal push) while the last half of the stroke (diagonal draw) moves the canoe forward and draws the stern toward the paddle, which also turns the bow toward the opposite side.

The cross bow rudder is a stroke in which the paddle is held against the resistance of the water and the momentum of the canoe actually creates the force which turns the canoe.

There has been much discussion of "bent arm" and "straight arm" paddling. Bent arm paddling has the advantage of using a leverage action of the arms since the top arm can push while the lower arm pulls. Its disadvantage is that much of this action is accomplished by the muscles of the arms and shoulder girdle which are weaker than the larger back and trunk muscles. Straight arm paddling involves more of a pull with both arms, accomplished to a great degree by the larger back and trunk muscles. When paddling in a situation that does not require a great deal of force, and much of the paddling that is done is of this type, the bent arm stroke probably conserves energy. However, when maximum power is needed, the straight arm stroke, which does away with dependence on the weaker arm muscles and uses the stronger back and trunk muscles to advantage, is more effective. Paddlers should be familiar with both methods and understand the advantages of each so that they can choose intelligently according to the demands of a particular situation. In paddling for a long period of time a change from one method to the other could give considerable relief to tired muscles.

FIELD HOCKEY

Field hockey is essentially a game of running, changing direction, and striking with an implement. The underhand throw pattern is involved in rolling the ball onto the field from out of bounds. The principles discussed in Chapter 12, Running, and Chapter 19, Striking, are applicable to this sport. Only a few of the applications of mechanics that are unique to hockey are discussed here.

In many sports, e.g., tennis and badminton, the momentum of the oncoming object adds to the effectiveness of the return hit. In hockey, however, it is wise, for safety, to absorb the force of the oncoming ball before applying force to reverse its direction. Since the ball approaches the vertical hitting surface of the stick with forward spin it tends to rise as it rebounds. As players are close and the ball is hard, injury is likely when a ball rebounds into the air. In hockey, loss of control is likely if the momentum of an oncoming ball is not absorbed when the purpose is to reverse the ball's direction. Since the ball tends to rebound upward, the handle of the hockey stick should be held forward of the blade when a ball is to be stopped. Then as blade gives to absorb the force of impact, the angle of the stick causes the ball to rebound toward the ground rather than upward.

Two methods for preventing the foul of "sticks" are most frequently suggested. One involves a tight wrist on backswing which keeps the blade of the stick low and a rotation of the blade downward on follow-through. This method makes the use of wrist action to produce force impossible, but is successful in avoiding "sticks." In the second method, the well bent right elbow is swung away from the body and up on the backswing and, on follow-through, the left elbow is well bent and swung out from the body. This method allows for the use of wrist action and makes it impossible for the stick to rise above the shoulder. Some individuals are more successful with the first method and others with the second.

In performing the scoop the stick is used as a combination first and third class lever. This can be likened to the use of a shovel (Chapter 6). While the scoop movement, being a light task, is rapid and the heavy task for which the shovel is employed demands a slower movement, the leverage employed is the same.

There is some disagreement among teachers as to the best method for carrying the hockey stick while running any distance on the field. Some have insisted that the stick be carried low with both hands well up toward the end of the handle. The advantage of this position is that the stick is close to the ground at all times and is always in position to play the ball. Its disadvantage is that, being a long implement, it takes considerable effort to control the head of the stick in this position and it is in the way of the forward moving legs of the player as she runs.

Others have taught their students to carry the stick in a horizontal position close to the front of the body, the left hand at the top of the stick and the right well down on the handle. The advantages of this position are that the stick is easier to hold and control and is out of the way of the player's legs as she moves forward. Its disadvantage is that the hand position must be adjusted and the blade of the stick dropped before control of the ball is possible. However, the right hand can slide up the handle very rapidly. It would seem that instead of insisting on the use of one method or the other, the wise teacher discusses the advantages and disadvantages of each and allows the student to select that method which she is able to use most effectively.

A study of the effect of position in the striking circle from which the ball is hit, on the degree of error possible if the ball is to pass through the goal, is interesting.[4] Except when the ball is hit from directly in front of the goal, the "opening of the goal," that is, the area through which the ball must pass to go into the goal, is actually smaller than the 12 foot width of the goal (Fig. 132). Just as in basketball, the opening of the goal available to the ball varies with the angle of the ball's approach. The size of the angle is important to the forward since this indicates the error in her shot which is possible if the shot is to pass through the goal. The opening of the goal is important to both the defense and the forward since it is easier to defend a small area. When a ball is approaching from a point which is 11 feet toward the sideline from the center of the goal and six

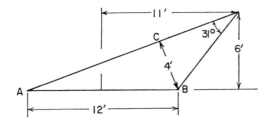

Figure 132. *Ball must pass through area BC in order to enter goal AB.*

feet out from the goal line, it must pass through a four foot
space if it is to pass between the goal posts (Fig. 132). Thus,
if the goalie stands diagonally out from the near goal post
facing the oncoming ball she must guard only the four foot
area.

If shooting from (approximately) opposite the center of
the goal, the angle through which the path of the ball may
vary and still go into the goal is greater as the player approaches the goal line, and the entire width of the goal is always
available.

Feet in Front	Feet to the Side	Angle	Opening of Goal
41	0	17°	12 ft.
21	0	32°	12 ft.
6	0	90°	12 ft.

Therefore, it is advantageous for the center forward to come
in close to the goal line before shooting (assuming that she
has passed the opposing defense with the exception of the
goalie). The center half should tackle her opposing center
forward to force her to shoot as far out in the striking circle
as possible. The farther out, the less area the defense must
cover to prevent the ball from passing between the goal posts
(Fig. 133).

When the ball is hit from a point farther toward the sideline, away from the center of the goal, the opening of the goal
diminishes as the player approaches the goal line. The angle
increases slightly and then, after the player reaches a point
approximately midway to the goal line, it also diminishes.

Feet in Front	Feet to the Side	Angle	Opening of Goal
41	21	13°	10 ft.
21	21	17°	8 ft.
6	21	9°	3 ft.

It is advisable, therefore, for the inner to shoot for the goal
from a point approximately halfway from the edge of the circle

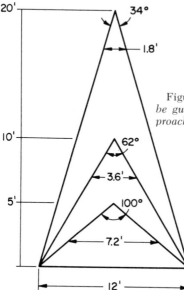

Figure 133. *Increase in width of area that must be guarded to prevent a goal as the forward approaches the goal line.*

to the goal line, since the angle of possible error is slightly larger at this point. This is true if she is not too far out toward the sideline. After the player reaches a point approximately 30 feet out toward the sideline both the angle and the opening of the goal diminish as she approaches the goal line. The fullbacks should attempt to force inners to shoot from far to the side and close to the goal line to decrease the margin of error possible for the shot and the area that must be guarded.

Feet in Front	Feet to the Side	Angle	Opening of Goal
31	31	11°	8 ft.
21	31	10°	6 ft.
6	31	4°	2 ft.

Since wings are normally far from the center of the field any shot taken from their positions must be extremely accurate. These shots are easy to guard since the opening of the goal is small. It is advisable, therefore, for wings to pass to inners or the center forward since these players are in more advantageous positions for shooting. Obviously, the halfbacks should attempt to force the wings to stay out and should be alert for passes toward the center of the field.

It is important that the goalie come out to meet a forward *who has passed all other defense and is well ahead of the rest of her forward line* so that she forces the forward to shoot at a point which results in less area needing to be guarded. She must know where to stand to cover the opening of the goal through which a ball must pass when shot from various angles.

If two forwards are approaching together she must stay back since the shot for goal could come from either.

Strings stretched out on the field to indicate angles and the width of the opening of the goal at various points clearly demonstrate to the student the reason for the coaching suggestions that are given.

SKIING

In many skiing techniques, gravity is the force that causes the movement. The position of the skier on an incline gives him potential energy. The reduced friction between his base (the skis) and the surface offers little resistance to gravity's force as it moves the skier downhill. The skier's main problems involve balancing his center of gravity above a moving base and producing forces which will cause his skis to rotate when he wishes to change direction, or which will overcome the forces of gravity and momentum when he wishes to stop.

Walking on the Level. The reduction of friction presents a problem when walking on skis on the level. Since there is little friction between the ski and the snow, the backward push of the foot, through the ski, against the snow cannot be as great as in walking, or slipping will result. To compensate for this, the poles are used for a point of contact to apply force by use of the arms and shoulders. Since the tips of the poles actually sink into the snow, the backward force against the poles is more directly backward and causes counterpressure from the snow which sends the skier forward. To increase the horizontal component of the force the pole is planted in the snow slightly behind the foot. In order to apply force as much as possible in line with the center of gravity to decrease the rotatory force, the hands are kept close to the sides of the body. The body is inclined forward from the ankles (as in walking) to move the center of gravity ahead of the pushing foot and pole so that there will be a horizontal component to the force applied.

The amount of lean and the push of the foot need to be adjusted according to the friction between the ski and the snow. This depends upon snow conditions and the wax on the skis. In general, the stickier the wax and the wetter (heavier) the snow the greater the friction between the two surfaces. As friction becomes less, less pushing force can be exerted by the feet and the body lean must be decreased. Use of alternate leg and arm gives more effective application of force and better balance since any force applied away from the center of gravity has a rotatory effect. If the push of the arm coincides with the push of the opposite foot, the rotatory tendencies tend to balance.

Downhill Running. The potential energy of the skis is imparted to the body of the skier since he is attached to the skis by the bindings. Since the force is applied to the skier at considerable distance from the center of gravity of his body, there is a tendency for this force to produce rotatory movement of the body which tends to move the legs forward and out from under the body. To compensate for this the skier must move his center of gravity forward. This forward lean should take place from the ankles with the heels kept down so that the surface area between boot and ski is as large as possible, thus making use of the entire ski as a base of support.

The forward lean of the body is in proportion to the degree of steepness of the slope. In general, the body is usually very slightly ahead of the line that is perpendicular to the skis so that air resistance to the body of the skier is counteracted. The faster the skier is moving the greater the air resistance and the greater the forward lean necessary to counteract it.

If the center of gravity of the body gets behind the line perpendicular to the skis (perpendicular to the slope) the body weight tends to push the skis forward and there are then two forces acting on the skis in a forward-downward direction, the body weight and the force of gravity. The skis move out from under the body.

The degree to which the motion of the skis caused by the force of gravity is imparted to the skier is dependent upon the angle of the skier to the skis. The speed of the skis depends upon the angle of the slope and the friction. The steeper the slope, the greater the downhill component of force in relation to the force pulling the skier against the slope and therefore, the skier moves down the hill faster (Fig. 134). The less the friction between the surface of the slope and the skis, the less the resistance offered to the motion of the skier. The less solid the surface (in general, the deeper and less packed the snow), the more the skis drop down into the snow and the greater the resistance to the forward momentum.

In applying this principle the wetness of the snow must be considered. Very dry, powdery snow, even though fairly deep, may offer little resistance. If the crust is thick enough so that the skier does not break through, it offers little resistance. In fact, so little resistance is offered that control is difficult. If the skier does break through the crust, the crust becomes a wall that the tip of the ski must break, and great resistance to forward motion is offered.

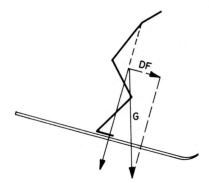

Figure 134. *Greater. downhill component of force with steeper grade.*

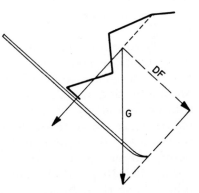

Skiing with one ski ahead of the other reduces the surface offering resistance, and puts the skier in a position to apply pressure which is effective in moving the center of gravity of the body backward or forward more easily. The base is enlarged in the direction of the force and therefore, the body is more stable. When one ski is forward the base is enlarged in the forward-backward direction which is the direction of any probable impacts from bumps or change in snow conditions. If a slowing of the skis is anticipated, the skier must be ready to shift his center of gravity back to be in position to resist the tendency for the upper body to continue moving ahead at the faster speed. Because of the inertia of the trunk it tends to keep moving forward at the same speed. Also the force causing the slowing of the skis is applied against the body at the feet which are a long way from the body's center of gravity and therefore, the lever arm is long.

Since the speed of the skier is affected considerably by the conditions of the snow, it is dangerous for a beginner to ski when the snow conditions vary on the same slope. It takes a great deal of control to adjust the center of gravity as the speed of the skis changes. It takes a skillful skier to control skis on ice since the lack of friction causes any slight change in weight to send the skis off in the opposite direction.

The skier skis with bent knees to lower his center of gravity and thus increase his stability and to make it possible to absorb the shock caused by bumps. The knees should not be bent so far that further bending is impossible when it is necessary to absorb shock.

The principle that the more nearly the center of gravity is over the center of the base the more stable the body, is important in skiing. When the center of gravity is over the center of the width of the base the skis are weighted evenly and they move at the same rate. If the center of gravity is off-center one ski is weighted more than the other. This causes the skier to turn.

Because it is more disastrous to catch an outside edge than an inside edge, some instructors teach students to edge slightly toward the inside to avoid catching an outside edge. Catching an inside edge of a ski places the foot in such a position (ankle rotated in and sole of the foot facing out) that the body weight exerts force away from the center of the stance and the ski moves away from the center. The base is widened and, up to a point, balance is not reduced. The foot is in position to push out against the wall of snow and to push the body in, over the other ski so that the ski that had a caught edge can be lifted and brought back into position. When an outside edge is caught the foot is placed in such a position (ankle rotated out and sole of foot facing in) that the body weight exerts pressure toward the center of the stance and the ski moves in, tending to cross the other ski. The base is narrowed and stability is reduced. If it does cross, the momentum is sharply reduced and, because of the inertia of the body, the skier is likely to fall forward. It is difficult to exert pressure in the direction that will move the center of gravity over the flat ski. When an edge is caught the weight must be moved onto the flat ski so that the weight can be removed from the edged ski and it can be flattened.

Snowplow. In a snowplow the skis are more or less on their inside edges. Hutter[5] states that since the ski is longer in front of its binding than behind it, the resistance of the snow is greater in front of the foot and the ski turns around this pivot point. The resistance in front of the binding can be increased by dropping forward into the knees more and the greater the difference in resistance between the front and rear of the ski, the tighter the turn.

Sideslip. To slide sideways the weight must be kept evenly distributed over the length of the skis. In discussing this technique Hutter[5] states that leaning too far forward puts too much pressure on the tips of the skis, the resistance is increased and they turn to point uphill. The skier then slides backward. If the pressure is placed too much on the back part of the skis they tend to turn downhill.

Parallel Skiing. For the past several years there has been a swing from stem skiing to parallel skiing.[6,7,8] In general, the parallel turns are made by first unweighting the skis and then thrusting the heels in the direction opposite to the direction of the turn. (The tails move to the right when making a left turn.) A forward-upward motion of the body effected by extending the knees and ankles, in combination with a push against the pole which has been placed in the snow about three feet ahead of the foot on the inside of the turn, unweights the tails of the skis and shifts the weight onto the tips. The pole must be placed well ahead of the foot since the body is moving forward and will be even with the pole by the time of the push. It is the inside pole that is used since it is the pivot point for the turn. The momentum of the skier causes him to turn around the pole. This reaching with the inside pole turns the shoulders away from the turn and puts them in position to counterbalance the heel thrust. The heel thrust, which moves the tails of the skis farther around, occurs as the weight drops back and the legs again go into flexion.

The forward-upward movement of the body which unweights the tails of the skis and shifts the weight forward can be demonstrated by standing on a bathroom scale and bending and then straightening the knees. As the knees bend there is a split second drop of the needle to zero and then the needle returns to the original reading. If the legs are extended, the needle jumps higher as the body pushes down against the scale to initiate the movement, drops to zero as the feet follow the body's upward movement, and then settles back to the beginning weight as the upward momentum of the body is overcome by gravity. It is at the moment during extension (when the scale needle would drop) that the tails of the skis are unweighted and the skier's momentum is effective in causing him to turn about the fixed point, his pole. As the turn is completed the skis are edged on the uphill edge to prevent side slipping down the slope.

DANCE

The application of the principles of mechanics to the various types of dance is as important as to any other activity. All principles that deal with equilibrium, motion, leverage, and force application and absorption must be applied in any dance activity. On the whole the rhythm of body movement is set by an outside stimulus. This fact causes problems for some individuals who find it difficult to move in a superimposed rhythm. (Chapter 26.)

The dance walk is a modification of the natural walk necessitated by a difference in purpose. While the purpose of normal walking is to conserve energy over a long period of time, the purpose of the dance walk is to produce a smooth gliding movement which allows for easy and immediate change of direction. Moving the toes forward rather than walking heel first and rolling forward onto the toes, keeps the ball of the foot along the floor, resulting in a gliding movement, and places the ball of the foot and the toes in a position which makes possible immediate application of force whenever change of direction is desired. The reduced friction between the surface of the dance floor and the foot makes it possible to slide the foot along the floor with ease and necessitates a smaller step to reduce the forward or backward component of the force exerted against the floor in order to prevent slipping.

Dance differs from most of the other activities of the physical education program in that its purpose may be to convey to others certain emotions and ideas or to demonstrate body control and patterns. These purposes are accomplished through position or movement and various degrees of energy expenditure. While other activities may seek to produce force with the least expenditure of energy, in dance energy may be sacrificed in order to create a given impression or to express a certain mood or emotion. The sole tool is the body. While properties may be used to create atmosphere, they are not generally used as instruments for the production of force as are the various pieces of sport equipment.

In all dance activities an understanding of the importance of the eyes and the semicircular canals of the ears to balance is extremely important. When turning rapidly the dancer fixes his eyes on a spot and quickly turns the head to that spot so that the eyes have a point of focus and the head is stationary for a part of the time that the body is executing each turn.

Contemporary dance and folk dance use walking, running, sliding, galloping, leaping, jumping, hopping and many combinations of these activities. Although they may be modified slightly because of purpose, the basic mechanics are the same as when these techniques are used in the performance of any other activity.

The buzz step turn which is used frequently in folk dance is unique with the dance activities, although the pivot used in basketball is certainly related to it. In executing this turn, an off-center application of force by one foot causes the body to move in a circle about the other foot which is the center of rotation. In this way it is the same as any pivot. When this turn is performed by two individuals double rotatory force is produced. Since the dancers are moving in a circle centrifugal force acts to pull them apart. This force becomes greater as the dancers lean farther away from each other since the radius of the circle is increased. The dancers must realize that greater force will need to be exerted to keep them together.

The techniques involved in leading are important in both social and folk dance. The best position for a man's right hand for leading differs somewhat according to the dance involved. The accepted position for most dancing involves placement of the man's right hand just below the girl's left shoulder blade. The flat hand increases the surface contact and makes possible the application of force over a broad surface area. Pressure of the whole hand applies force which moves the girl forward. Pressure with the heel of the hand applies off-center force which rotates her to her own right. In order for pressure of the fingers to rotate the girl to her own left, the fingers of the man's hand would need to extend beyond the girl's spine so that the force is applied on the right side of her back. Use of both hands, the right to push on one side or the other of the girl's back and the left to pull or push the girl's hand, makes possible excellent control of rotatory movement. Two forces, both off-center, can be applied at the same time to produce rotatory motion in either direction. *The pressure exerted in leading is slight, giving a suggestion of desired direction of movement more than force.* For difficult leads requiring considerable hip movement, such as those found in the Latin American dances, the man is in a better position to assist rotation of the hips of the girl when his hand is placed nearer to her hip rather than her shoulder.[9]

Tap dance requires that the student become adept at maintaining his equilibrium on one foot, a small base, while moving the other foot in various ways. It involves rapid transference of weight from one foot to another. The use of the arms to counterbalance the movements of the legs is extremely important. As in several other activities the student must learn to use the loss of equilibrium to initiate movement while maintaining an erect position.

In contemporary dance the body must frequently supply the resisting force as well as the force being applied. For example, when the dancer wishes to convey the idea of forceful pushing, the antagonists to the muscles of the arm and shoulder which produce the pushing force, must be contracted to resist the prime movers. The mechanical principles are followed in order to convey the idea rather than to apply force to an object.

In teaching beginners, practice of fundamental contemporary dance techniques is started with the students sitting or lying on the floor. A wide base of support and low center of gravity make it possible to concentrate on the movements being practiced without concern for the maintenance of balance. Practice at a bar is useful in minimizing balance problems while learning certain techniques which cannot be executed in a sitting or lying position. In general, the student progresses from a wide base to a narrow base, from a low to a high center of gravity, and from performing a technique over a stationary base to performing it over a moving base.

Because of the importance of the length of the lever, small light movements of the extremities can be performed away from the center of gravity but strong heavy movements need to be executed close to the body.

In performing the various dance falls the center of gravity is lowered as far as possible before it is allowed to move beyond the edge of the base. The weight is then rapidly spread over as large an area as possible so that the force per unit of area will be small. All of the principles of force absorption are extremely important since the dancer must continually absorb the kinetic energy produced by a leap, jump, or even a run.

In general, the dancer must become skilled in the control necessary to maintain positions and to move under conditions that make equilibrium difficult. He must know the principles of mechanics in order to be able to produce the amount of force desired for the particular technique or to convey the desired impression to others. He must be able to apply the principles of force absorption if he is to avoid injury.

BODY CONDITIONING EXERCISES

As in dance the lying and sitting positions, because of the broad base and low center of gravity, make it possible to concentrate on an exercise without concern with the maintenance of balance. The difficulty of some exercises is increased by changing the starting position from the sitting or lying position to a standing position and finally to performing the exercise above a moving base.

The force of gravity is used to increase the stretch placed on muscles and thus to aid in the development of flexibility. It is also used as a resistive force in the development of strength. In the forward-downward bending of the trunk gravity assists in pulling the upper body downward and increases the stretch of the muscles of the leg, hip, and lower back. In exercises in which the weight of the body itself, or of a body part is lifted or lowered slowly, gravity supplies the resistance against which the muscles must work. When lying on the side and lifting the leg upward the weight of the long lever must be lifted against gravity's pull. In lowering the leg effort is increased by controlling the speed of the drop so that again gravity's force must be resisted.

An understanding of the importance of the length of the lever is extremely important in the choice of body conditioning exercises. Since more momentum can be developed at the end of a long lever, the lengthening of the lever is important in producing additional force to stretch tight muscles. For example, a certain amount of stretch of the trunk muscles results from trunk twisting performed with the hands on the hips. However, when the arm on the side toward which one is twisting is flung diagonally upward and backward, the stretch is increased considerably because of the momentum which is transferred from the long arm lever to the trunk to which the arm is attached.

Lengthening the lever being lifted or slowly lowered against the pull of gravity greatly increases the effort required. Therefore, those exercises which use long levers are more effective for the development of strength. In the well known sit-up exercise the long trunk must be lifted against the force of gravity. Adjustment of the position of the arms and hands varies the degree of difficulty of this exercise because of the change in the distance of the weight from the fulcrum for the movement (the hips). When the arms are held forward the center of gravity of the upper body is as close to the fulcrum as possible. Reaching forward with the arms increases the ease of the sit-up since the momentum of the arms is transferred to the trunk and aids the abdominal muscles in overcoming inertia. When the hands are placed on the hips, the center of gravity moves slightly upward from the hips and the arms are no longer useful in supplying initial momentum. Therefore, this is somewhat more difficult. Crossing the arms over the chest and placing each hand on the opposite shoulder further lengthens the distance from the hips to the center of gravity of the upper body and increases the difficulty of the lift. The position with the hands placed at the back of the neck is even more difficult as the weight is still further from the fulcrum. In this position there is a tendency for the performer to swing the elbows forward and thus gain momentum which reduces the difficulty of the exercise. If the strongest exercise is desired it is important that the elbows remain out to the side throughout the exercise. Placing the arms straight above the head lengthens the lever to its maximum. Because this makes the exercise so difficult (if the arms are really kept in this position) it is almost impossible to resist the tendency to swing the arms forward, and since the lever is so long, if this is done the momentum that can be developed is considerable, and when this is transferred to the trunk the exercise becomes easier instead of more difficult.

Since the psoas muscles, which are strong hip flexors, are put on the stretch when one lies on the back with the legs straight, they are in an excellent position to assist the abdominal muscles in causing the sit-up movement. Bending the legs and placing the feet flat on the floor releases the stretch of this muscle and it can no longer assist the movement *to the same degree.* When the feet are held down on the floor by placing them under a bar or a piece of furniture or by having them held by a partner, the psoas is more effective than when the feet are free. Therefore, for maximum exercise of the abdominal muscles the knees should be well bent and the feet should not be held.

The psoas and iliacus muscles have some attachments on the lumbar vertebrae and therefore, any strong pull by these muscles with the legs stabilized will pull on the lower back and can cause strain if the upper body is allowed to lag behind. Therefore, this exercise should always be executed with the knees bent and by curling the back rather than allowing the back to arch.

In developing the abdominal muscles through this exercise the position should vary with the present strength of the individuals in the group. All should have the knees bent and the feet flat on the floor. Some may need to reach forward with their arms in the beginning. Others may be able to place the hands on the back of the neck and still keep the elbow out to the side. Still others may find the other positions necessary. Many may be unable to perform a sit-up when the feet are not held. Since the holding of the feet brings the psoas muscle to the assistance of the abdominals it would be advisable for these individuals to use a curl-up exercise that can be performed without this assistance in place of the so overworked sit-up exercise. Effort to lift by curling and to hold the upper body a few inches off the floor is probably more effective in abdominal muscle development than the complete sit-up exercise.

The part of the sit-up exercise which calls for maximum expenditure of effort is the first part of the movement. As the trunk is lifted off the floor inertia must be overcome, the weight is the farthest from the fulcrum, and the angle of pull of the muscle is most disadvantageous. As the upper body nears the position above the base the exercise becomes progressively easier. Once the movement has started inertia helps the movement. The weight arm progressively shortens and the angle of pull becomes increasingly larger and therefore becomes more advantageous. It might be wise to change the concept of this exercise and instead of starting from a lying position, to start from a sitting position with the legs bent and feet flat on the floor and lower the curled trunk backward and downward as far as is possible, keeping the feet on the floor and holding the upper body suspended above the floor for a period of ten seconds.[10] As abdominal strength increases the individual will be able to hold a position closer and closer to the floor.

Analysis of the popular straight leg lifting, and slowly lowering exercise makes it clear that it should be used with caution. Since the strong hip flexors are attached to the pelvic girdle and the thighs, effort to hold the long leg lever against gravity results in a pull against the pelvis which is transferred to the lower back. As in the sit-up exercise, the greatest strain comes when the legs are closer to the floor or when the angle of pull (angle between muscle and thigh bone) is smaller. It is easy to hold the legs straight up above the hips. The force of gravity pulls them down onto their base and the angle at which the muscles are functioning is advantageous (large). As the legs are lowered this angle of muscle function becomes smaller and at the same time the distance from the center of gravity of the legs to the fulcrum is increased. Both factors increase the effort required to control the legs against the force of gravity. If the abdominal muscles are not strong enough to stabilize the lower back, strain may result. The leverage and angle of muscular pull involved in this exercise must be recognized so that injury to the lower back is avoided. If the individual *flattens his back* against the floor, draws the knees into the chest, straightens the legs and, at the instant he *begins* to feel the lower back leave the floor (when he is no longer able to stabilize), allows the knees to bend and the feet to drop to the floor, no strain of the lower back is involved. If he continues the exercise with an arched lower back, strain is likely. Placing one hand on the floor beside (touching) the lower back will make it possible for the individual to know immediately when the back begins to lift.

In suggesting body conditioning exercises the condition of each individual must be considered and exercises must be adjusted to the present level of strength, flexibility, coordination, and endurance. Application of the mechanical principles indicates adjustments in movements that increase difficulty and effectiveness, and reduce the possibility of injury due to strain.

REFERENCES

1. Houtz, Sara Jane: Personal communication, July, 1963.
2. Wilson, R. I. (Dick), Manager, Archery Division, Shakespeare Company, Kalamazoo, Michigan, personal correspondence, June, 1965.
3. Hickman, C. N., Nagler, Forrest and Klopteg, Paul E.: *Archery, the Technical Side.* Milwaukee, The North American Press, 1947.
4. MacLean, Dorothy and Broer, Marion R.: Angles in Hockey Goal Shooting. Unpublished study, University of Washington, 1949.
5. Hutter, Clemens Maria: How You Can Learn Wedeln, Part I: Boil Your Skiing Down to the Absolute Essentials. *Ski,* 21:22, November, 1956.
6. Schaeffler, Willy, Bowen, Ezra and Riger, Robert: The New Way to Ski. *Sports Illustrated,* 7:22:34–42, Nov. 25, 1957; 7:25:60–69, Dec. 16, 1957; 7:26:94–106, Dec. 23, 1957.
7. Throw Away that Stem. *Sports Illustrated,* 21:21:46–51, Nov. 23, 1964.
8. Hutter, Miki: Technique Today: An Evaluation: *Skiing,* 17:3:92, 154–157, Dec., 1964; 17:5:58–60, Feb., 1965.
9. Wilson, Ruth M.: University of Washington, Seattle. Personal Conference.
10. Waite, Elizabeth M.: Conditioning Exercises. Unpublished paper, University of Washington, 1958.

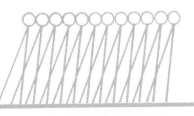

Part Five

Movement Education

27

Teaching Efficient Movement

The teacher is accorded a great privilege – that of guiding and often shaping, the thoughts and actions of others. This privilege carries with it grave responsibilities. It is the duty of every teacher to help each student with whom he comes in contact, gain as much knowledge, and as many skills as possible, so that the student will be able to use his capacities to the fullest as he meets and attempts to solve the problems of life.

Physical educators have a unique opportunity *and* a unique responsibility. Since movement is used in some way, to some degree, in almost every task accomplished by human beings the teaching of efficient movement becomes both an obligation and a challenge – a challenge to help each student develop the ability to use his body effectively in the performance of all tasks demanded of it, whether these tasks involve everyday living skills, work skills, or recreational skills.

How can physical educators, in the short period of time during which they have contact with a student, develop in him an understanding of, and skill in, such a variety of activities? In general, the recreational skills have received the focus of attention in recent years. However, if physical education is to make a real contribution to the total education of each student it must do more than give him a few isolated skills, most of which can be used only in specific recreational situations.

The challenge to the profession is: Can the teaching be broadened so that in the short period of time available to physical education each student can gain skill, not in a few isolated activities (most of them recreational), but skill in movement? Can physical education give the student such a thorough understanding of the only tool with which he can perform any task—his body—that he will be able to use it efficiently when he is faced with any new situation?

Physical educators have frequently experienced difficulty in the communication of their ideas in the field of movement education because of problems of semantics. To some, the term "Body Mechanics" has meant various postures or corrective activities. To others, the term has stood for the group of activities that include standing, walking, running, sitting, pushing, pulling and lifting, while still others have taken the view that all positions and movements involve body mechanics and, therefore, no such restrictive definitions are justified.

Discussion of the problem at the National Association for Physical Education of College Women Workshop in 1956 led to agreement on the following definitions:

Body Mechanics—the application of physical laws to the human body at rest or in motion. The term does not denote any specific set of activities or course content.

Basic Movement—movement carried on for its own sake, for increased understanding, or for awareness of the movement possibilities available to the human body.

Basic or Fundamental Activities—motor skill patterns that form the foundation for the specialized skills required in daily life, work, sports, dance (standing, walking, running, jumping, pushing, lifting, throwing, etc.).[1]

General acceptance of such a set of definitions could do much to further movement education since it would increase greatly the understanding of discussions in this field. If the physical educator is to accomplish his purpose of developing each individual's ability to meet effectively the majority of motor problems confronting him, he must teach body mechanics and basic movement and the application of these to the fundamental motor activities as well as to recreational activities.

If the physical educator understands the *basic* mechanical principles and their application to human motion he can teach knowledge important to *all* skills through any specific activity. This can be done only if he thinks in terms of movement education rather than in terms of specifics such as tennis, basketball, and softball. This does not imply that these specifics are not taught, but simply that they are used as vehicles to teach the students how to produce and control force, how to use their body levers, how to absorb force, and how to maintain balance or use instability to advantage. One cannot learn to play tennis without playing tennis. However, the learning of tennis can be facilitated and can contribute to more general knowledge of body movement through the application of previously learned patterns and knowledge of the way the body produces and controls force.

Students must be helped to gain insight into the relationships among various movement situations and into the broad application of basic principles and basic movement patterns. "Positive transfer is easier and more likely to occur when instruction. . . encourages the learner to be on the look-out for similarities and differences and if attention is drawn to underlying principles of wider application."[2] Knapp[3] also stated that if an individual practices an activity without perceiving relationships, his learning is likely to be highly specific to the situation in which it was gained.

The physical educator must be able to tell the student *why* he has failed to accomplish his purpose, why the ball went too low, or to the right, or beyond the end line. He must also be able to suggest possibilities for changes in movement and to make clear the ways in which these suggestions can contribute to more effective production of the desired results.

Over the years the methods of teaching physical education classes have varied considerably. "Most teachers, regardless of activity taught, have concentrated on skill patterns established authoritatively, and have presented them in the finesse of detail desired of the polished performer." [4] They have taken no notice of individual differences but have expected every student to reproduce the exact same movement. They have evaluated success in terms of what the student looks like as he executes the particular skill involved, rather than in terms of the efficiency of the performance for the particular individual. These teachers have taught by the "do it this way" method. Others have taught by the "do it this way *because*" method which, while it does include a reason for the suggested technique, may still require that all students look alike. Still others have used the problem solving approach.

The "do it this way" method ignores the fact that learning is an active process; that learning takes place as insight dawns — and this is as true of learning a motor skill as it is of any other learning. For effective learning, the student must be involved beyond simply going through a movement described and demonstrated by the teacher. He needs to be involved in considering the possibilities and deciding which movements have the greatest possibility for the best results according to his purpose. Further, this type of teaching demands the impossible, namely, that all students, regardless of physical and emotional makeup, perform an activity in exactly the same way. In demanding this the teacher may actually interfere with the development of skill. The case of the diver required by the teacher to lift her left knee on the hurdle (p. 17), although her normal movement pattern called for a right knee lift, is an excellent example of this type of teaching. Rarely, if ever, does this method of teaching lead to ability on the part of the student to apply material learned to any other activity.

When the reasons for the suggested technique are advanced by the teacher, application may be possible, at least to activities which are quite obviously similar. However, the teaching still may not involve the learner and may still interfere with learning if the teacher insists on the reproduction of a stereotyped pattern.

The problem solving method of teaching does involve the learner, and discussion of similarities makes possible a much broader application of the material of the course to other activities which may be encountered later. It also teaches students how to solve motor problems. The problem solving method of teaching movement defines the problem in terms of purpose. The student, *through meaningful exploration structured and guided by the teacher,* gains insights, and through application of these ideas determines the method for accomplishing his purpose with the least strain and least expenditure of energy.

In teaching the overhand throw the teacher might define the first purpose simply as that of hitting a specified height on the wall by a throw from a point approximately ten feet away. The students will be able to accomplish this purpose in a variety of ways since the task demands little effort. The next step might be to have the students move away from the wall and, at five foot intervals, throw the ball in such a way that it will hit the wall at the same height. Students working in pairs, or even groups of three or four, can observe the various adjustments in the movement which are made as the distance of the throw increases. The final distance should be sufficient to call for an all-out effort from the majority of students. Students may start using an underhand pattern of movement but as the distance is increased beyond their ability to throw underhand and hit the specified height on the wall, they will shift their patterns to allow for a longer backswing, more trunk rotation, etc. Discussion at various stages of this procedure can bring out the important principles of force production.

As various factors which contribute to increased distance are noted by members of the group, the teacher can suggest experimentation which will indicate the effectiveness of this factor. For example, when standing ten feet from the wall it will be easy to hit the wall with arm movement only. As the students move back they will soon discover that the backswing must be increased and, as the distance becomes even greater and they need an even longer backswing to work up sufficient momentum, they will find they must rotate their trunks to carry their arms back to the maximum position. Experimentation with swinging the arm back as far as possible without body rotation, holding this arm position and then rotating the trunk, quickly demonstrates the lengthening of the arc of the swing which is brought about by body rotation. The additional strength contributed to the throw by the trunk muscles when body rotation is used can also be demonstrated.

Experimentation with throwing as far as possible with the feet together, with the feet in a side stride, with the right foot forward, and finally with the left foot forward demonstrates the importance of a wide base in the direction of the force and the restriction of body rotation caused by the position which places the foot on the same side as the throwing arm, forward.

Experimentation with throwing the ball with as much force as possible at a low angle, a high angle, and a 45-degree angle demonstrates the importance of angle to the distance of the throw. If the teaching is taking place in a gymnasium, various rafters or points on the ceiling which the instructor knows will guide the releases at the approximate angles desired can be indicated as targets for the various throws. In each case the purpose is defined as throwing the ball with as much force as possible in the direction of a particular rafter. The student is asked to note the distance the ball travels (with each attempt) before hitting the floor.

Thus through structured experimentation the importance and the possibilities for application of various mechanical principles become obvious to the student. The more meaningful the learning experience the more likely learning is to occur. For further discussion of the overhand throw see Chapter 18, pp. 209–220. The teaching possibilities are as numerous as the ingenuity of the teacher permits.

A teacher who has, in the past, based his teaching upon the description of movements, at first may not see the many possibilities for structuring experiments for student learning. However, once he begins to attempt this type of teaching he will find that more and more ideas come to him. As in all learning, it is "by doing" that the teacher learns to teach through problem solving. He will probably need to start with only one or two structured problems a day but, if he thinks in terms of teaching movement rather than a specific sport skill, ways to make basic principles "dawn upon" his students will become obvious to him as he plans his lessons. Not all problems that the teacher structures will be effective in producing the desired perception on the part of the students, and many will not be equally successful with all students. However, the teacher can learn something from each attempt that will increase his effectiveness in the presentation of future problems. This type of teaching can be used with any age group. As with any teaching the vocabulary must be adjusted to the background of the particular group. The more technical terms can be brought into the teaching as they enter the curricula of other subjects. As the students study the laws of gravity and leverage in general science these terms can be incorporated into the physical education lesson. Simple experiments in movement which will clearly demonstrate the application of the various principles of motion, balance, force production, and absorption can be devised for the younger students. In this way a sound foundation in movement education can be laid at an early age.

A teacher needs to study carefully a student's ineffective performance in order to determine the *basic* reason for it. If it is caused by lack of strength, lighter equipment and exercises for the development of the particular muscular strength demanded by the task, can be prescribed. If faulty spatial concepts are involved, time to practice activities which will aid in the development of the new concept will be well invested. Lack of kinesthetic perception can be remedied by setting up a situation that will demand the use of the particular movement. For example, the previously discussed device of suspending a tennis ball at the height of the student's full racket reach aids in the development of a feeling for the movement pattern of the service, since the student must execute a full swing in order to contact the ball. Manual manipulation may also be effective in giving some students a feeling for a movement. This should be used as a last resort or in special situations since the kinesthetic sensations experienced by the learner are somewhat different from those he feels when performing himself and, as stated by Knapp[5] there is the risk that he will adopt a passive attitude which is never conducive to learning. However, in certain situations it can be extremely useful. For example, a girl having trouble with the overhand throw may gain the concept of "whip" rather than "push" by having her hand actually thrown by her instructor standing close behind her and holding her wrist so that her arm lies along that of the instructor and follows exactly its movement. If this is to be successful, it is important that the student's arm be completely relaxed. A lack of understanding can be dealt with by carefully structured problem solving situations. If any of the above is the basic reason for the student's lack of success, reiteration of the "correct" method of performance will be of doubtful value.*

Teachers "need to recognize that many somewhat different movements may be efficient and correct for a given purpose, depending on the individual doing the performing."[4] Carefully designed movement experiences can demonstrate to the student the reasons (in terms of basic physical laws) for the greater effectiveness of certain movement patterns over others. If the student is to understand the reason for the superiority of a technique, the teaching of each skill needs to be built upon the principles basic to efficiency in the particular movement being studied. It is only through such understanding that relationships between various movements of the body and between various activities become obvious to the student and he may then be able to apply his learning in other situations. However, the teaching situations must be geared for this carry-over. Teachers must teach for application. Students must be helped to generalize so that they will understand principles. They must be helped to see similarities in movement *and* in principles; to understand the ways of thinking about and attacking the solution to a new movement problem. They must learn to analyze the purposes of the movement in general terms, such as the amount of force that will be required and direction in which it must be applied to accomplish the specific purpose, and then, considering the basic principles, to determine the various ways that the segments of the body could be moved to produce the required force. Seldom is there just one way to execute any skill and there may be several possible methods, each with its advantages and disadvantages. Students must learn to weigh these and make a final choice on the basis of *all* the factors involved.

The student approaching the learning of golf should realize that the principles which he learned in tennis can guide him in determining the most effective method for hitting the golf

---

*For further discussion, the text edited by Ainsworth (Reference 6) is recommended.

ball. If the knowledge and skills gained through instruction in one activity are to give the student a base on which to build in other movement situations, the teacher must help the student make applications to other sport techniques and to activities of everyday living. Students should, through such teaching, realize that each activity is not completely new and unfamiliar but that previously acquired knowledge and skills can be applied to accomplish a new purpose. Thus learning time can be shortened. Kilby's use of the layup shot pattern in teaching a basketball player to dive (Chapter 23) is an example of such teaching.

In the teaching of movement there needs to be less concern with what the student looks like and more concern with the efficiency of the movement—its mechanics, degree of energy expenditure, and rhythmic quality.

Degree of energy expenditure is dependent upon purpose. If the purpose of the particular activity demands an all-out effort, such as a throw for distance, all of the factors which can contribute to greater speed at the end of the throwing lever should be employed and maximum expenditure of energy is called for. On the other hand, if the purpose is to serve the badminton bird from the front of one service court to the front of the diagonally opposite service court (short service), few of the factors involved in force production are required. Since the movement of the arm alone can produce sufficient force for the purpose, the longer backswing and additional muscular strength which are added to the movement by body rotation simply waste energy. The foot position is unimportant since body rotation is not needed and the force produced is not sufficient to upset body equilibrium even if the base is relatively small.

How frequently do teachers insist that each student reproduce the entire pattern of the activity, regardless of the particular purpose involved? Actually there is not one basic pattern for any activity; there is a pattern for maximum force production and this is adjusted as less force is needed to accomplish the specific purpose. These adjustments to less force will be accomplished differently by different individuals. Of course, the purpose may be to deceive the opponent, in which case, the obvious factors involved in maximum force must be included in the movement and much more energy expended than needed for the flight of the ball or shuttle that is produced. In fact, additional energy is expended to reduce the force at impact. However, the movement is satisfying the purpose which is to deceive the opponent.

The most efficient throw for a given situation may be made with a short swing which, in a particular situation, may be accomplished most efficiently with the feet almost together. Yet, how frequently is the student required to stand in a stride position with the left foot forward for *every* throw, regardless of whether this position contributes to the purpose of the movement? If the student understood that the left foot forward increases equilibrium by enlarging the base without restricting body rotation to the right, he would realize when it was necessary to assume this position.

Much teaching has become a matter of weaving together many devices which, although useful in correcting certain faults, are not necessary to the effective performance of the movement. Instead of using these devices one or two at a time *as the need becomes evident,* some teachers have lumped them together to form a stereotyped movement pattern required of all. Golf is probably the best example of this and a more detailed discussion can be found in Chapter 20.

Another example might be the teaching of floating in the swimming program. The placing of the arms in the water above the head and drawing of the legs toward the body in the frog position are devices for redistributing the body weight around the center of buoyancy. Some individuals, depending upon body build, need to make use of all possible devices while others need to use none. It is useless to teach all, regardless of buoyancy, to assume the same position. The principles involved in floating should be understood by all and each student should then make the adjustments in position demanded by his own body build. *The teacher needs to recognize the difference between devices which may be successful in helping some students, and the basic mechanical factors necessary to the successful accomplishment of the particular purpose and which, therefore, apply to all.*

Studies have indicated that the learning of a motor skill which involves both speed and accuracy proceeds most effectively when both are emphasized from the beginning. Accuracy developed at a slow tempo may be lost when the movement is speeded up, but there is little loss of speed when emphasis is placed on accuracy. Therefore, while it may be expedient for the student to go through a pattern of movement in slow motion in order to develop an understanding of sequence, continued practice at this tempo is a waste of time.

Some teachers have superimposed their own speed and rhythm of movement on their students. It must be recognized that individuals have different body rhythms. Some can adjust easily to superimposed speeds and rhythms, others cannot. Those who can, are successful in the various dance activities, gymnastics, and synchronized swimming. Those who cannot, even though they may move easily in activities which they can perform in their own rhythm, experience great difficulty in activities demanding a set rhythm. For example, consider the individual who is a skillful skier, basketball player, and swimmer but who cannot move efficiently in a dance class. Research is needed to determine methods of teaching which can most successfully help such individuals so that they need not forego the pleasure which can be experienced in taking part in this type of activity.

In situations in which movement in a superimposed rhythm or at a specified speed is not necessary to the purpose of the activity, the teacher would do well to allow the student to develop his skill in his own tempo. Using music in the teaching of various swings, such as the golf swing, may be useful in helping to induce a relaxed swinging motion as opposed to a more percussive hitting motion. For some students it may also be an aid in the establishment of a feeling for the rhythmic pattern involved. However, it would seem unwise to continue the musical accompaniment for a long period or to insist that all students maintain its rhythm. This, again, may be a useful device in helping some students to relax but it must be realized that it may hinder the learning of those who have difficulty in moving to an outside rhythmic stimulus.

In summary, if physical educators would focus on the process of learning and would guide the students through experiences which would cause ideas to "dawn upon" them, more efficient learning would result. If they would set up problem solving movement situations which would lead to student insight into the scientific facts of efficient movement instead of superimposing stereotyped movements, they could save time for themselves, their colleagues, and their students; the students would not be confused by attempting to give attention to many small details that do not actually affect the efficiency of the movement. Time and energy should be spent in teaching the basic mechanics that are essential to effective accomplishment of the purpose. The student should be free to develop his own style so long as his mannerisms do not interfere with the basic mechanics of the movement. The teacher must realize that no two students can, or should, look exactly alike as they perform a specific activity.

If physical educators would also structure movement situations which demonstrate similarities between various movement experiences, both in basic movement patterns and in mechanical principles involved, their teaching would become a more vital force in the lives of their students. Not only would the students gain understandings and skill which can be applied in a variety of situations, they would learn ways of attacking new problems. They would learn "how to learn" and this is perhaps the greatest contribution a teacher can make to any student.

REFERENCES

1. Movement Group Report, *Workshop Report: Purposeful Action*. Washington, D.C., The National Association for Physical Education of College Women, 1956, p. 89.
2. Knapp, B.: *Skill in Sport*. London, Routledge and Kegan Paul, 1963, p. 111.
3. *Ibid.*, p. 112.
4. Movement Group Report, *Workshop Report: Purposeful Action*. Washington, D.C., The National Association for Physical Education of College Women, 1956, p. 93.
5. Knapp, B.: *Skill in Sport*. London, Routledge and Kegan Paul, 1963, p. 25.
6. Broer, Marion R.: Teaching Individual Sports, in Ainsworth, Dorothy (ed.): *Individual Sports for Women*. Philadelphia, W. B. Saunders Company, 1963, particularly pp. 6–7.

28

The Foundation Course and Its Application to Physical Education Activities

A foundation course of some type has become an important part of many physical education programs and many other physical educators are planning to introduce such a course into their programs. At present, such courses are common for women at the college level and frequently are being offered to men, or in a coeducational situation. They are being introduced also at the junior and senior high school level. Many of the more recent curriculum guides published at state and local levels include units of instruction in movement fundamentals. This course has been given various titles, "Fundamentals," "Basic Activities," and "Basic Skills," to name a few. In general, the purposes are to give students a broader base of experience on which to build future motor performance and to maintain at least the minimum fitness levels demanded by their patterns of living. The accomplishment of these purposes is being approached differently in different situations. The content varies more in emphasis than in the broad areas of knowledge and skill included.

Content usually includes such areas as relaxation techniques, body conditioning, movement exploration, and the basic skills of standing, walking, running, leaping, sliding, stopping, jumping, landing, falling, pushing, pulling, holding, lifting, carrying, throwing, catching, and striking. Understanding of basic principles involved as well as skill in moving have been emphasized. More recently the importance of including background material dealing with physiology of exercise has been recognized.

The ability to relax the body at will, particularly the ability to relax, during movement, those muscles which can in no way contribute to the movement demanded by a particular task, contributes greatly to motor achievement. In general, unnecessary tension interferes with the smooth sequence of muscular action necessary for a coordinated movement.

Many students have difficulty in learning various physical education activities because of a lack in certain of the physical prerequisites discussed in Chapter 2. Body conditioning exercises are included in the foundation course for the purpose of causing bodily changes which will improve function, as well as to give the students an understanding of the mechanics and physiological effects of exercises which can be effective in the development of various elements of physical fitness. A well designed exercise program can increase the level of endurance, flexibility, strength, speed, and coordination. While not all of these are necessary to the same degree for success in every activity, each contributes to the effective performance of many of the activities commonly engaged in every day as well as those offered in a physical education program.

For example, lack of strength may make it impossible for the beginning bowler to swing the ball in a straight line because he does not have the strength to control this weight at arm's length from the body, or it may make it impossible for the dancer to perform a successful leap; lack of endurance may cause the hockey or soccer player to be ineffectual in defensive action because he cannot keep running at the speed needed, or it may cause the basketball player to lose accuracy because of fatigue. Without a minimal level of development in these physical prerequisites effective performance of physical activities is impossible.

Since physical condition constantly fluctuates according to the activities of the particular individual, it is not enough for the student to develop these elements of fitness during the time he is enrolled in the foundation course, it is necessary for him to gain an understanding of the methods for *keeping* the body at a desirable fitness level. Many students leave school with at least acceptable skill and knowledge in some sports as well as a knowledge of exercises which could be useful in maintaining a satisfactory level of physical fitness, and yet rarely use this skill and knowledge thereafter. If students are to be expected to make future use of learning, they must clearly understand the contribution of exercise to the effective functioning of the human body. The physical education instruction must present such information in a way that makes it vital to each student.

Through exploration of the movements possible for the various body segments, the student is able to perceive the movement potential of his body. For example, he not only can determine the possible range of motion of his upper extremities, but he can also determine the extent of this range which is within the limits of stability and can perceive this in relation to the various bases which his body can establish. Fundamental movement education should include extensive exploration of the movement possibilities of the body, both of itself and with a great variety of objects. If small children were given unlimited experiences in movement exploration and a wide variety of movement problems to solve, by the time they reached junior high and high school they would have a vocabulary of movement patterns which could be used with understanding in the development of more specific skills. However, since most high school and even college students have not had such experience, movement exploration becomes an important part of a foundation course.

The physical principles that determine the effective method for the performance of the basic skills are applicable to all movement, and the skills which make up the various physical education activities use basically many of these same patterns. There may be some modification owing to difference in purpose. The broadness of this application is shown in Table 2. The activities in the physical education program which use the various basic skills, either the identical movement patterns or patterns which are basically the same although somewhat modified, are listed under each basic skill classification.

Since the individual is on his feet in all of the activities taught, with the exception of canoeing, crew, riding, and swimming, knowledge of the principles of, and skill in maintaining a well balanced standing position have broad application. Actually, although the individual is in a horizontal position in swimming, the principles of alignment of the various body segments are no different from the vertical position and the knowledge and skill gained in discussion and practice of standing are applicable even to swimming.

TABLE 2. APPLICATION OF FOUNDATION COURSE TO SPECIFIC PHYSICAL EDUCATION ACTIVITIES

A. Content leading to development of physical, mental, and emotional prerequisites necessary for successful performance in any activity.

Body Conditioning Exercises   Relaxation Techniques   Movement Exploration

B. Content areas leading to development of knowledge of mechanical principles and skill involved in many movement patterns utilized in successful performance of the various specific activities noted under each area.

Standing	Walking	Running and Stopping	Jumping, Leaping, Hopping, etc.	Landing and Falling	Sitting	Pushing and Pulling	Holding, Lifting, Carrying	Throwing° and Catching	Striking°
All activities except: Canoeing Crew Riding Swimming	All activities except: Archery Canoeing Riding Shuffle-board Weight Lifting Note: use of walking coordination in crawl kick, in swimming	Badminton Baseball-Softball Basketball Dance Football Handball Hockey Lacrosse Speedball Speed-away Squash Rackets Tennis Track and Field	Apparatus Basketball Dance Diving Skiing Track and Field Tumbling Volleyball	Apparatus Baseball-Softball Basketball Dance Football Skiing Tumbling Track and Field Volleyball Wrestling	Canoeing Crew Contemporary Dance Riding	Archery Canoeing Crew Dance Fencing Riding Shot Put Shuffle-board Swimming Wrestling	Canoeing Dance Tumbling Weight Lifting Wrestling Note: Carrying equipment for many activities such as: Golf, Skiing, etc.	Apparatus (spotting-catching) Baseball-Softball Basketball Bowling (throwing) Deck Tennis Football Lacrosse Track and Field Tumbling (spotting-catching) Speedaway Speedball Some application of throwing to: Hockey (Roll-in) Soccer (Goalie)	Badminton Baseball-Softball Basketball Bowling Boxing Football Golf Handball Hockey Pool and Billiards Squash Rackets Soccer Speedaway Speedball Table Tennis Tennis Volleyball

°Use the same basic movement patterns.

Canoeing, crew, and riding involve sitting rather than standing and the principles of a well balanced sitting position, which are the same as those of a well balanced standing position, are applicable to these activities.

In many of the activities which include running—and the list is long—only short runs with rapid changes of direction are involved. This is true of basketball and all of the racket games. Men's basketball involves longer distances than does women's. The field sports of softball, football, hockey, soccer, speedball, speedaway, and lacrosse demand that longer distances be covered quickly. However, in all of these the ability to stop and change direction suddenly is also important. Only in some of the track events, in running to first base in baseball or softball, or in dance, can the individual gradually slow his run to a stop. Skill in running and stopping is the same whether one is learning basketball or tennis, hockey or a dance technique.

To be successful in basketball, volleyball, or diving one must be able to lift the body weight into the air. Many tumbling and apparatus activities also demand height of body projection. In dance, as in track and field activities, the individual must be able to apply a projecting force upward or outward depending upon the particular purpose.

Any type of projection of the body into the air is, of course, inevitably followed by a forceful contact of the body with the floor or ground. Also at any time that the body is moving rapidly a fall may result. Therefore, it is important that individuals taking part in any motor activity understand the principles of force absorption and become skilled in their application. In some physical education activities, such as dance and tumbling, force absorption is involved in the performance of the actual skill. In others, it is the natural aftermath of the skill, as in landing from a jump in basketball, volleyball, and track and field activities. While falling or landing is not involved in the actual skill of skiing, the importance of the knowledge of the principles of force absorption and skill and their application cannot be overlooked if injury is to be avoided in the performance of this activity.

Many physical educators, while agreeing that it is important to understand the principles of pushing, pulling, holding, lifting, and carrying because of their application to daily living activities, fail to appreciate the importance of this knowledge in the learning of sport activities. In the past, the teaching of these activites probably has been approached with the least enthusiasm on the part of both pupils and teachers of any of the areas included in the foundation course curriculum because frequently they have been taught as isolated and routine skills. What is the skill involved in archery except pulling? The body, the canoe, the shell, the rowboat move through the water as a result of a push or pull exerted against the water. The horse slows as a result of pressure against his mouth caused by a pull on the reins. The action which moves the fencing foil toward the opponent is essentially a push, as is the action which projects the shot.

A canoe must be lifted and carried to and from the water and launched without damage to the canoe or strain of the back of the carrier. Partners must be supported in tumbling and sometimes in contemporary dance or even folk dance. In coeducational dance the man frequently lifts his partner. Many activities involve the carrying of equipment which is heavy and if carried or lifted incorrectly strain can result. The golf cart has relieved the golfer (or caddie) of the task of carrying the heavy bag of clubs. However, the golf bag must still be pulled. Knowledge of the physical principles involved in tasks of pushing, pulling, lifting, and carrying can be skillfully applied in a wide variety of physical education activities.

While it is impossible, in a foundation course, to teach all of the specific types of "throws" or "strikes" that are involved in the physical education activity program, the three basic patterns (pp. 216–220 and Figures 2, 3, 4, pp. 11–15) and the principles of balance, force production, projection, angle of rebound, and spin can be included. If skill in these three basic patterns and an understanding of the principles involved are gained through such a course, much time can be saved in learning specific activities later.

It is interesting to note that striking is used in more activities than is throwing. It is a common concept that throwing is the most used of the basic skills with the possible exception of standing, walking, and running. Probably one of the reasons for this concept is the wide use of throwing in various games of low organization. It is reasonable that the student should be taught the basic throw-strike patterns with the object held in the hand. These can be applied later to the more difficult tasks involving contact with an object (striking).

Many of the common physical education activities use both throwing and striking. Throwing is more important in some and striking in others. Some individuals may question the inclusion of basketball in the list of striking activities. In dribbling, the player does strike rather than throw the ball, and in turn, the ball strikes the floor and the principles of rebound operate. The principles of striking are also important to success in basket shooting whenever the backboard is used.

With imaginative teaching the student can, through a foundation course, gain knowledge and skill which will be of great value in all future motor learning experiences. For example, he can gain skill and an understanding of the principles involved in quick starts, stops, and changes of direction and this is useful in such activities as badminton, basketball, tennis, softball (baseball), fencing, track, field hockey, and many other activities. Balance is important in any movement, but a clear understanding of the principles is particularly necessary in such activities as skiing, gymnastics, riding, to name a few. He can develop the ability to time his body movements with the movements of objects and this is required in badminton, tennis, basketball, field sports, volleyball, fencing, etc. The coordination of trunk rotation, transference of weight, and arm movement is met over and over and if, each time, the student's attention is directed to this coordination and its effectiveness for the particular purpose, he can gain an understanding of the principles involved and skill in its use, and it can become a tóol which he will be able to apply effectively as needed in many sports. He can learn not only the physical principles by which the body operates and many basic movement patterns, but he can also learn the ways of attacking a movement task so that, in the future he can determine for himself the most effective method for accomplishing a desired purpose.

Application of the knowledge and skill gained in a foundation course can facilitate the learning of specific activities in the physical education program. If the teaching of these activities is based upon problem solving, the student's skill in determining effective movement according to purpose can be strengthened.

If no foundation course is offered, or if it is impossible to provide such a course for all students, it is important that each specific activity be taught in such a way that the students learn as many of the principles of movement as are applicable to that activity, and that the teacher help the students to make broad applications to a variety of motor tasks. For example, a student in tumbling can gain skill and knowledge in the areas of balance control, motion, force production and absorption, and leverage. He should, after such a course, be able to apply the knowledge gained to such tasks as lifting heavy objects in his home or garden and he should be able to determine how to attempt to avoid falling injuries when he takes up skiing. A student in tennis should gain skill and knowledge that he could apply to any throwing or striking activity in which he might care to participate in the future.

Many departments of physical education have placed certain restrictions on the free election of physical education activities. Some have completely specified the physical education program. Others have required that students elect a team sport, an individual sport, a rhythmic activity, or swimming. They have expressed concern that each student have contact with an activity that has the potential for teaching social values as well as certain motor skills (team sport); one that has high "carry-over possibilities" (individual sport); one that requires adjustment of movement to an established rhythm (rhythmic activity). Swimming for those who cannot swim has been added because of its survival benefit. Perhaps it would be wise to consider as well, the possibilities that each activity offers for the teaching of basic movement patterns and physical principles and make certain that any requirement assures each student's exposure to all of the mechanical principles involved in human motion.

Index

Absorption of force, 79–81
  catching, 220–221
  falling, 159–162
    into water, 161–162
  hockey, 345
  landing from jump, 155, 156
Acceleration, 49, 70, 79
  of gravity, 37
Acuity of senses, 25, 30
Agility, 31
Air resistance, 27, 37, 38, 58, 101–102, 215, 247, 259, 261, 274
American twist serve (tennis), 281–282
Analysis of movement, 5
Angel balance, 327–329
Angle(s)
  of arched shot (basketball), 304–305
  of muscle pull, 75–76
  of projection, 97–102
  of rebound, 82–83, 87–93, 229–246
    effect of spin, 87–93, 229–233, 246
  shooting (hockey), 346–349
Angular motion, 51–52, 55, 65, 76
Apparatus, 377
Application of basic mechanical principles, to fundamental skills, 107–247
  to sports and dance, 251–360
Application of force, 69–79
  direction (angle) of, 73–76
  distance of, 77–78
  point of, 76–77
Approach (bowling), 285–286
Archery, 337–339, 377, 379

Archimedes' principle, 39, 309
Arm swing, in running, 145
  in walking, 131–132

Back stroke, elementary, 314–315, 321
Backswing, golf, 255–256
  tennis, 280–281
Backward roll, 334, 335
  to head stand, 334
Badminton, 27, 225, 273–282, 377
  clear, 12
  grip, 275
  serve, 11, 275, 276, 370
Balance. See *Equilibrium.*
Balance control, 29, 31
Balance stunts, 324–330
  angel balance, 327–329
  chest stand, 329
  head stand, 324–327
  knee shoulder stand, 329–330
  planché, 329
  shoulder stand, 327
Ballroom dance, 355, 377
Barnet, Nan, 297
Barr, George, 307
Baseball, 377, 378. See also *Catching, Running, Striking,* and *Throwing.*
Basic activities, defined, 364
Basic mechanical principles, 35–103
  applied to fundamental skills, 107–247
  applied to sports and dance, 251–360

Basic movement, defined, 364
  patterns, 6–19
    one foot jump for height, 18–19
    overhand, 7, 12–13
    sidearm, 7, 14–15
    underhand, 7, 8–11
Basic skills, 107–247
  defined, 364
Basketball, 299–307, 355, 377, 378
  lay-up, 18, 153, 300, 304
  pivot, 355
  throw (distance), 14
Basmajian, J. V., 67, 81
Batting, 15
Bent arm paddling, 344–345
Billiards, 377
Body angle (running), 144
Body build, 25, 108
Body conditioning exercises, 357–360, 375, 377. See also *Exercises.*
Body mechanics, defined, 364
Bow stroke, 343
Bowen, Ezra, 360
Bowen, Wilbur Pardon, 35, 39, 93, 323
Bowling, 26, 50, 283–298, 377
Boynton, Dorothy A., 122, 123, 208
Braun, Genevieve L., 123
Breast stroke, 322
Broad jump, 155, 157
Broer, Marion R., 23, 122, 223, 272, 307, 323, 360, 373
Brogdon, Elizabeth, 109, 122
Brouha, William, 196
Brown, Innis, 272
Brunnstrom, Signe, 13, 123
Bunn, John W., 81, 145, 147, 257, 272, 334, 336
Buoyancy, 38–39, 309–313, 340
Burke, Roger K., 103
Butterfly stroke, 322
Buzz step, 355

C stroke (sweep), 344
Canals, semicircular, 46, 354
Canoeing, 340–345, 377, 379
  bent arm paddling, 344–345
  changing positions, 342
  currents, 342–343
  entering and leaving, 340–341
  leverage, 340
  paddling position, 341
  straight arm paddling, 344–345
  strokes, 343–344
  wind resistance, 342–343
Carrying, 192–196
  application in physical education
    activities, 377, 378–379

Carrying (*Continued*)
  books, 195
  on head, 196
  suitcase, 3, 194
  tray, 195
  up and down stairs, 196
Carter, Don, 288, 289, 297
Cartwheel, 330
Catching, 80, 81, 220–221, 222–223, 377
Cates, H. A., 62, 67, 76, 81
Center of gravity, 35, 36, 37, 41, 42, 43, 44, 45, 73, 111, 193
  height of, 36
  method for determining, 36
Centrifugal force, 53, 54, 355
Centripetal force, 53, 54
Chair
  choosing, 176
  easy, 165–167, 172
  lifting, 201–203
  occasional, 165, 170
  straight, 164–165, 170–172
Changing position in canoe, 342
Chest stand, 329
Circular backswing (tennis), 280–281
Circular motion, 53
Cleats, 146, 257
Coefficient of friction, 56–57
  of restitution, 82, 226, 258
Conditioning exercises, 357–360, 377. See also *Exercises.*
Conservation of momentum, law of, 225
Contemporary dance, 355, 356, 379
Contour of ground (golf), 265, 271–272
Cooper, John N., 32, 40, 46, 47, 146, 147
Coordination, 31
Corrsin, Dr. John, 86
Crawl stroke, 316, 317–320
Cross bow rudder, 344
Crouch, James E., 81
Crouching start, 147
Culver, Elizabeth J., 293, 297, 298
Cureton, Thomas K., 320
Currents, 342–343
Curvilinear motion, 52

Dance, 354–356, 377, 378
  contemporary, 355, 356, 379
  dance walk, 354
  falls, 356
  folk, 355, 379
  leading, 355
  social, 355
  tap, 355–356

Davidson, Bill, 208
de Saint-Venant, M., 313, 323
Direction of force application, 73–76
  badminton, 280
  bowling, 284, 287–293
  golf, 258–261
  jumping, 154
  pushing and pulling, 183
  striking, 229–246
  swimming, 314
  tennis, 280
  throwing, 213–215
Distance of projection, 97–98, 246–247
  golf, 261–268
  jumping, 155
  striking, 246–247
  throwing, 215–216
Diving, 19, 153, 157
Downhill running (skiing), 350–352
Draw stroke, 343–344
Dribble (basketball), 300
Driver, Helen Irene, 282
Driving (golf), 264, 268–269

Easy chair, sitting down and arising, 165–167
  sitting position, 172
Efficient movement
  concepts, 3–32
  definition, 31
  prerequisites, 25–32
    emotional, 28, 30
    mental, 27, 30
    physical, 25–27, 30
  teaching, 363–373
Electromyography, 5, 7, 16, 109, 217, 252, 300
Elementary back stroke, 314–315, 321
Elftman, Herbert, 126, 141
Emotional prerequisites, to efficient movement, 28, 30
Endurance, 25, 30
Equilibrium, 41–47, 81, 111, 354
  catching, 220, 222
  holding and carrying, 193
  importance of sensory organs, 46–47, 354
  standing, 111–112
  throwing, 211
Exercises, 357–360
  flexibility development, 357
  strength development, 357–360
    sit-up exercise, 357–359
    straight leg lowering, 359–360
  use in foundation course, 375, 377

Exploration of movement, 375, 377
External weights, influence on center of gravity, 44
Eyes, 30, 46
  dominance (archery), 339
  in dance, 354

Falling, 17, 80–81, 159–162, 377, 378
  dance, 356
  into water, 161–162
  on land, 159–161
Falling bodies, law of, 37
Feet, position
  in golf, 256, 258–259
  in jumping, 154, 155
  in standing, 113–114, 117
  in walking, 130–131
  on stairs, 137–138
Fencing, 377, 379
Field hockey. See *Hockey.*
Fixation (stabilization), 70, 71, 133, 182
Flattening arc of throw, 211, 213–214
Flexibility, 25, 30, 108, 357
Flight of shuttle, 27, 101–102, 274
Flip, front, 331
Flitter, Hessel Howard, 142
Floating, 309–313
Floor, lifting objects from, 197–200
  sitting on, 167–170, 172–176
Folk dance, 355, 379
Foot, leverage of, 62–63. See also *Feet.*
Footwork, 276
Force, 69–81
  absorption, 79–81. See also *Absorption.*
  application, 69–79
  centrifugal and centripetal, 53, 54
  direction, 73–76. See also *Direction.*
  distance, 77–78. See also *Distance.*
  magnitude, 70–73. See also *Production.*
  point of application, 76–77
  production, 69–73. See also *Production.*
Force of impact, 79
Form, 17, 20
Forward roll, 330, 331–334
Foundation course, 374–381
Friction, 56–58, 73, 74, 124, 133–134, 136, 146, 154, 182, 183, 212, 257
Frog kick (wedge), 315, 321
Front flip, 331
Fuller, Dudley Dean, 123, 142

Fundamental activities, defined, 364
Fundamental skills, 107–247
  carrying, 192–196
  catching, 220–221
  falling, 159–162
  holding, 192–196
  jumping, 151–158
  lifting, 192–193, 196–208
  pushing and pulling, 181–191
  running, 143–150
  sitting, 163–180
  standing, 107–123
  stooping, 196–198
  striking, 224–247
  throwing, 209–222
  walking, 124–142
Fundamentals course, 374–381
Furniture
  desk, 177
  ironing board, 121
  kitchen counter, 121
  kitchen sink, 121
  kitchen stool, 178
  typewriter table, 178

Gardner, Ernest, 141
Goal shooting, basketball, 301–306
  hockey, 346–349
Golf, 252–272, 369
  contour of ground, 265, 271–272
  direction, 258–261
  distance, 261–268
  driving, 264, 268–269
  grip, 254, 257, 258, 259
  hill lies, 267–268
  iron shots, 262, 263, 266, 267
  putting, 269–272
  speed, 255–258
  spin, 259–261, 262–265
  stance, 256, 257, 258, 259
  wind resistance, 261
Gollnick, Philip D., 217, 223
Good form, 17, 20
Gravity, 35–38, 58, 151
  acceleration of, 37
  center of, 35, 36, 37, 41, 42, 43, 44, 45, 73, 111, 193
  line of, 37, 41, 111, 112, 134
Grip
  badminton, 275
  golf, 254, 257, 258, 259
  tennis, 275
Ground, contour of (golf), 265, 271–272

Hand, striking with, 226
Harmon, D. B., 172, 178
Harvey, T. D., 262, 263, 272

H'Doubler, Margaret N., 22, 23
Head position (standing), 116
Head stand, 324–327
Heels, effect on standing position, 120
  effect on walking, 127
Heidloff, Raymond Conrad, 331, 336
Height of kitchen sink and counter, effect on standing position, 121
Hellebrandt, Frances A., 20, 23, 107, 109, 112, 122, 123
Heusner, William W., Jr., 314, 323
Hickman, C. N., 339, 360
Hicks, Betty, 272
Hicks, Clifford B., 86, 93
Hill lies (golf), 267–268
Hockey (field), 345–349, 377, 378
  positions
    center forward, 346, 347
    center half, 347
    fullback, 348
    goalie, 347, 348
    halfback, 348
    inner, 347–348
    wing, 348
  scoop, 346
  shooting angles, 346–349
  stick, carrying, 346
  fouling prevention, 345–346
  stopping ball, 345
Holding, 192–196, 377
Hook (bowling), 289–290
Hopping, 151, 152, 377
Houtz, Sara Jane, 23, 122, 223, 272, 307, 323, 338, 360
Huelster, Laura J., 21, 23
Hurdling, 157
Hutter, Clemens Maria, 352, 360
Hutter, Miki, 20, 23, 360

Impact, force of, 79, 225
Incline, walking up and down, 134–136, 139–140
Inertia, 48
Injury, avoidance of, 79, 80, 81, 207
Iron shots (golf), 262, 263, 266, 267

J stroke, 343
Jones, Ernest, 272
Joseph, J., 112, 120, 122
Judgment, spatial, 27, 30
  timing, 27, 31
Jumping, 16–19, 73, 151–158, 377, 378
  angle of take-off, 154, 155, 157
  application to physical education activities, 377, 378
  arm swing, 152–153, 156

Jumping (*Continued*)
  backward, 157
  force, 152–153, 157
  height, 16–19
  landing, 155, 156, 158

Karpovich, Peter V., 62, 63, 67, 136, 142, 217, 315, 316, 322, 323
Kendall, Florence P., 120, 122, 123, 207, 208
Kendall, Henry Otis, 120, 122, 123, 207, 208
Kick, crawl, 319–321
Kidwell, Kathro, 293, 298
Kilby, Emelia-Louise, 300, 307
Kinesthetic perception, 5, 30, 108, 217–218
Kitchen counter and sink height, effect on standing position, 121
Klopteg, Paul E., 360
Knapp, B., 365, 368, 373
Knee shoulder stand, 329–330
Knees, position
  in jumping, 154, 155
  in running, 145–146
  in standing, 115, 117
Kraus, Hans, 32

Labyrinthine reflex, 109
LaDue, Frank, 55, 59, 100, 103
Landing, 80, 81
  application to physical education activities, 377, 378
  from fall, 159–161
  from jump, 155, 156, 158
  in water, 161–162
Lanoue, Frederick Richard, 100, 103
Laws. See names of laws.
Lay-up shot (basketball), 18, 153, 300, 304
Leaping, 151, 152, 377, 378
Lee, Mabel, 81
Leverage, 60–68, 340
Levers
  classes, 61–65
    first class, 61, 63–64, 206
    second class, 62, 63
    third class, 64, 207
  function of, 60
  human body, 66–67
  in pushing, 189, 191
  principle of, 65

Lifting, 192–193, 196–208
  application in physical education activities, 377, 378–379
  heavy chair, 201–203
  heavy object, from floor, 197–200
    from shelf, 203–206
  tray from table, 200–201
  suitcase, 200, 204–205
  with shovel, 206
Line of gravity, 37, 41, 111, 112, 134
Linear motion, 52, 53, 55, 76
Linear velocity, 54
Lissner, Herbert R., 40, 68, 142, 194, 208
Locomotor patterns, 17

MacLean, Dorothy, 360
Manning, Kenneth V., 40, 59, 68
McCormick, H. G., 109, 122
McDonald, F. W., 322, 323
McKee, Mary Ellen, 297, 298
Mechanical principles, 35–103, 376–377
  applied to fundamental skills, 107–247
  applied to sports and dance, 251–360
Mental prerequisites, to efficient movement, 27, 30
Metheny, Eleanor, 21, 23, 39, 128, 142, 172, 178
Methods of teaching, 365–368
Modern dance. See *Contemporary dance*.
Moment of force, 65
Momentum, 50, 70
  law of conservation of, 225
Morehouse, Laurence E., 32, 40, 46, 47, 146, 150
Morrison, Alex J., 272
Morton, J. Dudley, 112, 123, 142
Motion, 48–59. See also *Movement*.
  factors modifying, 56–58
  Newton's laws of, 48–51
  types of, 51–59
    angular (rotatory), 51–52, 53, 55, 65, 76
    circular, 53
    curvilinear, 52
    factors determining, 55–56
    linear (translatory), 52, 53, 55, 76
Movement. See also *Motion*.
  analysis, 5
  concepts, 3–32
  education, 363–381

Movement (*Continued*)
efficient. See *Efficient movement.*
exploration, 376, 377
patterns
jump, 16–19
locomotor, 17
overhand, 7, 12–13, 16, 216–217
sidearm, 7, 14–15, 16, 219
underhand, 7, 8–11, 218–219
teaching, 363–373
Movement tasks, types, 4
Mullaney, Dave, 305, 307
Muscle pull, angle of, 75–76
Muscular control, 31
Music, use in teaching, 372

Nagler, Forrest, 360
Newton's laws of motion, 48–51
first law, 48, 145, 183
second law, 49
third law, 49, 225
Norman, Jim, 55, 59, 100, 103

Observation, 5, 6
Occasional chair, sitting down and
arising, 165
sitting position, 170
Opening window, 188–189
Overhand pattern, 7, 12–13, 16, 216–
217
Overhand throw, 12, 213–214, 216–
218, 366–367

Paddling, 344–345
position, 341
Parallel skiing, 353–354
Patterns of movement, 6–19, 370.
See also *Movement.*
Pelvis, position in standing, 115, 117–
118
Physical education requirement, 381
Physical prerequisites, to efficient
movement, 25–27, 30
Pin bowling, 290–293
Pivot, basketball, 355
Planché, 329
Point-of-aim (archery), 338–339
Pool, 377
Posture
basic principles, 110–116
good, defined, 111
sitting, 163–180
standing, 107–122
values, 109–110

Power, influence on movement, 25, 30
Pregnancy, effect on standing position, 120
Prerequisites to efficient movement,
25–32
chart, 30–31
emotional, 28, 30
mental, 27, 30
physical, 25–27, 30
Principles, mechanical. See *Mechanical principles.*
Problem solving teaching, 366–368,
372–373
Production of force, 69–73
badminton, 273–274, 276, 280
bowling, 284–287
golf, 255–258
jumping, 152–154
pushing and pulling, 182–183
striking, 226–228
swimming, 317–322
tennis, 273–274, 276, 280
throwing, 210–213
Projectiles, 94–103. See also *Throwing* and *Striking.*
angle, 97–102
definition, 94
distance, 95, 97, 100
height, 97
methods of projection, 94–95
speed, 97
Proprioceptors, 47
Pulling, 74, 181–191
application in physical education
activities, 377, 378
canoeing, 343
efficient performance, 185–190
principles involved, 182–185
swimming, 317
Purposes of movement, 5
Pushing, 57, 71, 181–191. See also
Pulling.
Pushover stroke, 344
Putting (golf), 269–272

Rasch, Philip J., 103
Reaction force, 49, 225
Reaction time, 25, 30
Readiness, position of, 275–276
Rebound
angle of, 82–83, 87–93, 229–246
avoidance of, 79
basketball, 301–304, 305–306
bowling, 293–297
effect of spin on, 87–93, 230–234,
246
Reflexes, 109–110, 131–132

Relaxation, 374, 375, 377
Requirement, physical education, 381
Resistance, air. See *Air resistance.*
    water. See *Water resistance.*
Resultant of two forces, 73, 87
Rhythm, 5, 371
Riding, 377, 379, 380
Riger, Robert, 360
Rogers, James Frederick, 62, 63, 67
Roll. See *Rotatory stunts.*
Rolling, 218–219
Rotatory motion, 51, 52, 53, 55, 65, 76
    effect on stability, 45–46
Rotatory stunts, 330–336
    backward roll, 334, 335
        to head stand, 334
    forward roll, 330, 331–334
    front flip, 331
    somersault, 334, 336
Rotatory velocity, 54, 55
Running, 51, 73, 143–150
    application to physical education
        activities, 17, 377, 378
    arm swing, 145
    body angle, 144
    in circle, 147
    leg swing, 144
    speed, 145
    starting, 147–148
    stopping, 148, 377

Scatter rugs, 133
Schaeffler, Willy, 360
Scoop (hockey), 346
Second ball (bowling), 293, 294
Semicircular canals, 46, 354
Senses, acuity of, 25, 30
Sensory organs, in equilibrium, 46–47, 354
Sequence of force, 71, 72, 210
Serve
    badminton, 11, 275, 276, 370
    tennis, 13, 14, 276–279
        American twist, 281–282
    volleyball, 10, 21
Shelf, lifting object from, 203–206
Shoulder stand, 327
Shoulders, 116, 118
Shoveling, 188, 206
Shuttle, flight of, 27, 101–102, 274
Sidearm pattern, 7, 14–15, 219
Sidearm throw, 14, 219–220
Sideslip (skiing), 353
Similarities between activities, 6–19
Sitting, 163–180
    application in physical education
        activities, 377

Sitting *(Continued)*
    easy chair, 165–167, 172
    floor, 167–170, 172–176
    occasional chair, 165, 170
    straight chair, 164–165, 170–172
Sit-up exercise, 357–359
Skiing, 57, 349–353, 377, 378
    downhill running, 350–352
    parallel, 353–354
    sideslip, 353
    snowplow, 352
    walking on level, 349–350
Skills, basic. See *Basic skills.*
    fundamental. See *Fundamental skills.*
Smash (tennis, badminton), 279
Smith, Paul, 293, 298
Snowplow (skiing), 352
Soccer, 224, 377, 378
Social dance, 355, 377
Softball, 377, 378. See also *Catching, Running, Striking,* and *Throwing.*
Somersault, 334, 336
Spatial judgment, 27, 30, 275
Speed
    badminton, 273
    basketball, 267
    bowling, 284–287
    force production, 71, 72
    golf, 255–258
    leverage, 60, 61, 63, 67
    projection, 97, 98, 103
    running, 144, 145, 147
    striking, 226–228
    tennis, 277–279
    throwing, 210–213
    walking, 127–128
Speedaway, 377, 378
Speedball, 377, 378
Spin, 83–93, 216, 228–229, 230–234, 246, 281
    basketball, 300, 306
    bowling, 288–289, 296–297
    effect
        on flight, 84–87
        on rebound, 87–93, 230–234, 246
        on roll, 86–87
    golf, 259–261, 262–265
    striking, 228, 230–234, 246
Spot bowling, 290–293
Spot shooting (basketball), 300–304
Stability, 41–47
Stabilization, 70, 71, 133, 182
Stairs, ascending and descending, 136–140
Stance, archery, 338
    golf, 256, 257, 258, 259
Standing, 107–123
    application to physical education
        activities, 376, 377

Standing (*Continued*)
  basic principles, 110–116
  gaining concept of, 117–119
  on moving train, 42
  values of good position, 109–110
Standing start, 148
Stanley, Louis T., 254, 272
Starting (running), crouch, 147
  stand, 148
Stearns, W. J., 322, 323
Steinhaus, Arthur, 5, 14, 23
Sticks, prevention of (hockey), 345–346
Stock, Malcolm, 147, 150
Stone, Henry A., 35, 39, 93, 323
Stooping, 196–198
  advantages of, 198
Stopping (running), 148, 377
Straight arm paddling, 344–345
Straight chair, 164–165, 170–172
  sitting down and arising, 164–165
  sitting position, 170–172
Strain, avoidance of, 72, 207
Strength, 25, 26, 30, 72, 108
  increase of, 72, 357–360
Stretch reflex, 107
Striking, 209, 224–247
  application to physical education activities, 377, 379
  direction, 229–246
  distance, 246–247
  force production, 226–228
  spin, 228, 230–234, 246
  type of motion, 228
  with hand, 226
Strokes, canoeing and swimming. See names of specific strokes.
Stunts and tumbling. See *Tumbling.*
Suitcase, 200, 204–205
Sweep (C stroke), 344
Swimming, 308–323, 377, 381
  breast, 322
  butterfly, 322
  crawl, 316, 317–320, 343
  elementary back stroke, 314–315, 321
  floating, 309–313
  force production, 317–322
  wedge kick, 315, 321

Talbert, William F., 282
Tap dance, 355–356
Tasks, movement, 3, 4
Teaching
  efficient movement, 363–373
  golf, 268–272
  problem solving, 366–368, 372–373
  speed and accuracy skills, 371

Teaching methods, 365–368
Tennis, 13, 14, 26, 27, 253, 273–282, 377
  drive, 14
  grip, 275
  service, 13, 14, 276–279
    American twist, 281–282
Tepper, Rubye, 109, 122, 123
Terrell, Roy, 86, 93
Throwing, 209–220, 221–222, 379
  application in physical education activities, 377, 379
  direction, 213–215
  distance, 215–216
  flattening arc, 211, 213–214
  patterns, 6–16, 216–220
  speed, 210–213
  types, basketball, 14
    overhand, 7, 12–13, 16, 213–214, 216–218, 366–367
    sidearm, 14, 219–220
    underhand, 8, 10, 218–219
Timing control, 31
Timing judgment, 27, 31
Tittle, Y. A., 7, 23
Tonic neck reflex, 109
Track and field, 377, 378, 380. See also *Jumping, Running,* and *Throwing.*
Translatory motion (linear), 52
Tray, holding and carrying, 195–196
  lifting, 200–201
Tumbling, 324–336, 377
  angel balance, 327–329
  backward roll, 334, 335
    to head stand, 334
  cartwheel, 330
  chest stand, 329
  forward roll, 330, 331–334
  front flip, 331
  head stand, 324–327
  knee shoulder stand, 329–330
  planché, 329
  shoulder stand, 327
  somersault, 334, 336
Tuttle, W. W., 73, 81

Underhand pattern, 7, 8–11, 218–219
Underhand throw, 8, 10, 218–219

Values of well aligned position, 109–110
Velocity, 50, 70, 77
  linear, 54
  rotatory, 54, 55
Vision, 30, 46

Volleyball, 226
  serve, 10, 21
  spike, 18

Wagner, Miriam M., 81
Waite, Elizabeth M., 360
Walking, 42, 73, 124–142
  application in physical education
    activities, 17, 377
  arm swing, 131–132
  backward, 134
  body position, 129
  dance walk, 354
  foot position, 130–131
  friction in, 133–134, 136
  on ice, 133
  on incline, 134–136, 139–140
  on moving train, 42
  on sand (mud), 133
  on skis, 349–350
  on stairs, 136–140
  phases of, 125–126
  position of feet in, 130–134
  speed of, 127–128
  stability in, 127, 128–130
Warm-up, 73
Water, falling into, 161–162

Water resistance, 58, 308–309, 313–316
Watts, Diana, 22, 23
Weber, Robert L., 40, 59, 68
Wedge kick, 315, 321
Weights, external, 44. See also *Lifting.*
Weiss, Raymond, 153, 158
Wells, Katharine, 40, 53, 59, 81, 109, 122, 133, 142, 323
Wet floors, 133
White, Harvey E., 40, 59, 68, 81, 93, 103
White, Marsh W., 40, 59, 68
Williams, Marian, 40, 68, 142, 194, 208
Wilson, R. I., 338, 360
Wilson, Ruth M., 360
Wind resistance
  canoeing, 342–343
  golf, 261
  striking, 247
  throwing, 215–216
Window, opening, 188–189
Work, formula, 78

Zoethout, William D., 73, 81